UNRAVELED

unraveled

MANAGING *love* *sex* AND *relationships*

UNRAVELED

Contributors:
Heather Kolb, Ashley Jameson, Anna Philipsen, Debby Flanagan,
Diane Roberts, Patty Moreno, and Shari Chinchen

Published by
Pure Desire Ministries International
886 NW Corporate Drive, Troutdale, OR 97060
www.puredesire.org | 503.489.0230
ISBN 978-1-943291-09-0

1st Edition, June 2019

All the stories in this book are based on actual experiences. The names and details have been changed to protect the privacy of the people involved. In some cases, composites have been created.

Content editing by Heather Kolb

Cover design, interior design, and typesetting by Elisabeth Pearce

CONTENTS

ACKNOWLEDGMENTS

When it comes to creative projects, I am a firm believer in the philosophy "we are better together" and the development of *Unraveled: Managing Love, Sex, and Relationships* is evidence of this approach.

As the primary writer, I can tell you that this resource was written from a foundation of collaboration—not only through the personal and professional experiences of the writing team, but through the story of every woman who has struggled with unwanted sexual behaviors and destructive relationship patterns.

I would like to thank Ashley Jameson and Anna Philipsen. From conception to completion, you read, wrote, and advised on the best ways to make this resource applicable to the struggles women face today. Thank you for your practical and culturally relevant insights.

I would like to thank Debby Flanagan, Diane Roberts, Patty Moreno, and Shari Chinchen for your pastoral and clinical expertise. Your personal experience, professional awareness, and biblical wisdom enhanced the content and quality of *Unraveled*.

Finally, I would like to thank our heavenly Father. It is only through Your endless pursuit of relationship with us that we can experience lasting love.

Thank you, Father, for bringing our team together to write this resource. May it be a source of hope, healing, and transformation for many women. May You be glorified through this work.

Heather Kolb

INTRODUCTION

Why are you here? You may have decided to join this group to connect with other women. Perhaps you struggle with relationships—not just with men, but with anyone. It could be that you're hurting, that you want to find love but are continually disappointed by relationships. Maybe you are tainted by negative sexual experiences and mistakes from your past. You might be feeling distant from God, separated by the weight of shame and regret. Whatever it is that brought you to this group, we're excited you're here!

Many women are unable to sustain long-term relationships with romantic partners, family members, and friends. They feel isolated and alone. They desperately want connection—to feel a sense of acceptance and belonging. They want to be seen and heard. They want a safe place where they can discover their true identity: the person they are deep inside that they are afraid to show. They want to be known.

This requires risk for each of us: the vulnerability it will take to reach authenticity, the courage to move past the pain of brokenness and strive toward health, the willingness to release control in the hidden areas of our life in order to experience God's grace, and the strength for all of this to happen through community.

Isolation breeds shame, fear, and loneliness, but community breeds life. Community leads to healing.

Fellowship is a place of grace,
where mistakes aren't rubbed in but rubbed out.[1]

The goal of *Unraveled* is that we create a community—a place of grace—where women can find healing regardless of their past behaviors, current circumstance, and season of life. While the foundation and focus is for women who struggle with love, sex, and relationship issues, this resource promotes healing in many areas.

This workbook was written for any woman who has found herself:

- unable to find and/or keep a lasting relationship.
- struggling with sex or love addiction.

[1] Warren, R. (2002). *The Purpose Driven Life: What On Earth Am I Here For?* Grand Rapids, MI: Zondervan.

- engaging in unwanted sexual behaviors: pornography use, masturbation, hookups, affairs, same-sex attraction.
- met with disappointment when looking for love and connection.
- having little to no self-awareness.
- preoccupied with fantasy, to the point where it is interfering with work, family, and commitments.
- wanting to understand why she self-sabotages relationships.
- unable to maintain many forms of personal relationships with family, friends, and coworkers.
- stuffing down feelings, not allowing herself to feel emotion.
- compromising moral and personal boundaries to feel loved and accepted.
- afraid to voice her opinion or speak out, fearing the loss of relationship.
- with unprocessed trauma, creating problems in current relationships.
- hiding behind the facade of social media.
- seeking relationships with unavailable men.
- feeling so much shame about secrets that she has nowhere else to turn.
- pretending to have it all together on the outside, but broken inside.

If you see yourself on this list, you are not alone.

We all want relationship. God designed us for relationship. The challenge comes with understanding and recognizing the difference between unhealthy and healthy relationships.

Throughout this study, we will learn why we do what we do: how all of our past experiences—the good, the bad, and the ugly—contribute to the choices we make. We will learn how our sexuality and identity are God's design, but our past experiences interfere with our ability to recognize and live out God's plan for us. Through the use of weekly exercises, strategic tools, and self-care focus, we will learn how to live in health—**how to unravel the messiness of relationship**. We will discover how lifelong healing comes from a greater understanding of who God is and who He created us to be.

God has a plan for our lives: to bring us to a place of health and wholeness. He is going to use this study and this group to help us change and grow. Embrace the adventure!

Allow God to do what only He can do in you and through you.

CHAPTER OUTCOMES

This resource is created for women who struggle with relationship issues: anything from sex or love addiction to behaviors that lead to a destructive lifestyle. The content in each chapter is intended to facilitate a path toward healing. While it is true that growth and change take time, the content and focus of each chapter will provide the stepping-stones we need in order to create a new path of sustainable, lifelong health—physically, mentally, emotionally, and spiritually.

Over the next several months, we will gain insight into our behaviors, discover what is at the core of our actions, and develop a greater understanding of how we can move to a place of health. Here's a snapshot of what we'll learn in each chapter:

CHAPTER 1: THE TRUTH ABOUT LIFE

- Assess the extent of problematic behaviors
- The masks we wear and why
- How our distorted beliefs keep us stuck in unhealthy relationship patterns
- The significance of God's grace in healing
- Self-Care: The Importance of Sleep

CHAPTER 2: DERAILED

- How our thoughts and feelings contribute to our behaviors
- The neurochemistry of addictive behaviors
- How our sexual behaviors become unhealthy
- Self-Care: Exercise

CHAPTER 3: EMOTIONAL AWARENESS

- The truth about our behaviors
- Establish emotional self-awareness
- The power of our personal story
- Self-Care: Minimizing Stress

CHAPTER 4: WHERE WE COME FROM

- How our childhood experiences contribute to our relational response
- The way our family system impacts our current behaviors
- Where our trauma comes from
- Self-Care: Eating/Nutrition

CHAPTER 5: TOXIC RELATIONSHIPS

- The Cycle of Addiction
- Our reaction style and how it developed
- Unhealthy relationship patterns
- Self-Care: Taking Control of Our Time

CHAPTER 6: IN LOVE WITH LOVE

- The truth and origin of love
- How to develop genuine connection
- Our attachment style in relationship
- Living without codependency
- Self-Care: Developing Gratitude

CHAPTER 7: FACING LOSS

- Survival after painful life experiences
- The role of grief and anger in healing
- Forgiving others
- Self-Care: Stages of Grief

CHAPTER 8: BEYOND YOURSELF

- Why we hold on to unhealthy behaviors
- How consequences help us change and grow
- Generational cycles: choosing something different
- Facing our fears
- Self-Care: Replacing Unhealthy Behaviors

CHAPTER 9: MY VALUE

- Why shame holds us hostage
- How to create healthy boundaries
- Forgiving ourselves
- Self-Care: Saying No

CHAPTER 10: SECURITY IN CHRIST

- Our identity is found in relationship with God
- How personal promises shape our self-perception
- Our healing is not just for us, but to help others
- Self-Care: Biblical Meditation

CHAPTER 11: THE REAL ME

- Stepping out from behind the mask
- Embracing healthy sexuality
- Discovering true intimacy
- Self-Care: H.A.L.T. Awareness

CHAPTER 12: INTENTIONAL LIVING

- Recovery in practice
- Cultivating healthy relationships
- Living in health
- Helping others find hope
- Self-Care: Fire Drills

chapter one

THE TRUTH ABOUT LIFE

LESSON 1: PROBLEMATIC BEHAVIOR

How did I get here? Many of us wrestle with this question, trying to reconcile who we want to be with who we see ourselves becoming and trying to escape the negative behaviors that plague our life. The origin of our unwanted behavior started in early childhood or during our teen years. For many of us, we have struggled in relationship for decades. We carry so much buried pain. We have come to believe that change is impossible.

At first, we may feel like a woman with a broken leg that didn't heal properly and now we walk with a limp. As a result, we could not participate in many of life's wonderful activities. Wanting to fix the problem, we seek counsel from a physician who says, "I can fix your leg so you will no longer experience limitations. However, I will have to re-break your leg to set it properly. It will require some initial pain."

As we face the issues that contribute to our unwanted, out-of-control behaviors, we will experience some intense pain. The painful areas of our past that we have hidden away will come to the surface so we can begin the healing process. We must recognize how our life was built on our environment, family background, childhood trauma, life stresses, genetics, and more—each element shaping a unique path that led us to where we are today.

When it comes to assessing our own behaviors, we often have a skewed perspective. This is especially true when it comes to relationships. We think our behaviors are normal and only question this reality when something goes sideways.

This can be challenging. We are commanded to live in harmony with one another (Romans 12:16), but how is this possible when we struggle with relationship: gaining, maintaining, and keeping relationships? For many of us, when our relationships fall apart, we don't know ourselves, or others, well enough to understand what went wrong. We rarely take the time and energy to assess what happened. We simply move on to the next relationship, where we experience a similar outcome. This is not a healthy way to live.

If we were to honestly look at the significant relationships in our lives—family, friends, and romantic relationships—we would probably see a pattern emerge. Not necessarily the same pattern in every relationship, but patterns that lead to unhealthy relationship dynamics.

Sandy has a heart for people. She loves being around and serving others. Having many friends is important to Sandy. Although they only met a few months ago at a college event, she would do anything for her new friend Jan. They meet for coffee about once a week, but Sandy is constantly texting Jan, asking if she wants to hangout or go shopping. Jan is often unavailable for anything more than their occasional coffee get-together.

Recently, while meeting Sandy for coffee, Jan mentioned that her neck was sore. Immediately, in the middle of the coffee shop, Sandy got up, stood behind Jan, and started massaging Jan's neck. This went on for a couple minutes, while Sandy continued to talk about what she had learned from a friend who took a kinesiology course. Jan sat in silent shock, not knowing how to make this uncomfortable situation stop.

When Sandy returned to her seat, their conversation lagged and Jan quickly created an excuse to leave. Sandy wondered if Jan was bothered, but dismissed the thought as she sent a text to another friend.

Since this incident, Sandy has invited Jan for coffee several times, but Jan is always busy. Jan feels uncomfortable around Sandy and has no desire to continue the relationship; she plans to distance herself from Sandy, hoping that Sandy will eventually stop texting her. Sandy recognizes that Jan is distant, but doesn't know why.

What problematic behaviors do you notice about Sandy?

Unaware of her neediness - texting too much
Relationship isnt reciprocal
shes willing to go further for her friends than they for her
Boundary issues
looking for something Jan can't give her

Why do you think Jan responded the way she did?

Boundaries were violated - physical touch (not on Sandy's Radar)
Neck massage didnt match the closeness of their relationship
Jan avoids conflict + honest communication.
Jan unaware of her behaviors, why is Jan drawn to Sandy anyways

Sandy is a boundary buster: she doesn't recognize when she crosses the personal boundaries of others. Let's look at another example.

Noel has a first date tonight. She has many first dates. She wants to be in a lasting relationship but cannot seem to find the right guy. When she meets a new guy, she tries to develop their common areas of interest, which often involves her pretending to be interested in the same things. Ultimately, she gives them whatever they want—whatever she thinks will make them happy.

Noel has a hard time saying "no" to people, especially men. In an attempt to preserve a relationship, she will sometimes do things that make her feel uncomfortable. When the relationship ends, as they always do, Noel convinces herself that she is just being kind in considering their needs above her own.

As she gets ready for her date, she tries to push her feelings of guilt, shame, and worthlessness to the back of her mind. While getting ready, Noel received a text from a friend: *I met the perfect guy for you. Okay looking, but super funny! Told him you were available. Gave him your number. Okay, right?*

With a heavy sigh, Noel responded: *Yes, I'm available. Look forward to meeting him.*

☐ *What problematic behavior do you notice about Noel?*

prentending to be what others want
bonndary issues
can't say no—
doesn't know her needs, limits or what she wants
pushing shame down/aside → not dealing w/ it
comprimising her discernment, limits compatability

☐ *Do you think Noel knows that her behaviors are problematic? Why or why not?*

not really
Shame is a symptom trying to tell her — but she's fighting facing it
I think she may think this is just how it is...

Noel has no boundaries: she feels powerless in forming any type of boundary, even those that would protect her.

Of all the women described in these scenarios, which do identify with most? Why?

pretending to be interested in same things - giving them what they want. I would compromise, look down on my sense of self/identity - as if others were better. Compromising boundaries to not rock the boat or make people mad - or loose relationship

THOUGHTS → FEELINGS → BEHAVIORS

Whether we understand the significance of this cycle and the role it plays in our relationships, the truth remains: our thoughts influence our feelings and our feelings influence our behaviors.

Throughout this study, we will learn how our thoughts and feelings are closely linked and become the motivating force behind our behaviors. We will learn the importance of 2 Corinthians 10:5 (NASB) and the role it plays in our healing:

> *We are destroying speculations and every lofty thing raised up against the knowledge of God, and we are taking every thought captive to the obedience of Christ,...*

Those of us who struggle with relationships often don't recognize the control our thought life has over us. We live "in the moment" and are continually held captive by our black-and-white, all-or-nothing thinking. This can interfere with our ability to connect with others, limiting our capacity to cultivate deep, long-lasting relationships.

childhood

How do we know if our behaviors are problematic? Does it mean we have relationship issues if one relationship ends badly? Not necessarily; but if many of our relationships exist in tension—or we find ourselves doing things we don't really want to do or shouldn't do—it may require further investigation into our behaviors.

If we want to change our behaviors, we have to develop a self-awareness of why we do what we do. We have to take an objective approach and assess the reality of our behaviors. The following two assessments will help us identify some areas in our thoughts, feelings, and behaviors that contribute to unhealthy relationship dynamics. This is the starting point to creating lifelong change.

This week, take the following Love Addiction and Sexual Addiction Screening Tests. Be prepared to discuss the results in your group.

LOVE ADDICTION EVALUATION

Put a check next to any statements that describe you in the present or have described you in the past.

☐ **1.** I am driven by one or more compulsions (relationships, sex, food, drugs, shopping, etc.).

☐ **2.** I think my self-esteem is low.

☐ **3.** I think that my happiness depends on having a loving relationship.

☐ **4.** I often fantasize to avoid reality or loneliness.

☐ **5.** I feel I need to be "good" enough to earn love from others.

☐ **6.** I will do almost anything for that desired loving relationship.

☐ **7.** I find it difficult to say "no" and set healthy boundaries, especially in relationships.

☐ **8.** I keep looking for a relationship to fill what is missing or lacking in my life.

☐ **9.** I find myself thinking that things will (or would) be better in this new relationship.

☐ **10.** I have always felt a distance and/or lack of love from my dad and/or my mom.

☐ **11.** I have a difficult time having an intimate relationship with God.

☐ **12.** I vacillate from over- to out-of-control in any of these areas: relationships, sex, food, money, drugs, shopping, etc.

☐ **13.** I crave and fear intimacy at the same time.

☐ **14.** I have used sex to get love.

☐ **15.** I have used sex and/or seduction to dominate another person, be in control, or get what I want.

☐ **16.** I take responsibility for people, tasks and situations for which I am not responsible.

☐ **17.** I find myself in relationships that echo my past abuse.

☐ **18.** I was sexually abused as a child or adolescent.

☐ **19.** I have stayed in romantic relationships after they became emotionally or physically abusive.

☐ **20.** I often find myself preoccupied with sexual thoughts or romantic daydreams.

☐ **21.** I have trouble stopping my sexual behavior when I know it is inappropriate.

☐ **22.** I have hurt others emotionally because of my sexual/romantic behavior.

☐ **23.** I feel bad at times about my sexual behavior.

☐ **24.** I have worried about people finding out about my sexual activities.

☐ **25.** I feel controlled by my sexual desire or fantasies of romance.

☐ **26.** I have been sexually or romantically involved with inappropriate people such as a boss, a married person.

☐ **27.** When I have sex or am involved in sexual activity, I often feel depressed afterward.

☐ **28.** I have become emotionally or sexually involved with people I don't know.

______ **TOTAL NUMBER OF ITEMS CHECKED** | If you scored a total of 3-6 items checked, we recommend going through the *Seven Pillars of Freedom* Kit (for men) or *Unraveled* Kit (for women). If you scored over 6 checked items, we recommend seeking counseling from a certified sexual addiction therapist. For more information and resources visit www.puredesire.org.

1

SEXUAL ADDICTION SCREENING TEST (SAST-R V2.0)[2]

The Sexual Addiction Screening Test (SAST) is designed to assist in the assessment of sexually compulsive or "addictive" behavior. Developed in cooperation with hospitals, treatment programs, private therapists and community groups, the SAST provides a profile of responses that help to discriminate between addictive and non-addictive behavior.

- To complete the test, answer each question by placing a check next to it if it is true for you.
- Although the statements are written in the present tense, if the statements have ever applied to your life, then place a check next to that item.
- Statements are considered false only if they have never been a part of your life. If in doubt, let your first reaction be your guide.
- Please complete the scoring, filling out the Core Item Scale, the Subscales and the Addictive Dimensions on the page that follows the test. Pay close attention to your results on the Core Item Scale as a score of 6 or more indicates an addiction may be present.

☐ **1.** Were you sexually abused as a child or adolescent?
☐ **2.** Did your parents have trouble with sexual behavior?
☐ **3.** Do you often find yourself preoccupied with sexual thoughts?
☑ **4.** Do you feel that your sexual behavior is not normal? *
☑ **5.** Do you ever feel bad about your sexual behavior? •
☐ **6.** Has your sexual behavior ever created problems for you/your family?
☐ **7.** Have you ever sought help for sexual behavior you did not like?
☐ **8.** Has anyone been hurt emotionally because of your sexual behavior?
☐ **9.** Are any of your sexual activities against the law?
☐ **10.** Have you made efforts to quit a type of sexual activity and failed?
☑ **11.** Do you hide some of your sexual behaviors from others? •
☐ **12.** Have you attempted to stop some parts of your sexual activity?
☑ **13.** Have you felt degraded by your sexual behaviors? •
☐ **14.** When you have sex, do you feel depressed afterwards?
☐ **15.** Do you feel controlled by your sexual desire?
☑ **16.** Have important parts of your life (job, family, friends, leisure activities) been neglected because you were spending too much time on sex? •
☐ **17.** Do you ever think your sexual desire is stronger than you are?
☐ **18.** Is sex almost all you think about?
☐ **19.** Has sex (or romantic fantasies) been a way for you to escape problems?
☐ **20.** Has sex become the most important thing in your life?
☐ **21.** Are you in crisis over sexual matters?
☐ **22.** The Internet has created sexual problems for me.
☐ **23.** I spend too much time online for sexual purposes.
☐ **24.** I have purchased services online for erotic purposes (sites for dating).

[2] © 2008, P. J. Carnes, Sexual Addiction Screening Test - Revised (Used by permission)

intimate w/God

- ☐ **25.** I have made romantic or erotic connections with people online.
- ☐ **26.** People in my life have been upset about my sexual activities online.
- ☐ **27.** I have attempted to stop my online sexual behaviors.
- ☐ **28.** I have subscribed to or regularly purchased or rented sexually explicit materials (magazines, videos, books or online pornography).
- ☐ **29.** I have been sexual with minors.
- ☐ **30.** I have spent considerable time and money on strip clubs, adult bookstores, and movie houses.
- ☐ **31.** I have engaged prostitutes and escorts to satisfy my sexual needs.
- ☐ **32.** I have spent considerable time surfing pornography online.
- ☐ **33.** I have used magazines, videos, or online pornography even when there was considerable risk of being caught by family members who would be upset by my behavior.
- ☐ **34.** I have regularly purchased romantic novels or sexually explicit magazines.
- ☐ **35.** I have stayed in romantic relationships after they became emotionally abusive.
- ☐ **36.** I have traded sex for money or gifts.
- ☐ **37.** I have had multiple romantic or sexual relationships at the same time.
- ☐ **38.** After sexually acting out, I sometimes refrain from all sex for a significant period.
- ☐ **39.** I have regularly engaged in sadomasochistic behavior.
- ☐ **40.** I visit sexual bath-houses, sex clubs, or video/bookstores as part of my regular sexual activity.
- ☐ **41.** I have engaged in unsafe or "risky" sex even though I knew it could cause me harm.
- ☐ **42.** I have cruised public restrooms, rest areas, or parks for sex with strangers.
- ☐ **43.** I believe casual or anonymous sex has kept me from having more long-term intimate relationships.
- ☐ **44.** My sexual behavior has put me at risk for arrest for lewd conduct or public indecency.
- ☐ **45.** I have been paid for sex.

SCALES	ITEMS	CUT-OFF	MY SCORE
Core Item Scale	1-20	6 or more	4 past
Internet Items	22-27	3 or more	
Men's Items	28-33	2 or more	
Women's Items	34-39	2 or more	
Homosexual Men	40-45	3 or more	
Preoccupation	3, 18, 19, 20	2 or more	
Loss of Control	10, 12, 15, 17	2 or more	
Relationship Disturbance	6, 8, 16, 26	2 or more	1
Affect Disturbance	4, 5, 11, 13, 14	2 or more	3

RELATIVE DISTRIBUTIONS OF ADDICT & NON-ADDICT SAST SCORES

This instrument has been based on screenings of tens of thousands of people. This particular version is a developmental stage revision of the instrument, so scoring may be adjusted with more research. Please be aware that clinical decisions must be made conditionally since final scoring protocols may vary. A score of 6 or more on the Core Item Scale indicates an addiction may be present.

What are your thoughts regarding the two assessment tests and your results? What did you learn about yourself?

I have struggled with boundaries and compromise

Which statements on the two assessments do you relate to most? Why?

I take responsibility for people, tasks + situations for which I am not responsible

Setting healthy Boundaries + saying no

Looking Ahead

Complete the Group Check-In, Self-Care lesson, and Change & Growth Analysis in your *Unraveled: Weekly Tools* before the next group meeting.

Jessica - Family

alyson - Family

LESSON 2: THE MASKS WE WEAR

Many of us are familiar with the saying, "What you see is what you get," but do we really live this way? Are we the type of people who have nothing to hide and live a completely transparent life?

Whether we can admit it or not, many of us live our lives through a series of masquerades. We have an extensive array of masks we put on and take off without giving it much thought. We may not even recognize when and what masks we put on, especially the masks we've worn for most of our lives. Our masks, in the moment, serve a purpose. What purpose do they serve?

As I went through the process of healing from a broken marriage, an eating disorder, and alcohol abuse, my eyes were opened to the fact that I had been wearing masks—not just one mask, but several masks—since my teen years. Masks that were used to cover my pain, shame, and fear. I not only wore masks that covered my feelings, but masks that helped me become someone else: someone I thought others would like better, someone more fun and sexy than the real version, someone who could become what others wanted.

I was 16 years old when I started wearing masks. I had been dating Steve since the beginning of my sophomore year. A couple months into my junior year, Steve broke up with me. There were new freshman on campus and Steve was interested in someone else. I was devastated. I was heartbroken. I felt lost and alone. This was the first time I remember thinking, "I'm not enough." I felt worthless.

Not wanting to show my devastation, I put on the mask of independence and confidence—my identity was no longer shaped by having a steady boyfriend. In fact, I recognized that putting on a flirty and especially friendly mask with all the guys provided a constant stream of admiration and attention I had never before experienced. At the time, I had no idea how much power and pain would come from wearing masks.

Jesse

Why did Jesse think she had to put on a mask?

She'd been 'rejected'

What did Jesse discover about the power of masks?

Power + pain

the masks had power + caused pain

When we live our lives hiding behind a series of masks, we are attempting to avoid reality. We convince ourselves that if we maintain this charade long enough, then others will accept our masked reality. We become so determined to sustain the masquerade that we create justifications of our behaviors: we attempt to deceive ourselves in order to preserve and protect what hides behind the mask.

Raising awareness is the first step in changing our behavior. We all have used excuses to justify our behaviors—to rationalize our need to stay hidden behind our masks.

In the table below, list three justifications that are most characteristic of your behaviors. Then, list the painful truth: the fear behind your behaviors.

* Not be a burden | cassi ariel chris | others not help out when I ask

JUSTIFICATION	THE FEAR BEHIND MY BEHAVIOR
I was fearful in my marriage and thought having an affair would take away the pain.	Another man's attention made me feel wanted—I didn't feel secure in my marriage.
1. "I am afraid others will not do things as good as me", so I try to do everything myself or "will let me down or drop the ball"	fear of failing, Rejection, being criticized, left alone Performance Based
2. I needed attention to be seen worth something	Fear that I'm not enough, my identity - who I am isn't okay - looking to be validated
3. I'm lonely or want to feel emotion + love (chick flicks) / Social Media	fear that real Relationships will come up short true my needs / connection
4. won't like me if I don't like what they like - Be rejected if have my own ideas	Fear of my own Personal autonomy of my own independence that it will leave me alone -

Mark any of the following justifications you have used to keep your masks firmly in place.[3]

SPIRITUALIZE: TWISTING SCRIPTURE TO JUSTIFY OUR BEHAVIOR.

- ☐ It doesn't say anything in Scripture about masturbation.
- ☐ God wouldn't want me to be alone.
- ☐ We committed our relationship to one another before God; we don't need a piece of paper.
- ☐ I've been hurt by past relationships; I'm just looking for my soulmate now.
- ☐ He's a Christian, so it must be alright to cross sexual boundaries.
- ☐ We are engaged so being sexual is okay.
- ☐ God would want me to be happy and my husband isn't showing me love and attention like ______.
- ☐ I married the wrong man; now I found my soulmate.

MINIMIZE: ADMITTING THERE IS A PROBLEM BUT MINIMIZING ITS IMPORTANCE, COMPARING OUR PROBLEM TO THE PROBLEMS OF OTHERS AND THINKING, "MY PROBLEMS ARE NOTHING COMPARED TO ____________."

- ☐ We're only experimenting.
- ☐ I only masturbate when I am stressed.
- ☐ Oral sex isn't really sex.
- ☐ We keep our clothes on while we pleasure each other.
- ☐ I send suggestive messages to other men that my husband probably wouldn't like, but there has been no sex.
- ☐ It's only online. It's not real sex.
- ☐ My boyfriend has done worse things than I have.
- ☐ I'm only hurting myself—no one else.
- ☐ All my friends have sex. At least I'm still a virgin.

BLAME: FINDING FAULT WITH OTHER PEOPLE OR SITUATIONS RATHER THAN TAKING PERSONAL RESPONSIBILITY.

- ☐ My boyfriend/husband got me hooked on pornography.
- ☐ My friends were pressuring me to send nude photos.

---

[3] Bradley, R. & Roberts, D. (2012). *Behind the Mask: Authentic Living For Young Women*. Gresham, OR: Pure Desire Ministries International.

- ☐ My boyfriend would dump me if I don't "put out" sexually.
- ☐ My husband doesn't understand me or give me attention like ________ does.
- ☐ My parents wouldn't let me date, so I started "messing around" with some of my girlfriends.
- ☐ My husband is not meeting my sexual needs therefore I ____________.

RATIONALIZE: USING EXCUSES FOR OUR BEHAVIOR OR THE BEHAVIORS OF OTHERS WHO HAVE HURT US.

- ☐ I just met him for coffee; I didn't mean for it to go that far.
- ☐ We became close on the job; it just happened.
- ☐ I drank too much and couldn't say "no."
- ☐ My friends have gone all the way; we are just having oral sex.
- ☐ I am lonely and sexting helps me feel wanted.
- ☐ I am lonely, so I need a guy to fill the void.
- ☐ He shows me more attention than my husband does.
- ☐ Romance novels help me escape my problems.
- ☑ Everyone else is doing it.

What are the most powerful justifications you have used to keep your masks firmly in place? Explain.

→ My standards having a propensity to slide - Based on others around me.
→ Minimizing - not real sex
Excuse
Fear wouldn't date me/ be alone/rejected

Bathsheba knew what it was like to wear a mask (2 Samuel 11). Her husband, Uriah, served in King David's army and often put his loyalty and service to the king above his relationship with his wife. Perhaps Bathsheba felt lonely and unwanted in her marriage. Did she know that the king's balcony overlooked her bathing area? Did she put on a mask of seduction to entice King David? Bathsheba, like Jesse, probably felt ignored and was looking for someone to admire her, want her, give her attention—and it worked.

What do you think Bathsheba was thinking when she bathed on her roof?

Have you ever gone to extremes to get attention and fill the void of love with a seductive mask? Explain.

Why do we wear masks? We are hiding from our fears, failures, and shame. We are hiding from the fear of feeling worthless or not being enough, not recognizing the consequences that will follow. We are hiding from the judgment and condemnation from others. We are hiding from ourselves—the person we see in the mirror, the person we don't want to be alone with, the person we have become. Ultimately, we are hiding from God.

Wearing masks or hiding is nothing new; it has been a part of human behavior since the beginning of human existence. We see the first example of this behavior in Genesis 3, where the serpent is tempting Eve to eat of the forbidden fruit. After giving into her desire and sharing with her husband, "*At that moment their eyes were opened, and they suddenly felt shame at their nakedness. So they sewed fig leaves together to cover themselves.*"[4]

When God came looking for Adam and Eve, which He did regularly, they hid from God. Their shame not only caused them to hide from each other—cover up a part of their identity—but hide from God. One author offers this perspective:

[4] Genesis 3:7 NLT

"

Adam and Eve's entire frame of reference is one another, and God, in His perfect, unspoiled garden. But one decision against God changes their brain to believe they have something wrong with themselves and they need to hide. This is what shame does to all of us! It tells us, with no logical basis, that we are broken and we better hide.[5]

It's easy to look at this example and think that Eve had everything any woman would want: a perfect husband, the perfect father, and a perfect living environment. What more could any woman want? But have we ever thought about what motivated Eve to eat from the forbidden fruit—what caused her to be vulnerable to sin?

What do you think was going through Eve's mind that led to her vulnerability?

____

____

____

____

____

____

In what way is wearing masks part of the fall: something that started in the Garden of Eden?

____

____

____

____

____

____

When we put on a mask—when we hide—it is often attached to some distorted belief that we have about ourselves or others. The source of our distorted thinking can come from several places: traumatic experiences, childhood environment, lifestyle choices, and others.

[5] Stumbo, N. (2017). *Safe: Creating a Culture of Grace in a Climate of Shame*. Pure Desire Ministries International.

We all wear masks at different times in our lives and for many reasons. In the table below, identify the masks you have worn at various times throughout your life.[6]

MASKS I'VE WORN	DISTORTED BELIEF
☐ Self-sufficient mask	People may need me, but I don't need anyone. They will only disappoint me.
☐ Fortress mask	Protects me from getting close to people who could hurt me.
☐ Take charge mask	I have to feel in control, so I won't get hurt.
☐ Superior mask	If I look better than others, I will be accepted.
☐ Victim's mask	Everyone is trying to hurt me.
☐ Party mask	I have to be the life of the party to be accepted.
☐ Pleaser mask	I can't say "no" because I will be liked if I'm needed. I want to feel accepted.
☐ Vanity mask	My value comes from my outward appearance.
☐ Rescuer mask	I feel responsible for making others happy.
☐ Performance mask	My value is based on my performance and how well I measure up.
☐ Happy mask	People only like me when I am happy and fun to be with.
☐ "I can do it" mask	Asking for help is a sign of weakness. I can't depend on others.
☐ Perfectionist mask	I won't be liked if I make mistakes. I don't want to feel rejected.
☐ Rebel mask	I don't like feeling told what to do.
☐ Flirtatious mask	I feel accepted when I am pursued.

[6] Bradley, R. & Roberts, D. (2012). *Behind the Mask: Authentic Living for Young Women*. Pure Desire Ministries International.

Since our experiences, fears, and perceptions shape our lives, they also contribute to our thinking and the masks we wear. While we may be able to identify with many of the masks provided, there are those masks that are unique to us.

In the table below, list any additional masks you've worn and the distorted belief associated with that mask.

TYPE OF MASK	DISTORTED BELIEF
Responsible mask	
up to me mask	

Looking Ahead

Complete the Group Check-In, Self-Care lesson, and Change & Growth Analysis in your *Unraveled: Weekly Tools* before the next group meeting.

LESSON 3: UNMASKING GRACE

When we begin to recognize the masks we wear in life, it is important to understand why we choose the masks we wear. What happened that caused us to need a mask, to need that specific mask? What need is the mask filling? This is an interesting observation about human behavior: when we do something—healthy or unhealthy—we do it because it meets a need.

At one point, our mask may have been necessary to keep us safe. If we had an abusive parent, we may have worn a Pleaser Mask to avoid harsh punishment, but now, as an adult, we can't figure out how to function without it.

Masks provide a disguise. Masks are convenient. Masks create the illusion that they will keep us safe. They hide our insecurities and give us a false sense of control. Masks can be impressive: concealing more than they protect, hiding our weaknesses, loneliness, and fears. With the masks we wear, we create a sophisticated facade in hopes of being loved and accepted—hoping no one will discover what lies beneath.

Our need for acceptance motivates us to behave in a way that opposes our core values. We seek unhealthy toxic relationships under the false belief that they will bring happiness and reveal the control we have in our life. The pressure to meet perceived social expectations drives us to cross harmful sexual boundaries.

I was raised with parents who were lenient with rules, so it was easy to be sexually promiscuous. My parents were not home much and I often felt lonely. My parents had big plans for my future that included college and a strong career, so getting pregnant was not an option. At one point, I hid an unwanted pregnancy and, with the help of my boyfriend, had an abortion. I tried to be more careful with my sexual behaviors, not wanting to get pregnant again but this didn't last long. Unfortunately, because of unprotected sex, I contracted a lifelong sexually transmitted disease (STD).

I committed my life to Christ, then met and married the man of my dreams. We tried for many years to have children, but realized the abortion and the STD led to my inability to have children. We were devastated, but began thinking about adoption. I realized I had to process the grief of the choices I made many years ago.

As I began to process my grief, I prayed for a child. I held onto the promise of Jeremiah 29:11-12 (NKJV):

[11]For I know the thoughts that I think toward you, says the Lord, thoughts of peace and not of evil, to give you a future and a hope. [12]Then you will call upon Me and go and pray to Me, and I will listen to you.

God miraculously provided a way for us to adopt a child. Adoption usually takes years, but within months, we were told that a young woman who had considered abortion, decided instead that she wanted a Christian couple to adopt her baby. As I held my newborn baby for the first time, with tears of joy I declared: "her name is 'Grace.'"

Mia

Why did Mia engage in toxic relationships and risky sexual behaviors?

This list provides some common reasons that women engage in toxic relationships and risky sexual behaviors.[7] Circle any reasons that relate to your experiences.

To feel loved	Gain acceptance	Social media
Peer pressure	Hormones	Wanting to control men
Feeling lonely	Needing a sexual high	To keep a relationship
Rebellion	Drug/alcohol influences	Wanting male attention
Curiosity	Not feeling loved by spouse	Wanting to feel good

[7] Bradley, R. & Roberts, D. (2012). *Behind the Mask: Authentic Living for Young Women*. Pure Desire Ministries International.

Can you identify a point in your life where you developed similar feelings that led to a toxic relationship?

Did your need to be involved in a toxic relationship increase or decrease over time?

Want the good news? **God loves and accepts us regardless of past choices.** Like Mia, we have amazing possibilities in our future, but we have to commit to the healing process. We have to recognize how our masks allow us to hide and ignore painful thoughts, feelings, and behaviors. If we want to experience the fullness of God's grace, we have to be willing to let go of our masks. We have to learn how to live authentically, without hiding who we are behind the mask; otherwise, only the mask receives the love and acceptance.

Last week, we identified the masks we wear and the distorted belief connected to that mask. Removing our masks is a scary process, but it is one that has to happen if we are going to pursue lifelong healing.

When we live behind a mask, it allows us to live in denial. We don't have to face our fears. In many ways, this creates a lose/lose situation. Keeping our masks securely in place may lead to negative consequences, but so could removing them. It was fear that caused us to put on the mask in the first place. Making the brave decision to face that fear will help us remove the masks.

Here are some things to consider: when the time is right, what masks will you remove first? Which mask is heaviest and the greatest burden to carry? Which mask is light and might come off easily in the safety of this group? What fear will you have to face in removing the masks? Use the following table to explore these options.

MASKS I'VE WORN	NEGATIVE CONSEQUENCES OF NOT FACING MY FEARS	WHAT FEAR MUST I FACE?
Self-sufficient mask	If I keep this mask, I will live a lonely life, not needing others.	If I remove the mask, I will have to face the fear that others will disappoint me and let me down.
1. Responsible mask	co-dependence, others can't grow in areas need	I won't be loved if I'm not helping others.
2. up to me mask	over worked	Balls dropped. Things aren't done perfect
3. Should've known better (Parents strong) Perfectionist not make a mistake	Caleb - hard on himself most opp. for grace physically	Can be loved if mess up can be SAFE if mess up can survive/live/thrive w/ mess or mistakes w/

As we begin to explore what life could look like without our masks, we need to stay focused on the healing path before us. We cannot allow our past behaviors—no matter how devastating we think they are—to hold us captive any longer. Instead, we need to face our fears and trust God's grace in our healing, allowing Him to do what only He can do in us and through us.

We may feel unworthy—as though our past behaviors forever taint us (contaminate, infect, or ruin us)—keeping us from experiencing the refreshing favor of God's grace. However, this is not how God works. Even in the genealogy of Christ, God used unlikely women to fulfill His plan. In Matthew's account of the genealogy, only five women are mentioned and all had been soiled by a fallen world.[8]

- Matthew 1:3: Tamar posed as a prostitute and tricked Judah into having sex with her (Genesis 38).
- Matthew 1:5: Rahab was a prostitute (Joshua 2:1).
- Matthew 1:5: Ruth, the Moabite, was a Gentile (Ruth 1).
- Matthew 1:6: Bathsheba had an affair with David while married to Uriah (2 Samuel 11-12).
- Matthew 1:6: Mary, the mother of Jesus, whose reputation was questioned (Matthew 1).

[8] Ibid.

God constantly moves in unusual ways to achieve His purpose, even within the lineage of Christ. God can use anyone: empowering the most unlikely of us to become His supernatural agents, using us to bring about His glory through His unbounding grace.

What is encouraging about the way God used the unlikely women in Jesus' lineage?

Despite your past, how do you think God will use you to fulfill His plan? Explain.

As you imagine life without masks, what makes you excited about this process?

What fears will you have to face?

RECOVERY ACTION PLAN

Prior to joining this group, many of us didn't have the tools or an appropriate level of awareness to navigate our relationships. Since we are beginning to learn why we have been stuck in our previously unwanted and problematic behaviors, the Recovery Action Plan will help us gain accountability for new, healthy behaviors.

The Recovery Action Plan is a valuable tool for any of us wanting to take a proactive approach to our recovery and relationships. It will help us identify reasonable and necessary steps to take in response to **relapse: when we engage in a behavior or find ourselves in an area we promised ourselves and others we would never go again**.

In the past, medicating our pain through unhealthy methods was a way of life—a means of survival. Now, as we learn to walk in sobriety, the Recovery Action Plan will give us a new tool to help transform our addictive and harmful behaviors, eventually changing the negative consequences we experience.

When creating a Recovery Action Plan, it is important to identify the logical and natural consequences if relapse occurs. Natural consequences are the inevitable results of the addict's own actions. Logical consequences happen as a result of the addict's actions but are intentionally imposed by the addict (their group or spouse) as a means of changing future behaviors. These consequences are not meant to be punitive, but designed to help us:

- feel safe and learn to respond, rather than react to the relapse;
- understand the natural and logical consequences if we choose to act out;
- stop trying to recover from relapse in an unhealthy way; and
- rebuild trust in relationships.

Whether we are single or married, creating a Recovery Action Plan will raise an awareness of how our behaviors affect us and our relationships. As we work through the process of creating a Recovery Action Plan, it is important to be intentional and thorough. This will be a foundational step to our healing.

Use the space on the next pages to create your Recovery Action Plan. A full explanation and examples can be found at puredesire.org/tools. Use a separate sheet of paper if more space is required.

Step 1: Identify your relapse—the actions you're committing to refrain from. This list should be re-evaluated at least every six months.

Examples: pornography use, masturbation, fantasy, manipulating relationships, alcohol use, obsessive social media use, Facebook stalking.

Blowing up in anger — throwing stuff or

binge eating
or

Shopping — @ whole foods $200+ not journaling

Step 2: Determine who you will need to share your relapse with and in what time frame. This typically includes a group member, a mentor or friend, and your spouse, if they are engaged in the recovery process. Share within 24 hours of the relapse. Knowing ahead of time that you committed to being honest about a relapse within a short time frame will help you combat one of the most common lies that lead to relapse: "No one needs to know."

Example: I will share my relapse with Sara and Angie from group for help and support. I will then share my relapse with my spouse/significant other...

- Melisa
- Jamie B.

Amanda: isolating avoiding netflix w/in 24 hrs
Ashley: shopping if struggling - mac.
Alyson: over eat. - amanda/whit.
Emily: pushing boundaries w/ marty

Step 3: Write out all the natural consequences of your relapse. If you are married and your spouse is engaged in recovery with you, share these with your spouse—note if they have any additional natural consequences you have not considered.

Examples: broken trust, hurting family and friends, job loss...

broken relationship

Step 4: Write out all the logical consequences you are choosing to follow if you relapse. Include a list of action steps you can take to rebuild and maintain trust. If married, your spouse can share the behaviors that will help to rebuild their trust.

Examples: I won't use my computer in my room alone; I won't use social media when home alone; I will sleep in a separate room from my spouse...

- counseling
- talk to friend

Step 5: Create an Escape Plan by visiting the Pure Desire Tools page at puredesire.org/tools and add additional alarms you recognize that lead to relapse. Add any necessary steps to handle the downward spiral differently next time.

Examples: have an accountability friend with me during girls' night out; don't have any male Facebook friends that are not friends with my husband; when feeling bored at home, instead of using social media, I'll...

stay away from edge
Self care plan
inconsistent journal - self awareness

Step 6: Describe your desired outcome for creating this plan. If you have a clear vision of how this plan will help your recovery, you are more likely to follow it.

Examples: I want to have lasting relationships with family and friends; I want to stop feeling like I need attention from every guy in the room; I want to stop thinking that sex equals love...

Resolving

When we are intentional about making the necessary changes to live in health, it changes the way we think, feel, and act. It begins to change the way we perceive our world. It changes our behaviors toward relationships.

Looking Ahead

Complete the Group Check-In, Self-Care lesson, and Change & Growth Analysis in your *Unraveled: Weekly Tools* before the next group meeting.

chapter two

DERAILED

LESSON 1: WHAT IS SOBRIETY?

What is sobriety? The dictionary would tell us that it's a state of living sober, but what does that mean? Regardless of who we ask or whose research we follow, the definition of sobriety can be complex, encompassing various elements that work together to move us to a place of health. It's important to take on this mindset when we are pursuing sobriety and lifelong health. Our pathway toward health is not paved with only one type of stone or based on overcoming only one area in our lives—it is paved with a variety of stones that change over time based on our needs throughout the process.

This process of healing and maintaining a steady condition of health often takes on a theme such as "living in sobriety" or "being in recovery," but what does this look like? We simply cannot stop harmful behaviors and expect a lasting change. It will require a process of changing our brain—how we think, feel, and act—which can only happen through self-awareness.

Look at this definition of sobriety.[9]

- Restoration: accepting life on God's terms, with trust, grace, mercy, vulnerability, and gratitude
- No current secrets
- Working to resolve problems
- Identifying fears and feelings
- Keeping commitments to meetings, prayer, family, church, people, goals, and self
- Being open and honest, making eye contact
- Increasing in relationships with God and others
- True accountability

We have already approached some of these issues through assessment tests, facing our fears to remove the masks we wear, weekly commitments for better sleep, and developing our Recovery Action Plan. As we go through this workbook, we will continue to gain new tools, insights, and understanding of what sobriety and restoration will look like for each of us.

There is no single "quick fix" pathway to healing. What makes matters worse is that many of us have never been here before. We've started the path toward healing, only to feel

---

[9] Dye, M. (2012). *The Genesis Process: For Change Groups, Book 1 and 2, Individual Workbook (4th ed.)*. Auburn, CA: Michael Dye.

defeated and give up a short time later. It's difficult to maintain direction when we don't know which way to go.

If we want to sustain lifelong healing, it requires a submission to God's leading. We have to follow Him because we don't know where we're going. When it comes to following God's lead, what was true for the Israelites as they crossed the Jordan River is true for us.

> *Early in the morning Joshua and all the Israelites set out from Shittim and went to the Jordan, where they camped before crossing over. [2]After three days the officers went throughout the camp, [3]giving orders to the people: "When you see the ark of the covenant of the Lord your God, and the Levitical priests carrying it, you are to move out from your positions and follow it. [4]**Then you will know which way to go, since you have never been this way before.** But keep a distance of about two thousand cubits between you and the ark; do not go near it."*
>
> **JOSHUA 3:1-4**

The Israelites were instructed to follow the Ark of the Covenant, which was a representation of God Himself, so that they would know which way to go. They had "never been this way before" and needed God to lead the way.

It may seem scary to not know the way or to give up the control we want in our own healing and trust God's leading. However, when we submit to God's leading, we experience His grace and blessing like never before. The next verse of Joshua 3 reveals this truth:

> *[5]Joshua told the people, "Consecrate yourselves, for tomorrow the Lord will do amazing things among you."*

It is exciting to think of what God is going to do in us and through us as we move toward health! None of us will experience true sobriety if we do not yield to God's leading in our lives. This will require a new level of trust and faith for many of us, and in return, the development of a deep love relationship with God.

As you consider the process of discovering lifelong healing, what are your initial fears?

____

____

____

____

____

____

What is one thing you are excited to see God do in your healing?

____

____

____

____

____

____

My late night, online activities are not hurting anyone. I've tried to stop, but why should I? This is really no different than the fantasy video games my husband plays online. It's not really real, so what's the harm?

For the past year, I have developed a pattern of staying up late after my family goes to bed. Initially it was to catch up on chores. At one point, while perusing various online chat rooms, I stumbled into romantic and sexually explicit conversations with men. I have been married for nine years, and until now, found our sex life mundane. Initially I felt guilty, but my online fantasy chat-life has given me a new-found sense of exhilaration, even providing more enthusiasm and energy during sex with my husband. In many ways, this is a win-win situation for everyone.

I am very careful to delete my browser history every night, leaving no trail of my online activity. It's not really a secret, but I would hate for my husband to see it. I don't want to hurt his feelings. Besides, he's really the one benefiting from my newly acquired sexual appetite.

Sonja

At what point do we have a problem that needs to be addressed? When does our behavior become the problem?

These are great questions. So often, especially when we hear the word "addiction," we immediately tell ourselves, "I'm not an addict! That's not me!" All of us have an image that comes to mind when we think of someone who is addicted, but many times it reflects a stereotypical, Hollywood version that is far from reality.

But, what happens when we use this language or ask these questions:

1. Is our behavior something we've struggled with for a long period of time?
2. Is our behavior something we've tried to stop on our own, but can't?
3. Is our behavior causing us harm or harming those around us?

Looking at Sonja's story, does she have a problem? What concerns do you see in her pattern of behavior?

____

____

____

____

Take a minute and review the Sexual Addiction Screening Test (SAST) based on Sonja's behaviors. What is her score? Is she a sex addict?

____

____

____

What indicators on the SAST would help Sonja break denial that she isn't hurting anyone?

____

____

____

Sonja has convinced herself that her behavior is not hurting anyone. This is a lie. Her behavior is hurting her. It may seem exciting in the moment, but she had to work past the feeling of guilt to get to a place of justification. In many ways, she has readjusted her moral compass and made changes to her thought process. This is contributing to how she feels about her current behavior, as well as influencing her future behaviors.

THOUGHTS → FEELINGS → BEHAVIORS

There is no way around it: our thoughts influence our feelings and our feelings influence our behaviors.[10] Having an awareness of this cycle and how it contributes to our relationships is foundational to our healing. For many women, not only separating their thoughts and feelings, but also identifying them in this process takes time.

Defining the difference between thoughts and feelings is imperative. We've all heard someone say, "...it made me feel like they were judging me because I was letting my kids eat snacks..." This is not a feeling, but is a perfect example of a thought. Feelings are best described as one word: happy, sad, playful, excited. Feelings reflect an emotional state. A thought is a full sentence that leads to a feeling.

[10] Riggenbach, J. (2013). *The CBT Toolbox: A Workbook for Clients and Clinicians*. Eau Claire, WI: PESI Publishing & Media.

Here are a few examples of how our thoughts lead to how we feel:

- I thought they were going to raise my rent, so I felt worried.
- I thought we were having a girls' night tomorrow, but it was canceled. I am disappointed.
- I thought my big work project would be completed soon, but it has been delayed. I feel frustrated.

So often, we know what we're thinking but can't identify what we're feeling. Or, we know how we feel, but are not sure why or where the feeling is coming from. Use the following exercise to further explore the relationship between our thoughts and feelings.

CHALLENGING UNHEALTHY THOUGHTS

When it comes to our inner voice—talking to ourselves in our head—many of us understand the analogy of a tape recorder. Over time, the messages we pick up about ourselves, our identity, and our behaviors are recorded on imaginary tapes. These tapes rewind and replay—over and over—throughout our lifetime. Unfortunately, it is our negative messages—our unhealthy thoughts—that replay with the greatest frequency, especially when, in the moment, we are feeling frustrated, stressed, or lonely.

Research suggests that we talk to ourselves at a rate of 4,000 words per minute; for some people, this is as much as 10 times faster than they can talk out loud.[11] This is possible because when we talk to ourselves, it is more condensed—we have a greater understanding of the meaning behind what we are saying.

As previously discussed, **thoughts are full sentences and feelings are one word**. Our thoughts and feelings are closely related, in that many of our feelings originate from what we are thinking.[12] The conversations that take place in our mind—the tapes that continually play—influence how we are feeling.

What are some of the messages that play in your mind? If there were a tape recorder in your head recording your every thought, what would the replay sound like?

____

____

____

____

____

____

[11] Beck, J. (2016). *The Running Conversation in Your Head*. November 23. Retrieved from www.theatlantic.com.

[12] Riggenbach, J. (2013). *The CBT Toolbox: A Workbook for Clients and Clinicians*. Eau Claire, WI: PESI Publishing & Media.

Scripture instructs us to "take every thought captive" (2 Corinthians 10:5) and we can only do this if we are aware of how our thoughts impact our feelings and, ultimately, our behaviors. Use the following table to connect your thoughts and feelings throughout the week.[13]

I FELT...	BECAUSE I THOUGHT...
Fear	I thought my ex-husband was trying to manipulate our kids; he has always wanted to take them away from me.
Sad	I thought I was getting a promotion at work, but they gave it to someone else.
Happy	I thought I was going to have to work late, but made it to my son's baseball game, where he hit a home run.

[13] Riggenbach, J. (2013). *The CBT Toolbox: A Workbook for Clients and Clinicians*. Eau Claire, WI: PESI Publishing & Media.

I FELT...	BECAUSE I THOUGHT...

What observations can you make about how your feelings and thoughts are related?

Raising awareness to how our thoughts and feelings influence our behaviors will help us gain insight into the motivating factors that drive our behaviors in relationship.

Looking Ahead

Complete the Group Check-In, Self-Care lesson, and Change & Growth Analysis in your *Unraveled: Weekly Tools* before the next group meeting.

Note: Since lesson 2 covers the neurochemistry of addiction, it is longer than the previous lessons. Be sure to set aside enough time to complete this lesson before group next week.

LESSON 2: THE NEUROCHEMISTRY OF ADDICTION

This week, we are going to focus on understanding the neurochemistry of addiction. It's not enough that we recognize how our behaviors and thought life create problems in relationship. To gain lasting sobriety from any destructive behavior, we have to learn what's happening in our brain so we can initiate change from the inside out.

As we dig into our past throughout the course of this study, we will discuss many factors that contribute to addictive and problematic behavior. Typically, it is not one single life event or circumstance where coping behaviors were developed to soothe the painful feeling in the moment. It is important to recognize that the road to addiction is multifaceted and often explained through a biopsychosocial perspective—meaning that our biology (genetic and chemical makeup), psychology (mood, personality, behavior), and the social environment (culture, family, socioeconomic status) of our life each plays a role in our behaviors.

The brain structures and functions discussed in this lesson will provide a foundation for all neurochemistry discussions in the following lessons.

> *Jesus replied, "'You must love the LORD your God with all your heart, all your soul, and all your mind.'*
>
> **MATTHEW 22:37 NLT**

We are commanded to love God with our heart, soul, and mind; but how can we do this if we don't understand how our mind—our brain—works and contributes to our behaviors?

While it is not necessary to know all the intricacies of the brain, it is essential to know both the structures and functions of some basic processes. For this reason, this lesson is primarily about learning what we need to know—what is necessary for creating a road map to recovery—followed by practical application.

THE BRAIN

The human brain is one of the most mysterious of God's creations. It contains approximately 100 billion nerve cells or what we refer to as **neurons**.[14] A single neuron communicates or sends information by passing a chemical—**a neurotransmitter**—to another neuron. The connections between neurons—**the synapse or synaptic gap**—can span from 10 trillion to 100 trillion points of contact within the human nervous system.

NEURONS

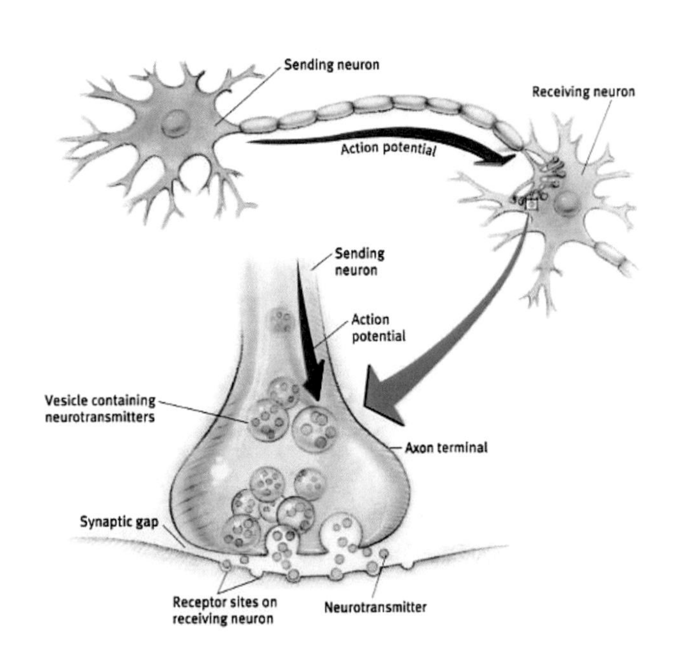

[15] The primary function of a neuron is to process information.[16] Neurons vary in both form and size depending on their specific function; some less than fractions of an inch and others up to 3 feet in length. **They are also specific to which type of neurotransmitter they respond: dopamine, serotonin, or norepinephrine, for example.**

In very simple terms, an electrical impulse travels down the **axon**, producing a chemical reaction—releasing neurotransmitters into the synaptic gap. A receptor on the receiving cell will bind to a specific neurotransmitter, in many ways reflecting a lock-and-key scenario, absorbing the neurotransmitter, yielding a specific action. This is called **synaptic transmission**. The excess neurotransmitters not used by the receiving cell are taken back into the sending cell—recycled—through a reuptake process for repackaging and reuse.[17] Although this process is extremely complex, down to the most minuscule detail, it is important to understand how these mechanisms work in connection to addictive behavior.

---

[14] Beatty, J. (2001). *The Human Brain: Essentials of Behavioral Neuroscience*. Thousand Oaks, CA: Sage Publications, Inc.

[15] Hall, R. AP Psychology course. http://www.rhsmpsychology.com/Handouts/synapse.htm

[16] Beatty, J. (1995). Principles of Behavioral Neuroscience. Dubuque, IA: Wm. C. Brown Communications, Inc.

[17] Beatty, J. (2001). *The Human Brain: Essentials of Behavioral Neuroscience*. Thousand Oaks, CA: Sage Publications, Inc.

Take a Break: *In your own words, write out a definition that will help you remember the terms described above.*

Neurons: ____

Neurotransmitters: ______________________________________

Synapse/Synaptic Gap: ___________________________________

The **limbic system** is located in the center of the brain—often referred to as the emotional center of the brain. It is not one isolated part of the brain, but rather a collection of structures associated with processing emotion, mood, and memory.[18] The limbic system is made up of several distinct areas, interconnected by their function. Three specific areas of the brain play a significant role in addictive behavior.

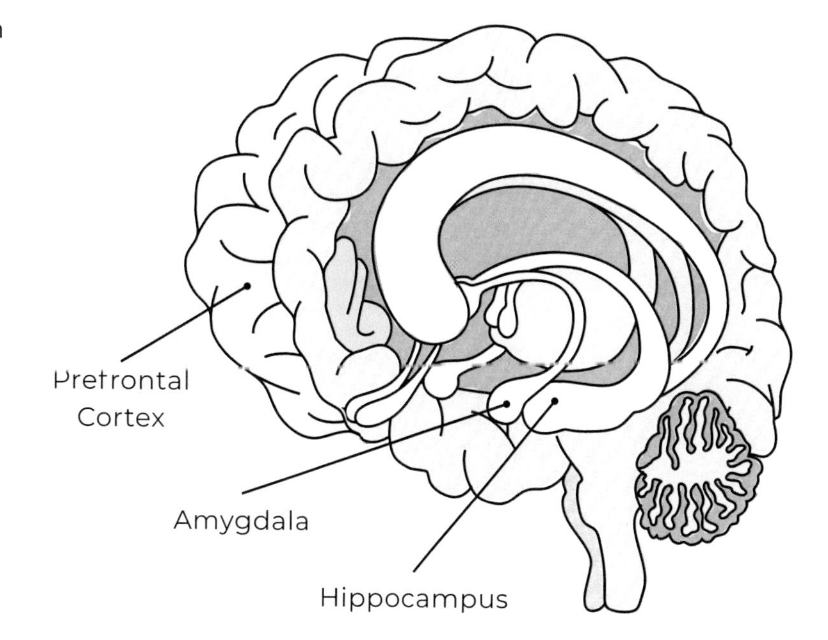

The **prefrontal cortex**, which interacts with the limbic system, does many amazing things for us: regulates positive and negative emotion, helps with problem-solving, and self-awareness, to name a few.[19] Most importantly, when it comes to addictive behavior, the prefrontal cortex contributes to decision-making, planning, and impulse control.

The **hippocampus** gathers information from many sources—from our environment and life events—and links them together to form memories.[20] It is responsible for consolidating (moving) our short-term memory into long-term memory while we sleep (another reason why sleep is so important).

---

[18] Abrahams, P. (2015). *How the Brain Works: Understanding Brain Function, Thought, and Personality.* New York, NY: Metro Books.

[19] Hines, T. (2016). *Anatomy of the Brain.* Mayfield Clinic, University of Cincinnati, Department of Neurosurgery.

[20] Siegel, D.J. (2012). *Pocket Guide to Interpersonal Neurobiology: An Integrative Handbook of the Mind.* New York, NY: W.W. Norton & Company, Inc.

The **amygdala** regulates our emotional response and assigns meaning based on our environment.[21] Both positive and negative emotions are produced in the amygdala as a result of a rapid assessment of the situation. For example, when someone we love walks into the room, our face will display an emotional response of happiness or pleasure. Or, if someone unexpected appears in a dark setting, we may respond with fear because the amygdala has determined that there is a threat or the situation may be dangerous.

When we have an experience, especially an event that is perceived as threatening or dangerous, the hippocampus and the amygdala work together to process the event—the specific details of what happened and the way it made us feel are stored together in our limbic system.

The disconnect: research suggests that the limbic system—the emotional center of the brain—is fully functional by age six.[22] However, the prefrontal cortex—decision-making, planning, and impulse control—is not fully developed until the mid-twenties.

The reality of this physiological disconnect: *most of us will spend almost 20 years interpreting our world—what is happening to us and around us—through a highly emotional filter; through a limbic filter. Not because we are overreacting or overly emotional, but because our brain is not yet capable of rational thought.*

I couldn't understand my reaction. The look on my husband's face was that of shock, confusion, and disappointment. We were out on a date, having a great time, when he leaned in to kiss me. Without even thinking about it, I turned my head and pulled away. In the moment, I felt the need to protect myself; but why?

As a girl, I remember boys trying to kiss me when I didn't want them to. In high school, with many boyfriends, they kissed me aggressively—like they were taking something from me that I was not willing to give. At times, especially in sexual situations, they forced themselves on me, trapping me into submission. I felt afraid and unsafe. I had no control over what was happening to me.

This doesn't make sense. If I'm in a happy, committed marriage, why would I respond to my husband this way? I really love kissing him, so why is this happening?

Aspen

[21] Abrahams, P. (2015). *How the Brain Works: Understanding Brain Function, Thought, and Personality.* New York, NY: Metro Books.

[22] BetterHelp (2018). *Adolescent Brain Development And What It Means.* Retrieved from https://www.betterhelp.com/advice/adolescence/adolescent-brain-development-and-what-it-means/.

What is causing Aspen to react this way? Is she experiencing a ***limbic*** *reaction?*

God designed our limbic system for survival, to help us develop awareness and learn from our environment—whether we are safe or in danger. Collectively, the areas of the limbic system work together to influence and create emotion, mood, and memory. In response to an emotional trigger—a limbic reaction, if you will—the limbic system will set in motion a sequence of neurological actions.

If a situation is alarming or frightening, it will trigger our **fight-flight-or-freeze** response.[23] If we encounter a person as a friend, our memory will override the need or feeling to retreat, and produce the appropriate warm-hearted response.

Take a Break: *In your own words, describe the function of each area of the limbic system.*

Prefrontal cortex: ______

Hippocampus: ______

Amygdala: ______

Can you think of a situation when your fight-flight-or-freeze response was activated: when you felt fearful or threatened? Explain.

[23] Siegel, D.J. (2012). *Pocket Guide to Interpersonal Neurobiology: An Integrative Handbook of the Mind.* New York, NY: W.W. Norton & Company, Inc.

Can you think of a time when you exhibited a ***limbic*** *response or felt emotionally triggered by a fairly normal situation? This is evident when the level of our response doesn't match the level of the situation. Explain.*

Our limbic system is so important. When the Bible refers to our heart—when we ask Jesus into our heart—it is referring to this area of the brain: the limbic system. When it comes to our sexually compulsive and addictive behaviors, lifelong healing comes from a renewing of our limbic system.

Based on what you have learned so far, what is the significance of understanding what's happening in the brain?

THE REWARD SYSTEM

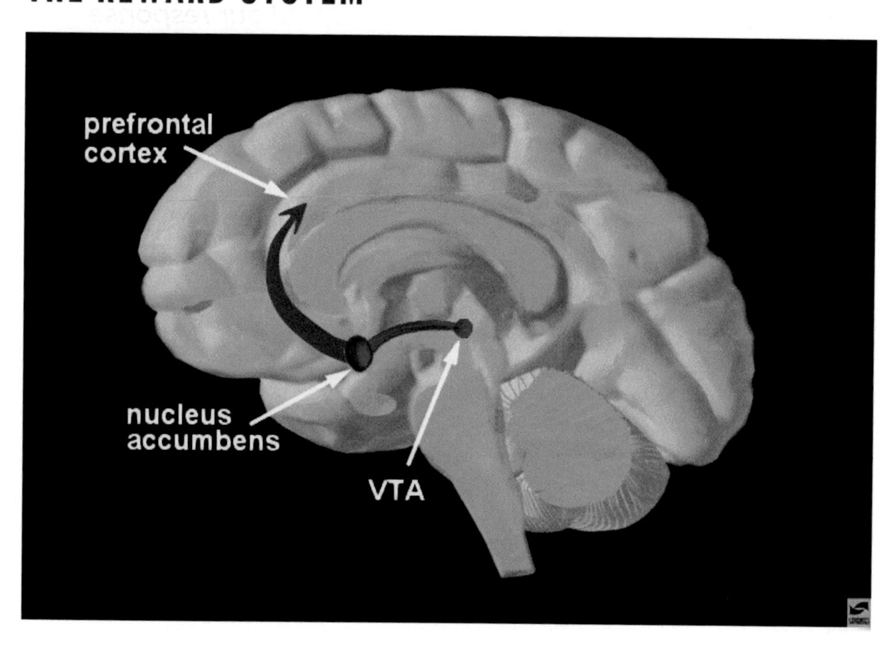

[24] Everything we do—all of our thoughts, feelings, and behaviors—originate in our brain. The motivation behind *why we do what we do* happens through a specific process. Here's how this works.

The **ventral tegmental area** (VTA) is highly responsive to the production of dopamine.[25] This is the origin of the dopamine system. It looks for excitement or novelty (stimulation) in our environment. Once it finds excitement, the release of dopamine increases and is projected to various regions of the brain: the nucleus accumbens, amygdala, and hippocampus of the limbic system, and the prefrontal cortex.

When dopamine is stimulated in the brain, it creates feelings of euphoria and pleasure. Who doesn't want that! When we participate in behaviors that stimulate the production of dopamine in our brain, we naturally want to repeat those behaviors. The reward system doesn't just create feelings of pleasure. It includes areas of the brain involved with motivation and memory. Logically, we determine that if we continue the same behaviors, we will get the same response. If it were only that simple.

Dopamine is a powerful motivator. In laboratory studies, rats will perform a specific action to receive an electrical stimulation to their brain—rewarding them with the production of dopamine—ignoring all other rewards such as food and water.[26] When it comes to stimulating the production of dopamine, rats will press a lever as rapidly as 2,000 times per hour, each time receiving an electrical stimulation. In fact, they will continue to press the lever at this same rate for 24 hours or more. This is just one example of the power of dopamine.

[24] Reward Pathway. http://www.drugabuse.gov/pubs/teaching/Teaching2.html

[25] Beatty, J. (1995). *Principles of Behavioral Neuroscience*. Dubuque, IA: Wm. C. Brown Communications, Inc.

[26] Ibid.

THE ADDICTED BRAIN

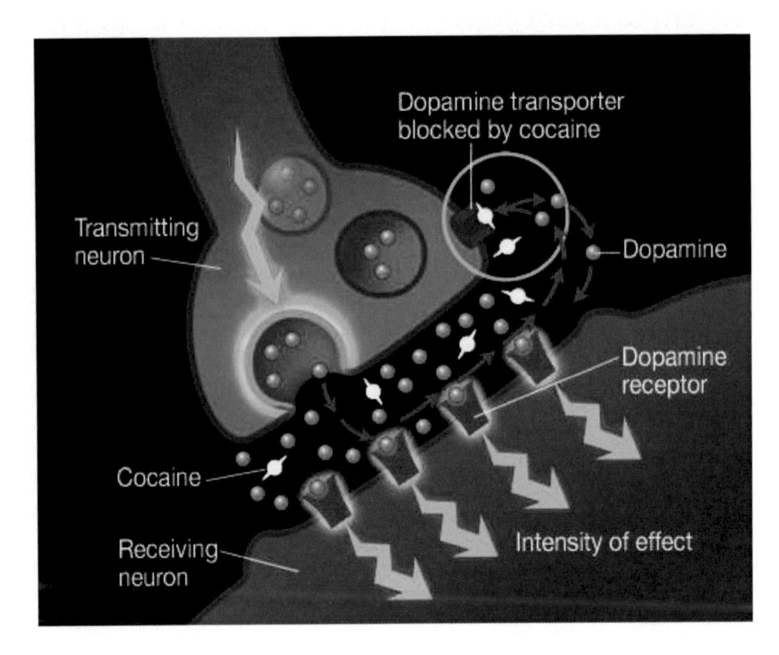

[27]Have you ever thought of addictive behavior as learned behavior? Think about this: learning produces changes in the way we think, feel, and act.[28] When our behavior is reinforced with a positive result—making us feel in control, happy, or safe—we naturally want to repeat the behaviors that created this specific response. The more we repeat the behavior, the more it changes our brain, strengthening neural connections.

Previously, we learned what is happening during synaptic transmission: the communication process among neurons in a healthy, non-addicted brain. Here's what is happening in an addicted brain.

The best way to illustrate this process is to begin with a brain addicted to cocaine. When an individual uses cocaine, it activates the VTA, stimulating the production of dopamine.[29] However, with cocaine on board, the cocaine binds to the dopamine transport system and blocks the reuptake process. As a result, dopamine floods the synaptic gap and over stimulates the receiving neuron.

What is most fascinating about this process is that **the brain registers all pleasure the same way, regardless of its origin**.[30] Whether we derive pleasure from shopping, a substance, a sexual encounter, or an accomplishment, the brain responds the same way. In fact, the brain doesn't discriminate based on the source—it will continue to produce dopamine in response to the stimulation of the VTA.

So what is happening in the brain if cocaine is not the issue but a behavior is the issue? What is blocking the reuptake of dopamine? This is an excellent question.

---

[27] Dopamine transporter blocked by cocaine. https://www.drugabuse.gov/publications/research-reports/cocaine/how-does-cocaine-produce-its-effects

[28] Carlson, N. (2007). *Physiology of Behavior* (9th ed.). Boston, MA: Pearson Education, Inc.

[29] Ibid.

[30] Unknown author (n.d.). *Understanding Addiction: How Addiction Hijacks the Brain*. Harvard Health Publications. www.helpguide.org

Based on research from the University of Florida, scientists liken the dopamine transport system to a very powerful and efficient "vacuum cleaner."[31] In a healthy brain, when dopamine is released in response to a pleasurable action, dopamine is eventually swept back into the sending cell via the dopamine transport system, returning the brain to a less-stimulated state. Our brain is all about balance. When the dopamine transport system is out of balance—unable to keep up with excessive amounts of dopamine in the system—problems occur.

A non-substance addiction is considered a behavioral or process addiction: the compulsion to continually engage in a behavior despite the negative consequences.[32] When it comes to addictive behaviors, we all can find ourselves becoming addicted to love, sex, food, shopping, relationships, gaming, and even social media. Our brain can become addicted to these behaviors the same way it becomes addicted to a substance.

TOLERANCE

Typically, when our reward system is naturally stimulated through the pleasures of our everyday lives, our brain functions accordingly. However, when we artificially increase the stimulation of dopamine through substance use or behaviors, flooding the brain with dopamine, the brain responds by producing less dopamine.[33] The brain recognizes when something is not right in its chemical makeup and makes adjustments to bring everything back into balance. Over time, the substance or behavior yields less pleasure, requiring an increased dosage of the substance or an escalation in the behavior to achieve the same dopamine high.

When it comes to developing **tolerance**, here's what we need to remember: **an increase in stimuli–the substance or behavior used to make us feel better–decreases the effect it has in the brain**.

This is also one of the main reasons why it is so difficult to stop using a substance or engaging in an unhealthy behavior. The downside of a dopamine high is often followed by anxiety and depression[34]—anxiety because we're now faced with living life without the protection of our addiction, and depression because our brain has decreased its dopamine production.

---

[31] University of Florida. (2016, January 25). Researchers uncover how dopamine transports within the brain. *ScienceDaily.* www.sciencedaily.com/releases/2016/01/160125184333.htm

[32] American Addiction Centers (2018). Retrieved from https://americanaddictioncenters.org/behavioral-addictions.

[33] Unknown author (n.d.). *Understanding Addiction: How Addiction Hijacks the Brain.* Harvard Health Publications. www.helpguide.org

[34] Carlson, N. (2007). *Physiology of Behavior* (9th ed.). Boston, MA: Pearson Education, Inc.

How does having a deeper understanding of what's going on in your brain personally impact your perception of addictive behaviors?

Think of a time when you attempted to stop using your drug of choice—a substance or a behavior—and found yourself feeling anxious and/or depressed. Describe the experience.

Examples: late-night eating, social media, masturbation or any unwanted sexual behavior, drinking wine or alcohol.

What was the end result of the above described experience? Were you able to fight past the physiological effects of tolerance, or did the experience end in relapse?

Identify how this experience made you feel. Circle the appropriate feelings.

Happy	Confident	Sad	Withdrawn
Motivated	Empowered	Disappointed	Guilty
Successful	Excited	Angry	Exhausted
Encouraged	Cheerful	Embarrassed	Lonely

Of the feelings you circled above, which one stands out most? What is the significance of that feeling in this instance?

____

____

____

____

____

____

EMOTION

All of this brain information would be incomplete without recognizing the practical way it impacts our relationships, especially when it comes to our emotional health.

Understanding the factors that influence emotion is challenging; however, emotion plays a significant role in our everyday lives, shaping and enhancing the human experience. It is important to recognize the difference between mood and emotion. Mood is often defined as a more persistent period of emotionality.[35] Emotions are typically short-lived, lasting anywhere from a few minutes to several hours, and often occur in response to an external stimuli.

We've all been there. It can be caused by another driver who almost hit our car, the past-due notice we get for the bill we've already paid, or the red sock that found its way into our laundry load of whites, and we now have the wardrobe of a pretty pink princess. We feel alarmed, exasperated, and frustrated (and a little sad), but only in the moment. These feelings soon fade and are replaced when our emotions are again evoked.

[35] Barlow, D. & Durand, V. (2005). *Abnormal Psychology: An Integrated Approach* (4th ed.). Belmont, CA: Thomson Wadsworth.

Experiencing emotion involves both physical and mental processes, which are dependent on what's happening (external stimuli) and an individual's interpretation of the event.[36]

While it has been argued that we have six basic or universal emotions—joy, sadness, anger, disgust, fear, and surprise—this remains a topic of controversy.[37] Not only are the terminology and definitions used ambiguous at best, emotion is subjective. While we may be able to infer, *generally* speaking, that in a *general* situation most people would emotionally respond in *generally* the same way, this is dangerous. Cultural influences, issues of mental health, and individual life experience profoundly affect emotion.[38] More importantly, all other emotions—love, delight, empathy, passion, gratefulness, and many more—are learned behavior.

When it comes to the development and regulation of interpersonal relationships, emotional expressions are crucial.[39] Much of human interaction relies on, and is often dictated by, our ability to learn and recognize emotional or facial expressions. Here are a few examples to illustrate this point:

- An infant will learn facial expressions from their primary caregivers—both positive and negative—during their early attachment years.
- When a teenager comes home from school, aggressively throws his backpack on the floor and yells at his brother, he is greeted by his parent with a defensive but curious facial expression, reacting to his hostility.
- While appearing in court after receiving a speeding ticket, the judge's somber expression and serious tone often set the mood for everyone in the room.

There are many instances we could discuss where we had the opportunity to practice our facial expression awareness. Throughout the course of this study, we will continue to build on what we learned about brain structure and function and the way it contributes to our behavior.

---

[36] Abrahams, P. (2015). *How the Brain Works: Understanding Brain Function, Thought, and Personality*. New York, NY: Metro Books.

[37] Dalgleish, T. & Power, M. (1999). *Handbook of Cognition and Emotion*. New York, NY: John Wiley & Sons Ltd.

[38] Abrahams, P. (2015). *How the Brain Works: Understanding Brain Function, Thought, and Personality*. New York, NY: Metro Books.

[39] Dalgleish, T. & Power, M. (1999). *Handbook of Cognition and Emotion*. New York, NY: John Wiley & Sons Ltd.

Prior to this lesson, what was your understanding of emotion?

Where and/or how did you learn about emotion? What was the emotional climate in your family while growing up?

Keep in mind that understanding emotion is more than our ability to recognize emotional or facial expressions. Emotion can also be the result of an internal stimuli—a feeling or a thought that creates an emotional response.[40]

Looking Ahead

Complete the Group Check-In, Self-Care lesson, Thoughts/Feelings Awareness Log, and Change & Growth Analysis in your *Unraveled: Weekly Tools* before the next group meeting.

[40] Carlson, N. (2007). *Physiology of Behavior* (9th ed.). Boston, MA: Pearson Education, Inc.

LESSON 3: MY SEXUAL BEHAVIORS

The more we understand how our childhood environment and life experience impact brain development, the more likely we are to recognize the source of our unhealthy behaviors. While it may not be obvious at first, over time, as we struggle to manage love, sex, and relationships, it becomes quite clear: our behaviors, especially our sexual behaviors, are interfering with our ability to create genuine connection with others.

Many women struggle with understanding how our sexuality affects our perspective, capacity for relationship, and even our daily lives. For many of us, our sexuality has brought us nothing but pain: we have been used and abused; we are wanted and rejected; we are shamed for being female.

We have bought into society's definition of sexuality: that our sexuality ultimately leads us to love and acceptance. We have been deceived.

Even as a little girl I loved the attention I received from men. I was raised by a single mom and never had much contact with my biological dad. My mom got pregnant at 17 and my parents never married. Over the years, I watched my mom's behavior toward men: fun and flirty, dressing for attention, and always interested in what the men were interested in. Despite a string of unhealthy, unsuccessful relationships, my mom was always looking for the perfect man.

I learned what womanhood should look like from my mom. I typically had more guy friends than girl friends. I was never without a boyfriend, often starting a relationship with a new guy before ending my current relationship. I learned that if I gave my boyfriends physical affection they would treat me well, say nice things to me, and buy me gifts: they would love me.

Although I participated in many sexual acts with all my boyfriends, I didn't officially lose my virginity until I was 14 years old, the summer before I entered high school, to a high school senior. I felt so loved!

I immediately told my mom about my first sexual experience. My mom gave me a brief talk about safe sex and scheduled a doctor appointment for me so I could get on birth control pills. She didn't want me to get pregnant. I finally made the connection: sex equals love.

Lara

In what ways do you relate to Lara's story?

What is Lara's core belief about her sexuality?

What was communicated to you about your sexuality from your family of origin?

What has been your core belief about your sexuality?

What is sexuality? While many think our sexuality is based on sexual orientation and preference, it is so much more. From birth we are identified as female. Our brain is female, organized differently than a male brain. For example, the female brain has language centers in both hemispheres; whereas, the language center of the male brain is in the left hemisphere.[41] Generally, this is why women cultivate relationships, socially connect, and communicate more than men.

[41] Jantz, G. (2014). Brain Differences Between Genders. *Psychology Today.* Retrieved from https://www.psychologytoday.com/us/blog/hope-relationships/201402/brain-differences-between-genders

It was once thought that gender and sexuality were culturally shaped, having more to do with how parents raised their children than actual biological differences.[42] Today, it is well-recognized that **the female brain is structurally and functionally different than the male brain**, contributing to the vast behavioral differences in memory potential, emotional sensitivity, learning capacity, and more.

We are created in the image of God and uniquely created female.

> *So God created human beings in his own image. In the image of God he created them; male and female he created them.*
>
> **GENESIS 1:27 NLT**

By God's design, our sexuality is a core characteristic of our human nature. We are sexual beings. It is part of our identity. However, when we don't understand the intent and purpose of our sexuality from God's perspective, it can become an area that is misused, manipulated, distorted, and a source of shame.

As illustrated in Lara's story, so many women confuse sexual activity with love. Ultimately, we all want to experience a deep, unconditional, sacrificial love. Seeking this "perfect" love, we continually exchange sexual favors and compromise our sexuality, only to be left alone, disappointed, and ashamed yet again. What we fail to recognize is that sex is not the glue that holds human relationships together.

In Mark 12:29-31 (NLT), Jesus clearly states that love, not sex, is the bonding agent in relationships: loving God and loving others.

> *[29]Jesus replied, "The most important commandment is this: 'Listen, O Israel! The LORD our God is the one and only LORD. [30]And you must love the LORD your God with all your heart, all your soul, all your mind, and all your strength.' [31]The second is equally important: 'Love your neighbor as yourself.' No other commandment is greater than these."*

So, if we were not raised in an environment where we learned this type of love and have not experienced it elsewhere, how is it that we develop a mindset for genuine love?

Use the following questions to begin identifying differences in the way love impacts our perceptions and behaviors.

---

[42] Brizendine, L. (2006). *The Female Brain.* New York, NY: Harmony Books.

What are some ways you feel personally loved by God?

What are some ways you feel loved in a non-sexual relationship (with a parent, sibling, or friend)?

What are some ways you feel loved by your spouse or in a romantic relationship?

In Lara's story, it's easy to see there was a huge void of love and connectedness in her family, so she was trying to fill a legitimate need in an unhealthy way. When have you tried to meet a legitimate need in an unhealthy way?

Love is a learned behavior. It is not one of our basic human emotions. From birth, we all learn what love looks like through experience. Not only do we learn what love should or should not look like, we assign meaning to love based on the behaviors of others. We spend a lifetime interpreting the intent and motivation behind the way we are loved, only to find that our interpretation was shaped through our misguided and distorted view of love.

Think about life as a child. When do we remember feeling loved and close to our parents? When we received emotional support and encouragement? When we received physical affection—hugs, kisses, snuggles? Going out to shop or explore? Eating new foods or treats together?

The way we experience love and our perception of love impacts our sexuality. We want to feel loved through genuine connection, but struggle when our desire for love and connection becomes enmeshed with our sexuality. At some point, our sexual behaviors enter a gray area: our mind grapples with what we know to be true and what we can justify, convincing ourselves that our behaviors are okay if we never fully cross sexual boundaries. In the moment, we often cannot see how the behaviors we have justified as "harmless" lead to unhealthy sexual perceptions and behaviors in the future.

I hated getting up in the morning for class. It was my second year of college and I shared a dorm room with three of my good friends. Some mornings, Claire's bed was empty. It didn't take long to see her on the top bunk spooning with Brittney—again. Claire must have slept there all night. Weird. I never understood why my friends needed to be so touchy and spoon with each other all the time.

I quickly did my morning stretches and then hopped in the one shower in our dorm room. I had to shower quickly: I knew my roommates' alarms would go off soon and I didn't want to be in the shower when they got up. I washed up, got out, and threw a towel around me. A few minutes later, one by one, my three friends got out of bed and made their way into the bathroom. Before long, they were all naked and getting in the small shower together, like they did nearly every morning.

The whole thing made me very uncomfortable. I always felt like I needed to rush through my shower just so they didn't all get in there with me. There was no way I was going to be squished in a shower with three other girls. I put on my clothes and a little makeup and headed out of the room. I didn't want to be there any longer than necessary. I knew they would stand around naked while putting on their makeup before getting dressed.

On my walk to the cafeteria, I couldn't help but question my friends' behavior. Why do they spoon all night? Why do they feel like they should be naked together in the shower? Are they attracted to each other? I could not figure it out. I sat down at the table and then noticed my boyfriend walking over. For a second I wondered, If I didn't have this amazing guy in my life, would I want to be naked with my girlfriends and cuddle with them all night? I really hoped the answer was no, but I wasn't sure.

None of my friends were dating anyone, though they wanted to be in relationships. Maybe my friends were trying to fill a void: since they were not in a dating relationship with a guy, they developed a closeness—too close—with one another. It didn't make sense to me, but I also couldn't imagine what it would be like to not be in a dating relationship. Maybe my roommates were trying to fill their desire for intimacy by being physical with each other? My thoughts quickly passed as I stood to greet my boyfriend with a hug. I couldn't imagine life without the connection we shared.

Kristi

Are the roommates' behaviors just "girls being girls," or is there another motivation?

Through this experience, what are the roommates learning about their sexuality?

How is this experience contributing to their perception of feeling loved and accepted?

THE CONTINUUM OF SEXUALITY

Human sexuality is complex and exists on a continuum.[43] Based on our experiences, both positive and negative, we form rules and expectations around our sexuality. Throughout our lifetime, the pendulum of our sexual behavior swings. So much of our physiology is all about balance, and this includes our sexuality. If we have experienced healthy sexual relationships, our sexual perception and behaviors reflect health. When we experience pain and trauma in sexual relationships, our sexual perception and behaviors swing between sexual extremes: sexual anorexia and sexual addiction.

Sexual anorexia is characterized by a distinct aversion to anything sexual. This includes rigid and judgmental attitudes toward sexuality and physical touch. Many of us who struggle with sexual anorexia carry extreme sexual shame and self-loathing related to previous sexual experiences or a negative perspective of sex. We may exhibit distortions in our physical perception and appearance.

Sexual anorexia is based on a core belief: "I am basically a bad, unworthy person. No one could love me as I am. My needs are never going to be met if I have to depend on others. Sex is bad and dirty. Sex is my most terrifying need."

Motivations: illusion of power, control, safety, and self-righteousness.

Sexual health is characterized by manageable sexual behaviors. This includes honest and vulnerable communication and realistic expectations of sex. We recognize that physical sex is only part of our sexuality, cultivating intimacy through commitment, trust, and healthy boundaries. We are expressive in our sexuality. We are content.

Sexual health is based on a core belief: "I am saved by God's grace, worthy of His love. I am created in God's image and I am loveable. My needs can be met through an intimate, loving relationship. Sex is an amazing part of God's design between me and my husband."

Motivations: emotionally and spiritually connected, present, and affectionate.

Sexual addiction is characterized by out-of-control sexual behaviors. This often includes excessive masturbation, pornography use, fantasy, and multiple sexual partners. Despite negative consequences, our compulsive need for sexual satisfaction persists—we seek out risk-filled sexual experiences. We're looking for a quick fix, a moment of instant gratification to mask our feelings of pain and fear. We feel socially isolated.

Sexual addiction is based on a core belief: "I am basically a bad, unworthy person. No one could love me as I am. My needs are never going to be met if I have to depend on others. Sex is my most important need."

Motivations: illusion of power, control, safety, freedom, and choice.

---

[43] Adapted from the International Institute for Trauma and Addiction Professionals, CSAT Certification Training Day Two: Module One.

THE CONTINUUM OF SEXUALITY[44]

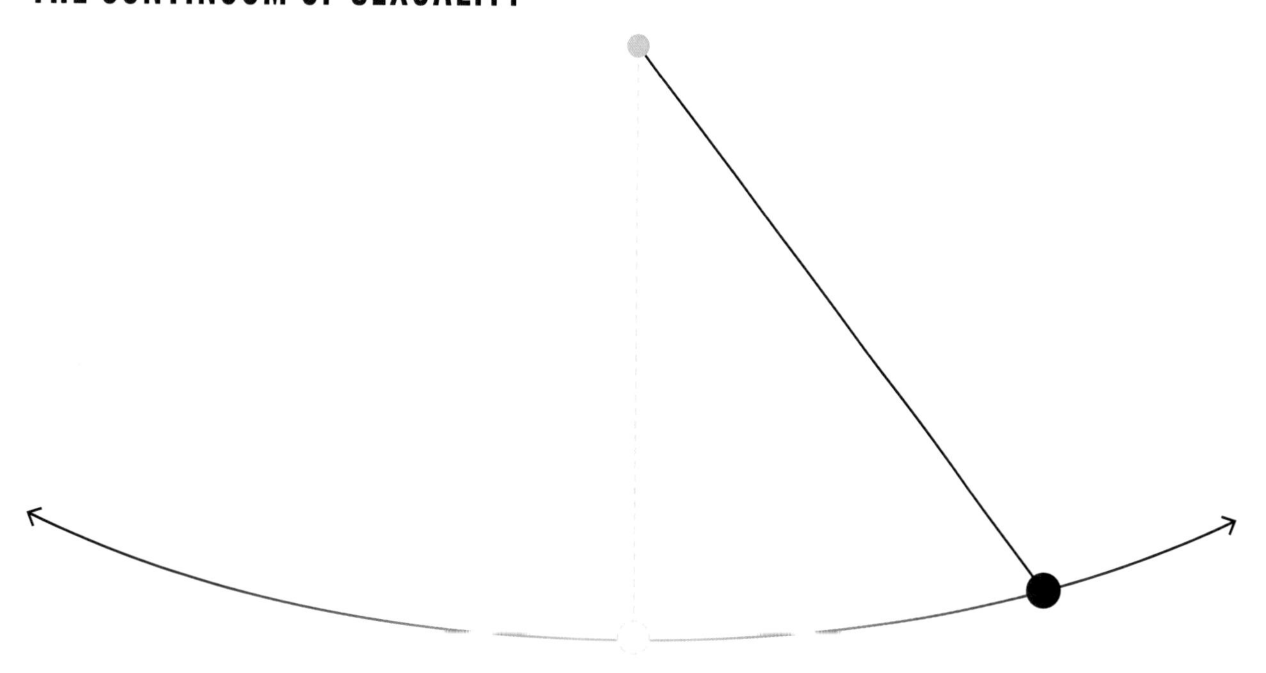

SEXUAL ANOREXIA/ACTING IN	SEXUAL HEALTH	SEXUAL ADDICTION/ACTING OUT
Rigid	Structure	Chaotic
Excessive	Boundaries	Collapse
Isolation	Intimacy	Emotionally Absent
Depression	Expressing Needs	Excess
Fear	Sharing Needs	Anger
Obsessive	Taking Responsibility	Defiant

Some of the motivations for sexual anorexia and sexual addiction are identical. Although many of the attitudes and behaviors are polar opposites, the motivation looks the same: we want to feel like we are the one with all the power; we want to feel like we have control in the relationship; we want to feel safe. As we continue to understand what healthy sexuality looks like, we will discover that this is essential for learning how to manage love, sex, and relationships.

[44] Adapted from International Institute for Trauma and Addiction Professionals CSAT Certification Training Day Two: Module One

Based on the descriptions above, which behaviors do you relate to most: sexual anorexia, sexual health, or sexual addiction? Why?

Since our sexual behaviors exist on a continuum, in what ways are your sexual behaviors healthy?

In what ways are your sexual behaviors unhealthy?

When do you feel the most sexual? When do you feel the least sexual?

In what area could you begin to change, moving you toward sexual health?

Our sexuality is a defining piece of who we are—a part of our core identity. When we understand our sexual behaviors, both healthy and unhealthy, it helps us recognize where change is needed.

Looking Ahead

Complete the Group Check-In, Self-Care lesson, Thoughts/Feelings Awareness Log, and Change & Growth Analysis in your *Unraveled: Weekly Tools* before the next group meeting.

chapter three

EMOTIONAL AWARENESS

LESSON 1: CONFRONTING DENIAL

Dr. Patrick Carnes suggests that breaking through the denial of our addictive, compulsive, and problematic behaviors is challenging. Many people "...hide the severity of the problem from others to delude themselves about their ability to control their behaviors and to minimize their impact on others."[45]

For many of us, denial is used as a defense mechanism. Perhaps we experienced something so terrible, so beyond comprehension, that we cannot consciously accept it as truth. In some ways, living in denial protects us. When we live in denial, we escape the emotional harm attached to a painful experience.

Honestly, we may not recognize the extent to which we are living in denial. We may try to convince ourselves that, "What happened in the past, should stay in the past. I'm fine. I'm going to keep moving forward." Inevitably, the emotional weight of our past will sabotage our forward motion, making each step forward much more difficult than the last. We will continue to trip over the denial we have created in our path.

At some point, we will face a decision: continue to struggle with denial, staying in one stagnant place, never really moving forward, OR confront denial and work to unravel our addictive, compulsive, and problematic behaviors; learning how to manage love, sex, and relationships in a healthy way.

I know something is wrong. Although my husband and I are separated and have not lived together in nine years, when he comes into town once a month, I become a different person. I am a nervous wreck anticipating his arrival, but became flirty and overly affectionate once he arrives, even inviting him to stay at my house. Why did I so desperately want his attention? I want to, but I'm too poor to get a divorce. Whatever this is, it is not healthy.

I originally left my husband because of his drug addiction. He was physically abusive but still claimed to love me, even now. He can't seem to keep a job and is constantly moving. Even though I know all of this, I am still attracted to him and

---

[45] Carnes, P. (2000). Sexual Addiction and Compulsion: Recognition, Treat & Recovery. *CNS Spectrums*, 5(10): 63-72.

give in to his sexual advances when he is in town. I can't explain why I turn into a lovestruck teenager when he's around. I feel like I'm going crazy.

Despite the fact that I am "legally" married, I continue to have many male friends. I've always had more guy friends than girl friends. Men are so much easier to get along with than women. I don't really have any close female friends. Let's just say I have many "friends with benefits." It's not like I'm having affairs, since I didn't really feel married.

Lately, I've found myself sexually attracted to much younger men. I'm 36 years old and pursuing a relationship with an 18-year-old. The younger guys seem so attentive and willing to spend time with me. Although they don't know much about my past, they genuinely care about the real me.

Christina

Based on Christina's story, where do you think she is struggling with denial?

What is Christina trying to hide with denial: what is the reality of her situation?

If Christina was your friend, how would you help her break through her denial and see the truth?

Learning to live in truth can feel overwhelming. Many of us haven't looked at the truth in years, let alone lived in it. We have become so comfortable living behind the wall of denial, unsure if we would even recognize the real version of ourselves.

Without question, confronting denial will be a big job. It will take more work than we think. It will be more painful than we anticipate. It will reveal more truth than we thought possible. It will bring more healing than we ever imagined.

When God wants to work in us—deep, life-changing, liberating work—it's going to take time and intention. It's going to take the women in this group to walk with us through the difficult times. It's going to take a measure of grace that only God can provide.

> *Let us then approach God's throne of grace with confidence, so that we may receive mercy and find grace to help us in our time of need.*
>
> **HEBREWS 4:16**

In what ways have you been living in denial?

____

____

____

____

____

____

____

____

____

As you consider confronting denial, how is Hebrews 4:16 empowering?

____

____

____

____

____

____

____

____

____

Identify one area in your life where you are ready to confront denial. What will be the greatest challenge in this area?

____

____

____

____

____

____

____

____

____

____

____

____

FINDING MY FEELINGS

The ability to identify our feelings, in the moment, can be challenging, not to mention the difficulty of trying to identify our feelings after the fact—sometimes many years later. Feelings are one word—happy, sad, energized, grateful. They are a single word that strikes at the core of how we were impacted by an interaction, experience, or event. Whether we recognize it or not, our feelings become placeholders in our memory, waiting to rise to the surface when we least expect it.

Much of the way we think about and process feelings comes from the environment in which we were raised. It has been suggested that we are hardwired with six basic emotions—anger, disgust, fear, happiness, sadness, and surprise.[46] All other emotions are learned behaviors. If we were raised in an environment where emotional expression was modeled, we will be more aware of our feelings, able to express how we are feeling in many situations. However, if we were raised in an environment where feelings and emotions were not expressed, we will be less likely to identify how we are feeling—in many ways, we will lack an awareness and the ability to describe our feelings.

Regardless of our past experience, it is never too late to start learning how to identify our feelings. Since we know that all of us experience the six basic emotions, we will begin with identifying these specific feelings. We will start off slow but continue to build on this exercise throughout the course of this study.

---

[46] Burton, N. (2016). *What Are Basic Emotions?* Retrieved from www.psychologytoday.com.

In the table below, write out a personal definition for the following emotions and/or a situation when you experienced the specific emotion.

PERSONAL DEFINITION	EMOTIONAL EXPERIENCE
I feel fear in an emergency and I don't know what to do.	My son fell off the swing and landed on his head. He was bleeding a lot. I didn't know if I should call an ambulance or drive to the emergency room.
	Anger:
	Disgust:
	Fear:
	Happiness:
	Sadness:
	Surprise:

Consider the following definitions:

- **Anger:** a strong feeling of annoyance, displeasure, or hostility.
- **Disgust:** a feeling of revulsion or profound disapproval aroused by something unpleasant or offensive.
- **Fear:** an unpleasant emotion caused by the belief that someone or something is dangerous, likely to cause pain, or a threat.
- **Happiness:** the state of being happy; exhibiting a positive mood or a sense of well-being.
- **Sadness:** the condition or quality of being sad; affected with or expressing grief or unhappiness.
- **Surprise:** an unexpected or astonishing event, fact, or thing.

When comparing your definition to the actual definition, what observations can you make?

If we are going to develop emotional health, we have to become more aware of how we are feeling in the moment. Over the next week, in the table provided, chart how you are feeling. Use tally marks (IIII) in the box below, so you can keep track of your specific emotional experiences that occur throughout a given day. Be intentional about recording your feelings and plan to share your experience in group next week.

FEELING	MON	TUES	WED	THURS	FRI	SAT	SUN
Anger							
Disgust							
Fear							
Happiness							
Sadness							
Surprise							

Based on your emotional data collected over the past week, what are your most common emotional expressions? List all emotions that show up with frequency.

Can you identify a pattern to when you are experiencing your most frequent emotion?

It is important to understand our feelings and how they contribute to our behavior. Our feelings have value. It might seem unnatural or scary to explore this feelings arena, especially if this is a new area of discovery. Don't back away. Be brave.

Looking Ahead

Complete the Group Check-In, Self-Care lesson, Thoughts/Feelings Awareness Log, and Change & Growth Analysis in your *Unraveled: Weekly Tools* before the next group meeting.

LESSON 2: SELF-AWARENESS

Raising an awareness of our behaviors—our self-destructive thought processes, feelings, and actions—is what allows us to recognize where change is needed. If we want to live in health, we have to risk change. Change not only requires risk, but also a willingness to embrace the truth regardless of the consequences. It is having a perspective and mindset of "reality at all costs."

Think of it this way: "**Reality at all costs** is not a mantra of extreme commitment or will power, but a state of mind—of being present and aware. **Reality at all costs** is about knowing the truth and being willing to admit where my behavior does not match."[47]

In this lesson, we will discover an amazing tool for helping us maintain a clear perspective of our behaviors—not that we will always like the results, but so we can continue to move toward health through realistic self-awareness. We cannot change our behaviors if we fail to recognize where change is needed. **When pursuing health, change is inevitable.**

I have always been an overachiever. I grew up in a home where achievement was highly valued and this shaped much of my identity. Throughout my childhood, career, marriage, and even in parenting, I always aimed for perfection. I know no one is perfect, but my expectation of perfection was part of my core beliefs, and from time to time this would cause problems.

In an effort to overachieve in all areas of life, I often neglected my feelings. I had trained myself to push past any negative feelings, not allowing myself to really feel the pain. I stayed very busy, which allowed me to have very little time alone and kept me from experiencing negative emotions. By staying busy, I also neglected my self-care on a regular basis. I got very little sleep, spent no time with God or friends, and experienced days when I felt too busy for basic necessities like showering. Those who knew me would never suspect any of this—I always gave the impression that I had everything together. I was admired for how much and how well I accomplished things in my life.

In my early 30s—juggling the demands of parenting, work, marriage, and trying to keep my house clean—I really started to break down. My lack of emotional awareness pushed me further and further from health. I continued to move past

---

[47] Roberts, B. & Kolb, H. (2018). *Digital Natives: Raising an Online Generation.* Gresham, OR: Pure Desire Ministries International.

any negative emotion without dealing with it. Eventually, I had pushed aside so many negative emotions that one day they all came to the surface. I exploded in anger and yelled at my young children.

I didn't know where this anger was coming from, but it continued to show its ugly face on a regular basis. Now that it was coming out, I felt like I couldn't control it. I honestly believed that I had never been angry in my life. In reality, I had been repressing anger and other negative emotions my entire life. I lacked so much self-awareness that I really didn't know how to process any emotions. Despite the guilt I felt for my uncontrollable, explosive anger, I was completely at a loss. I didn't know how to fix this or how to begin working on self-awareness.

Brooke

What were some of Brooke's core beliefs about herself?

____

____

____

____

____

Describe the symptoms Brooke exhibited that led to her breakdown.

____

____

____

____

____

Why is it important that we recognize and acknowledge our feelings in a healthy way?

____

____

____

____

____

____

____

THE FASTER RELAPSE AWARENESS SCALE

The FASTER Relapse Awareness Scale[48] (referred to as the FASTER Scale) helps us identify and understand our current behaviors in order to change our future behaviors. This unique tool is designed to raise awareness of the self-destructive patterns often exhibited in a person's life. The intent is to provide an intervention or an escape from relapse. **One of the greatest things we can do for ourselves is learn why we do what we do.**

Many times, when we feel overwhelmed or stressed, we relapse or return to our previous coping behaviors in order to gain control of what's happening. When we discover the trauma at the core of our addictive and compulsive behaviors and process our fear and pain, it leads to restoration and health. It leads to the behaviors we previously discussed (chapter 2, lesson 1) that become a continual part of establishing sobriety.

Every letter in the word "FASTER" reflects a downward step toward relapse.[49] Each step describes behaviors, attitudes, and feelings that hide or protect our pain and fear. While the behaviors may be the result of environmental or neurochemical factors, the pattern of progression toward relapse can become more obvious over time. Developing an awareness of our unique relapse patterns is critical for helping us create a mindset for health, as well as the strategies needed to avoid future relapse.

The FASTER Scale process is made up of two parts.[50] Part One helps us recognize the specific behaviors, attitudes, and feelings that are currently true about us in each section. Part Two allows us to focus on the most obvious behavior, attitude, or feeling with which we are struggling and answer three important follow-up questions.

In Part One we will go through all the steps on the FASTER Scale and circle what we identify with in each section—that we are experiencing on a daily or weekly basis.

In Part Two we will identify the single behavior, attitude, or feeling that is most powerful or problematic within each step and write it next to the corresponding heading.

Procrastination and isolation are two behaviors found consistently in all the steps of the FASTER Scale.[51] When we are faced with having to do something that is unpleasant, we often turn to procrastination and isolation. However, this has the tendency to make things worse over time. Failing to deal with what is happening in our environment moves us down the FASTER Scale and further from trusting God—toward relapse. Through the support and accountability of our group, we can overcome the behaviors that keep us stuck in addictive, compulsive patterns and continue on the path toward health.

---

[48] Dye, M. (2012). *The Genesis Process: For Change Groups, Book 1 and 2, Individual Workbook* (4th ed.). Auburn, CA: Michael Dye, 234.

[49] Ibid, 236.

[50] Ibid, 238.

[51] Ibid, 255.

FASTER SCALE

Adapted with permission from the *Genesis Process* by Michael Dye

PART ONE

☐ *Circle the behaviors on the FASTER Scale that you identify with in each section.*

RESTORATION – **(Accepting life on God's terms, with trust, grace, mercy, vulnerability and gratitude)** No current secrets; working to resolve problems; identifying fears and feelings; keeping commitments to meetings, prayer, family, church, people, goals, and self; being open and honest, making eye contact; increasing in relationships with God and others; true accountability.

FORGETTING PRIORITIES - (**Start believing the present circumstances and moving away from trusting God. Denial; flight; a change in what's important; how you spend your time, energy, and thoughts.**) Secrets; less time/energy for God, meetings, church; avoiding support and accountability people; superficial conversations; sarcasm; isolating; changes in goals; obsessed with relationships; breaking promises & commitments; neglecting family; preoccupation with material things, TV, computers, entertainment; procrastination; lying; overconfidence; bored; hiding money; image management; seeking to control situations and other people.

Forgetting Priorities will lead to the inclusion of:

ANXIETY – (**A growing background noise of undefined fear; getting energy from emotions.**) Worry, using profanity, being fearful; being resentful; replaying old, negative thoughts; perfectionism; judging other's motives; making goals and lists that you can't complete; mind reading; fantasy, codependent, rescuing; sleep problems, trouble concentrating, seeking/creating drama; gossip; using over-the-counter medication for pain, sleep or weight control; flirting.

Anxiety then leads to the inclusion of:

SPEEDING UP – (**Trying to outrun the anxiety which is usually the first sign of depression**): Super busy and always in a hurry (finding good reason to justify the work); workaholic; can't relax; avoiding slowing down; feeling driven; can't turn off thoughts; skipping meals; binge eating (usually at night); overspending; can't identify own feelings/needs; repetitive negative thoughts; irritable; dramatic mood swings; too much caffeine; over exercising; nervousness; difficulty being alone and/or with people; difficulty listening to others; making excuses for having to "do it all."

Speeding Up then leads to the inclusion of:

TICKED OFF – (**Getting adrenaline high on anger and aggression**): Procrastination causing crisis in money, work, and relationships; increased sarcasm; black and white (all or nothing) thinking; feeling alone; nobody understands; overreacting, road rage;

constant resentments; pushing others away; increasing isolation; blaming; arguing; irrational thinking; can't take criticism; defensive; people avoiding you; needing to be right; digestive problems; headaches; obsessive (stuck) thoughts; can't forgive; feeling superior; using intimidation.

Ticked off then leads to the inclusion of:

EXHAUSTED – (**Loss of physical and emotional energy; coming off the adrenaline high, and the onset of depression**) Depressed; panicked; confused; hopelessness; sleeping too much or too little; can't cope; overwhelmed; crying for "no reason"; can't think; forgetful; pessimistic; helpless; tired; numb; wanting to run; constant cravings for old coping behaviors; thinking of using sex, drugs, or alcohol; seeking old unhealthy people & places; really isolating; people angry with you; self abuse; suicidal thoughts; spontaneous crying; no goals; survival mode; not returning phone calls; missing work; irritability; no appetite.

Exhausted then leads to the inclusion of:

RELAPSE – (**Returning to the place you swore you would never go again. Coping with life on your terms. You sitting in the driver's seat instead of God.**) Giving up and giving in; out of control; lost in your addiction; lying to yourself and others; feeling you just can't manage without your coping behaviors, at least for now. The result is the reinforcement of shame, guilt and condemnation; and feelings of abandonment and being alone.

PART TWO

☐ *Identify the most powerful behavior in each section and write it next to the corresponding heading.*

☐ *Answer the following three questions:*

1. How does it affect me? How do I feel in the moment?
2. How does it affect the important people in my life?
3. Why do I do this? What is the benefit for me?

RESTORATION: ______________________________

1. ______________________________
2. ______________________________
3. ______________________________

FORGETTING PRIORITIES: ____________________

1. ____________________
2. ____________________
3. ____________________

ANXIETY: ____________________

1. ____________________
2. ____________________
3. ____________________

SPEEDING UP: ____________________

1. ____________________
2. ____________________
3. ____________________

TICKED OFF: ____________________

1. ____________________
2. ____________________
3. ____________________

EXHAUSTED: ____________________

1. ____________________
2. ____________________
3. ____________________

RELAPSE: ____________________

1. ____________________
2. ____________________
3. ____________________

DOUBLE BIND

Any time change is needed, we face a double bind: a lose/lose situation.[52] We have a choice to make and we don't want to do either option. However, when recognizing a choice is required, the right choice becomes obvious—not because it's the easier choice, but because of the direction it takes us. One choice will lead us further into isolation—stuck in our addictive behaviors—separated from God and others. The other choice will lead us toward relationship with God and others. In fact, many times the more obvious choice toward health is the most difficult choice.

When we face a double bind, we are facing our fears, just like we did when we anticipated removing the masks we wear (chapter 1, lesson 3). A double bind requires that we face our fears and step in the direction that we've been avoiding.

As with most choices we make, there are consequences. The same is true when faced with a double bind. Let's see if we can identify the double bind in the following story.

I am happily married. I love my husband and think our marriage is better than most. However, if there was one area that could use a little work, it would be in our communication styles. Whenever I initiate a conversation about something, especially a topic I'm passionate about, my husband interrupts me, takes over the conversation, and shuts me down. When this happens, I feel disrespected, unloved, and silenced. I don't feel like I have a voice.

Lately, this pattern has become more frequent. I spoke with a trusted friend about it and she advised me to discuss my feelings with my husband. I'm afraid that if I bring this up with him, he'll get angry and say, "You're too sensitive. You're overreacting again!" But, if I don't say anything and let this pattern continue, it will become divisive in our marriage. I'm already starting to feel resentful toward my husband. I don't know what to do. The thought of confronting him with this issue makes me feel anxious and physically sick. The thought of not saying anything and letting him walk all over me with his words makes me feel worthless and a little angry.

Debi

---

[52] Ibid, 57.

What is the double bind—the two negative choices—Debi is facing?

If you were in Debi's situation, what would you do?

It is normal to experience fear when trying to make the right choice for long-term health. Worry and fear can keep us from taking that step.

ARE YOU CONCERNED OR WORRIED?

Something is on your mind. You can't sleep. You are distracted. Are you worried or are you concerned? Is there a difference? Why does it matter?

When we make the choice to develop health in our lives—physically, mentally, emotionally, and spiritually—we have to be proactive. We have to put strategies in place that allow us to establish healthy control in our behaviors, thought processes, and attitudes.

Concerns are:

- Things we need to take care of: making a phone call, finishing a chore or task, spending time with the kids, getting into group, having a difficult conversation.
- Something we have control over and the ability to change: our attitude toward our spouse when they fail to do something we expected.
- Something that is our responsibility that we need to take ownership of: finishing a task well and letting go of our compulsive, perfectionist tendencies.

Worries are:

- Things that are not ours to fix: our spouse's relationship with their parents; our son's job search.
- Something we have no control over: our daughter's college is closing and she has to transfer; natural disaster; war.
- A future worry that hasn't happened: "What if I can't find a babysitter?" "What if my spouse can't find a better job?" "What if...?"
- Irrational fears that have no basis in reality: zombies, alien abduction.

When we are concerned about something, we need to be proactive: take control. Put action steps in place to help us resolve the concern. Do what needs to be done to minimize the stress surrounding our concerns.

When we are worried, when it is out of our control, we need to be proactive: allow God to take control. In these situations, find a scripture that provides comfort and assurance that God will take care of our worries.

Give all your worries and cares to God, for he cares about you.

1 PETER 5:7

This is a great tool for taking our thoughts captive (2 Corinthians 10:5). We don't want to allow negative and destructive thoughts to control us and poison our attitude.

Use the following tables to determine whether you are feeling concerned or worried. For each concern put an action step in place. For each worry, find a scripture that reminds you of God's grace and provision in your life.

CONCERN	ACTION STEP

WORRY/FEAR	SCRIPTURE

SCRIPTURE SUGGESTIONS:

Don't worry about anything; instead, pray about everything. Tell God what you need, and thank him for all he has done.

PHILIPPIANS 4:6

[28]Then Jesus said, "Come to me, all of you who are weary and carry heavy burdens, and I will give you rest. [29]Take my yoke upon you. Let me teach you, because I am humble and gentle at heart, and you will find rest for your souls. [30]For my yoke is easy to bear, and the burden I give you is light."

MATTHEW 11:28-30

Give your burdens to the Lord, and he will take care of you. He will not permit the godly to slip and fall.

PSALM 55:22

When have you ***experienced*** *God taking care of your worries and concerns?*

A personal promise from God is more than simply our favorite scripture. It often comes from an encounter with God—when we felt His presence in a unique and powerful way. Times when we felt God saying something to us, about us, and can link this experience to a specific scripture in His Word.

Our brain is changed through experience with God. When we see God working in our lives, experience His closeness, and hear His voice through His Word and personal promises to us, it changes us. It is this life-changing experience that leads to lifelong healing.

Looking Ahead

Complete the FASTER Scale, Group Check-in, Self-Care lesson, Thoughts/Feelings Awareness Log, and Change & Growth Analysis in your *Unraveled: Weekly Tools* before the next group meeting.

LESSON 3: IS LOVE A FEELING?

WHAT IS LOVE?

Love is probably one of the most studied, debated, and published topics in philosophy, science, and religion. Why do we want love? Why do we need love? Why is it easier to find love in some areas of our lives but not in all areas? Why do we continue to seek out love in relationship when we are constantly left heart broken and disillusioned? Will anyone ever meet our expectations for love?

Most of us would initially think of love in a positive way, but attached to love are many negative effects that play an equal role in our lives. While love can be confusing and subjective to define, we all have experienced the effects of love in our lives: joy, loneliness, sorrow, devotion, guilt, happiness, pain, excitement, grief, disappointment, surprise, freedom, sacrifice...and the list goes on and on.

Love is a learned behavior. We learn about love—what it is, how it is given, and how to get it—through experience: our family of origin, relationship, movies, music, social media, and more. It is an essential part of the human experience.

I can't remember a time when I felt so unloved. My husband wanted to sell our home and move to another town, to take a job making less money. We would be leaving our families, friends, and church community. We would be leaving the only life I had ever known. We were at an impasse in this decision. We were out for dinner one night and my husband's friend showed up. I thought it was a coincidence, but I was so wrong. My husband had invited his friend to dinner to coerce me into moving. I took the car keys and left the restaurant. I've never felt so angry, bullied, and betrayed.

Feeling frustrated and confused, I went to talk with my parents. They often provided a sound, godly perspective to life's problems. My mom wasn't home, but my dad was there to lend a listening ear. For the next hour, I ranted about my husband, his manipulative tactics, his self-centeredness, and his obvious lack of love for me. My dad just listened.

When I finally stopped ranting, my dad asked, "Who are the people in your life who love you?" I quickly named my parents, all my siblings and other family members, and many close friends. Then my dad asked, "How do you know they love you?" These seemed like trick questions. I quickly mentioned some simple things that expressed love and even described very specific instances where I KNEW I was loved. This conversation lifted my spirits and brought a smile to my face.

I'll never forget this: with an expression of peace and confidence, my dad smiled and said, "Then, how much more could the One who created love, love you?"

Audrey

Audrey is in a tough spot with her husband. Why do you think she feels unloved?

How will understanding God's love help Audrey deal with her husband and their relationship issues?

If we want to gain a full understanding of love, we have to learn from "the One who created love." We will never find satisfaction in a flawed, imperfect, self-centered, and sinful version of love. We have to go to the source.

Probably the most well-known verse among the churched and unchurched alike is John 3:16:

> *For God so loved the world that he gave his one and only Son, that whoever believes in him shall not perish but have eternal life.*

What does this verse tell you about love?

Read through the following verses about love. After each verse, write out a few words or a phrase that reflects the behaviors, characteristics, or attributes of love.

> *This is how we know what love is: Jesus Christ laid down his life for us. And we ought to lay down our lives for our brothers and sisters. If anyone has material possessions and sees a brother or sister in need but has no pity on them, how can the love of God be in that person? Dear children, let us not love with words or speech but with actions and in truth.*
>
> **1 JOHN 3:16-18**

> *The commandments...are summed up in the one command, "Love your neighbor as you love yourself." If you love others, you will never do them wrong; to love, then, is to obey the whole Law.*
>
> **ROMANS 13:9-10 GNT**

> *There is no fear in love. But perfect love drives out fear, because fear has to do with punishment. The one who fears is not made perfect in love.*
> *We love because He first loved us.*
>
> **1 JOHN 4:18-19**

> *Place me like a seal over your heart, like a seal on your arm; for love is as strong as death...Many waters cannot quench love; rivers cannot sweep it away.*
>
> **SONG OF SONGS 8:6-7**

☐ *Which of the above scriptures best illustrates love or resonates with you most? Why?*

____

____

____

____

☐ *How are the above scriptures similar or different from your previous understanding of love?*

____

____

____

____

Understanding God's love for us comes from knowing the heart of God. Nothing illustrates God's love for us more than the story of Hosea and the parable of the prodigal son.

The Lord told the prophet Hosea to marry Gomer, a promiscuous woman. Although they were married and had kids, Gomer was having affairs with other men. Despite this, the Lord instructs Hosea to go after her, to buy her back, and love her again. Israel had been unfaithful and worshiped false gods, but God still loved them. This was an example of God's relentless love for Israel.

> *"Go and love your wife again, even though she commits adultery with another lover. This will illustrate that the Lord still loves Israel, even though the people have turned to other gods and love to worship them."*
>
> **HOSEA 3:1 NLT**

Another great example of God's love is described in the parable of the prodigal son. When a rebellious son demands his inheritance, his father gives it to him. This was extremely hurtful behavior, since an inheritance was given after a father's death, not while a father was still living. The son squandered his wealth and decided to return to his father, even though he had sinned against his father and behaved badly. Without question or need for explanation, the father lovingly, unconditionally, and shamelessly welcomed back his son.

> *"But the father said to his servants, 'Quick! Bring the best robe and put it on him. Put a ring on his finger and sandals on his feet. [23]Bring the fattened calf and kill it. Let's have a feast and celebrate. [24]For this son of mine was dead and is alive again; he was lost and is found.' So they began to celebrate."*
>
> **LUKE 15:22-24**

If you were Gomer, the promiscuous woman, or the prodigal son, how would you feel about these demonstrations of love?

Have you ever experienced such a demonstration of love? Explain.

God's love for us is extravagant. God gave His only Son—God so loved the world—so that we could have a relationship with Him through Jesus.

In the box below, draw a picture of what God's love feels like to you.

Although Audrey felt unloved by her husband, she experienced the love of God through her parents, siblings, and friends. Others in our life may have tainted our perspective of God's love for us, but understanding God's outrageous love for us is paramount.

Love is more than a feeling. It is an action, decision, and choice we make. It is a mindset that infiltrates all our relationships. It shapes our worldview. It is only through God's perfect love and relationship with Him that we will ever find true and lasting love.

MY STORY

Why are we here in this group? We all have a story. For many of us, our story includes a foundation of love: a form of love that has impacted and shaped our perspective, influencing how and why we seek out love in relationship.

Truthfully telling our story, out loud, in a safe environment heals us.[53] At some point in our past, we suffered a deficiency in the way we formed attachments and bonded to others. This process helps us strengthen our ability to trust and bond with others in a healthy way.

In the space provided, write out your personal story. Why are you here? What life events and experiences contribute to your compulsive and addictive behaviors?

Your story can begin and end at any stage of your life: childhood, college, marriage. It could include a snapshot of your life—a time when a profound experience changed your perspective or the way you engage in relationship. What you write can be as broad or as narrow as you want. Feel free to leave out graphic details and specific names of others involved. Your story should take about three minutes to read out loud during your next group meeting.

---

[53] Roberts, D. (2010). *Pure Desire for Women: Eight Pillars to Freedom from love addiction & sexual issues.* Workbook 1. Gresham, OR: Pure Desire Ministries International. 59.

Facing the truth about our past and unpacking our addiction story can feel overwhelming. Some of us may need to take this assignment in stages, writing out a few sentences or a paragraph at a time. Others may want to just get it over with, writing it all out in one sitting. Whatever method we use, be intentional and thorough. It may not seem like it matters now, but this is an important step on our path toward lifelong health.

Looking Ahead

Complete the FASTER Scale, Group Check-in, Self-Care lesson, Thoughts/Feelings Awareness Log, and Change & Growth Analysis in your *Unraveled: Weekly Tools* before the next group meeting.

chapter four

WHERE WE COME FROM

LESSON 1: LOVE AS A CHILD

Our lives are made up of a million moments that have influenced, directed, and shaped who we are today. For many of us, how we ended up here remains a mystery. We may be able to rationalize various parts of our past—both good and bad—that give insight to some of our current thoughts, feelings, and behaviors. Yet, the question remains: how did we get here?

We're not talking about a philosophical "beginning of time" question, but more of an individual question: How did we get here, right now, to this place in our lives? Why do we continue to struggle in relationships? Why do we misinterpret the meaning of connection with others? Why do we relentlessly chase after love, only to find ourselves feeling rejected, discarded, and lonely?

Some of our current struggles and compulsive behaviors come from past experiences. Someone we expected to support us—to be responsible for us—failed. We have been disappointed and disillusioned by others. We survived, but not without scars. Our scars, while we hide them well, hinder our relationships, affecting the way we have learned to relate, trust, and love others.

We are not blaming others for our problems. None of us had perfect parents. In their brokenness they did the best they could. We are not blaming them. Instead, we are working to discover and reclaim what God wants to restore in our lives. We cannot make sense of our current relationship issues unless we understand the full impact of our brokenness.

In the table below, identify the people who have contributed to your brokenness.[54] *Describe the adverse effects of the relationship and the way it makes you feel.*

PERSON	ADVERSE EFFECTS	FEELINGS
1.		
2.		
3.		
4.		

[54] Roberts, D. (2010). *Pure Desire for Women: Eight Pillars to Freedom from love addiction & sexual issues*. Workbook 1. Gresham, OR: Pure Desire Ministries International. 129.

We have to recognize that our brokenness—our relational scars—are internal, not external, causing us to be oblivious to their effects. In many ways, we develop a blind spot—a place unnoticed by our peripheral vision, out of our natural line of sight.[55] This is significant. When we experience pain and fear in our lives, it can create a blind spot—an area we can't heal unless we are aware of its existence. Whether we know it or not, our blind spot has a direct line of sight to our soul—to our heart. When we experience brokenness, it leaves us vulnerable. As we begin to recognize our blind spot, we can be proactive in bringing our brokenness back into view, allowing us to heal in a healthy environment.

> *I prayed to the Lord, and he answered me. He freed me from all my fears.*
>
> **PSALM 34:4 NLT**

Describe a time when you reacted to your internal brokenness, your blind spot, but didn't realize it until after the fact.

In what ways are you becoming more aware of your blind spot?

[55] Dye, M. (2012). *The Genesis Process: For Change Groups, Book 1 and 2, Individual Workbook.* Auburn, CA: Michael Dye. 109.

I grew up in a very religious home and went to church three times a week. I heard very little about God's grace and much about His wrath. My mom and dad were separated off and on during my childhood; when they were separated, my siblings and I lived with my mom.

My mom struggled with depression and was overwhelmed most of the time. She would lock herself in her room for extended periods of time, so we learned to take care of ourselves and each other. When my mom was not in her room, she disciplined us in physical and harsh ways. We were taught that anything sexual was dirty.

Our home was not a safe place to learn, talk openly, or express negative emotions. Anger, sadness, hurt, frustration, and fear were not allowed. I learned to put all my negative feelings in a deep corner of my mind and lock them away.

I didn't know what it was like to feel safe and accepted for who I was; my mom never seemed happy with me. I felt like I was supposed to be someone else, but I didn't know how to make that happen. Many times, I was punished for things I didn't do. My mom called me a liar and told me, "God has shown me that you are a liar and need to be punished!" This was incredibly confusing. Over the years, I started to believe that I was a liar and didn't know how to tell the truth.

When I was seven years old, I was molested by the pastor of our church. He told me that I was worthless and that if I ever told anyone what he was doing to me, they wouldn't believe me. This reinforced what my mother continually told me: I am a liar. If my own mother thought I was a liar, then why would anyone else ever believe me? My little mind was so confused that, for years, even I didn't believe that the pastor had done anything to me. I learned to compartmentalize my pain and trauma. During the abuse, I created a place in my mind to escape my reality, a place I never went otherwise. The sexual abuse lasted for eight years, until I was 15 and my family moved away from the area. For years I struggled to trust myself, questioning whether the abuse had even happened. Every time I thought about it, I heard a voice in my head saying, "You're nothing but a liar. Everyone knows it."

Kit

With what Kit experienced from her mom and pastor, what kind of view would she have of God?

____

____

____

____

____

I grew up, got married, had children, and became very angry. Anger seemed to control me. I began to take out my anger on my children. I knew I needed help but didn't know how or where to get it. I longed to find a safe place.

When I was 30 years old, my husband's sexual addiction brought me to a Pure Desire group. As I worked through the material, it became obvious: being raised in an environment where I was unable to safely show emotion had disabled me. I was numb, moving through life without feeling—not feeling extreme pain, but also not feeling true joy. The abuse I experienced caused me to close myself off from others. I didn't know how to trust people. I lived with a crippling fear that if people really knew me, they wouldn't like me, so I lived under a guise of perfectionism.

I had never met women like those in my group. They were so open and honest: never judging or condemning, simply listening, understanding, and accepting. I found so much freedom when I went to group each week. Telling my story was painful, more raw and real than anything I had ever before felt. I cried tears of shame, regret, and loss. I cried for the little girl who never got to be a little girl—the little girl who had to grow up way before her time. That little girl had never known what it was like to be carefree, to run, play, and laugh without a big black burden following her around.

Today, I continue to experience how much God loves me, how much grace and compassion He has for me. I am learning to embrace all of the emotions that life brings. At times, I still want to shut myself away, where I feel safe, keeping people at a distance. God is showing me who I am in Him—loved, treasured, adored, worthy, chosen, redeemed, healed, and whole. Some days, these things are hard to believe. When I hear the old voices telling me lies, I remind myself of the experiences I've had in group and that God's Word is truth. His Word says that I am greatly loved. "For God so loved Kit, that He gave His one and only Son." John 3:16

Kit

As a child, what did Kit learn about love from the adults in her life?

____

____

____

____

____

____

____

After growing up, getting married, and having kids, why do you think Kit was so angry?

What made Kit's group instrumental to her healing?

Kit was able to experience healing through her group and God's promises in her life. It is only through new, positive experiences that we change our brain—that we begin to reconstruct new neural pathways in our limbic system, creating lasting and lifelong change.

So many of our internal messages—both positive and negative—were developed during our childhood through experience with others. For most of us, our primary relationships were with our parents.

Use the following questions to further explore the impact of the relationship with your parents.[56] If you were raised with a stepmother or stepfather, answer the questions pertaining to that relationship. This also applies if you were raised by any other person who took on a parental role: grandmother, grandfather, aunt, foster parent.

MOTHER'S ROLE

1. *While growing up, describe what you remember about your mother.*

[56] Roberts, D. (2010). *Pure Desire for Women: Eight Pillars to Freedom from love addiction & sexual issues*. Workbook 1. Gresham, OR: Pure Desire Ministries International. 139.

2. *Write down five adjectives or statements that describe your mother.*

3. *How are you the same as or different from your mother?*

4. *How did she encourage and affirm you? If she didn't, describe that loss.*

5. *How do you respond to women or female authority figures?*

FATHER'S ROLE

1. *While growing up, describe what you remember about your father.*

2. *Write down five adjectives or statements that describe your father.*

3. *How are you the same as or different than your father?*

4. *How did he encourage and affirm you? If he didn't, describe that loss.*

5. *How do you respond to men or male authority figures?*

As you think about the influence of your family of origin, what are your conclusions?

___

___

___

___

IDENTIFYING TRIGGERS

Identifying triggers can be challenging, but is a necessary part of the healing process. If we intend to change our behaviors, we need to understand why we do what we do. This level of awareness is directly tied to recognizing how we are triggered by our environment.

Simply put, a trigger is something that elicits or stirs up a feeling or an emotional response; and a trigger can be anything—a person, place, smell, object, or even another's behavior. In the moment, anything that propels us back to a time when we experienced pain, trauma, or a lack of control. In many ways, our triggers often magnify an area in our life where we continue to struggle: physically, mentally, emotionally, spiritually, and sexually.

Since we are all different and respond differently to similar situations—even among family members—it is important to recognize when we are feeling triggered. A good indication is when our emotional response to a situation is either extremely elevated or nonexistent.

Here's an example: Caroline enters the break room at work, where Matt, Caroline's colleague and friend, has brought in a box of doughnuts. In a kind and gracious gesture, Matt offers Caroline a doughnut. Caroline is immediately angered and responds, "Why would I want a doughnut? I'm gluten-free; and I don't even like doughnuts! Why did you even bring doughnuts? You look like you've had your fair share of doughnuts!" Caroline stomped out of the break room, leaving Matt shocked and confused by what had just happened.

Was Caroline's response appropriate to the situation? No. When Matt offered her a doughnut, wouldn't a simple "No, thank you" have sufficed? Yes. Was she triggered by something in her environment? Probably.

Here's what Matt doesn't know about Caroline: she has struggled with her weight most of her life, has bouts with bulimia, and is currently in Weight Watchers. She has been doing well with her eating behaviors over the past month, but at last night's weigh-in, she had gained three pounds. She feels frustrated, discouraged, and hungry. Although she knows her father loved her, she has memories of him joking with her and calling her "chubster." Every time she looks in the mirror, that's what she hears in her head. Caroline doesn't like being overweight—it makes her feel worthless and unlovable. She really does like doughnuts and feels horrible about what she said to Matt.

Caroline was triggered when Matt offered her doughnuts. Her response to Matt was out of proportion to what the situation warranted.

We all have **triggers: pressure points that are directly tied to our past pain and trauma**. As you work through the following questions, be specific and detailed in your answers.

Describe a situation in the past few months when you felt triggered, creating an unexpected emotional response.

What thoughts were going through your head during this situation?[57] (Remember, thoughts are described in a sentence: "I thought this would end badly.")

During this situation, what were you feeling? (Remember, feelings are described in one word: "I felt fear, anxiety, depressed.")

What other factors may have contributed to your response in this situation? (Sleep deprivation, stress, other life concerns.)

[57] Dye, M. (2012). *The Genesis Process: For Change Groups, Book 1 and 2, Individual Workbook* (4th ed.). Auburn, CA: Michael Dye.

Prior to the above described situation, when was the last time you remember feeling triggered in this same way?

Can you identify any themes between the two situations described above?

Following the situation that happened within the past few months, how did you feel?

In light of this situation, what are your triggers?

1.
2.
3.
4.
5.

When we work to identify our triggers, it helps us uncover the past pain and trauma that is interfering with our ability to cultivate healthy relationships. While this can be difficult at times, it is an essential step on our path toward healing.

Looking Ahead

Complete the FASTER Scale, Group Check-in, Self-Care lesson, Thoughts/Feelings Awareness Log, and Change & Growth Analysis in your *Unraveled: Weekly Tools* before the next group meeting.

LESSON 2: A FAMILY SYSTEMS ISSUE

As we continue to dig into our family of origin, it can make us feel uncomfortable. For many of us, we love our parents and understand that they did their best in raising us. For others, we may struggle with this process, uncertain of how exhuming our past is going to lead to healing. We are concerned that digging up our past will reveal areas we are not yet ready to process—areas that may change us, but also change our current relationships.

While change is good, we may have gotten to a point in our rocky relationships where things are not so bad right now. As it is, we can maintain the relationship, but if something "rocks the boat," we may not be able to handle the outcome. So why even go there?

You are a product of your environment.[58]

This is a fact: each of us is a product of our environment. While we were growing up, everything that happened to us and around us played a role in our development. This is especially true when it comes to the way we were parented.

PARENTING STYLES

Understanding the parent-child relationship is huge when it comes to gaining insight into our family system issues. It affects the way we develop our attachment skills and relate to others. It affects the way we process our world physically, mentally, emotionally, spiritually, and even sexually. It is a key element to recognizing why we do what we do in relationships.

Research into the effects of parenting on the physical, social, and emotional development of a child date back to the early 1930s.[59] The early parenting studies focused on only two factors: the quality of parent-child interactions (warmth) and the nature of parental

[58] BrainyQuote (2018). W. Clement Stone quote. Retrieved from https://www.brainyquote.com/quotes/w_clement_stone_193778

[59] Power, T. (2013). Parenting Dimensions and Styles: A Brief History and Recommendations for Future Research. *Childhood Obesity,* 9(1), August, 14-21.

discipline (control). However, in the mid-1960s, Diana Baumrind shifted the focus of her research, looking at the behavioral characteristics of children as the outcome of the way the child was parented. This was foundational in identifying three parenting styles.

Authoritarian parents require strict adherence to rigid rules.[60] This creates a parent-child dynamic that is based on obedience and compliance, not on relationship. Authoritarian parents have a commanding presence. They expect their children to not question authority, do as their told, and abide by the rules. They are quick to express their disappointment in their child's behavior, but reluctant to give praise or recognition for any acceptable behavior.

Permissive parents have few rules, give their children minimal responsibility, and do not hold their children accountable for their actions. Permissive parents provide little support, guidance, training, and discipline. Their children grow up with a lack of direction and purpose, and an unhealthy sense of entitlement.

Authoritative parents communicate clear boundaries and guidance for behavior, built on a foundation of love and affection. They train their children through responsibility, accountability, and consistent support. They encourage their children to be independent thinkers and to make good decisions in a safe and caring environment. They create and cultivate relationship through healthy communication and respect.

In the early 1980s, a fourth parenting style was added.[61] **Uninvolved or neglectful parents** attempt to meet their child's basic needs of food and shelter, but rarely provide more than the minimal necessities. They offer little, if any, support, guidance, training, or discipline. They are unresponsive to the physical, social, and emotional needs of their children. Uninvolved or neglectful parents tend to be indifferent toward their children and non-existent in their children's lives.

I felt the enormous weight of shame and embarrassment as I sat around the table with eight other women. I was new to this church and only agreed to attend the women's conference because a friend paid my way. If I had known that I might have to talk about my childhood, I never would have agreed to attend.

The main speaker was engaging and spoke empathetically about how our childhood environment can play a significant role in shaping our perspective and impacting our decisions. I knew this too well. I was 26 years old, married and divorced, and had two children that were given up for adoption at birth. My past was sprinkled with promiscuous sex, drug use, unemployment, and abortions.

---

[60] Coon, D. & Mitter, J. (2013). *Introduction to Psychology: Gateways to Mind and Behavior,* (13th ed.). Belmont, CA: Wadsworth, Cengage Learning.

[61] Cherry, K. (2018). Why Parenting Styles Matter When Raising Children. Retrieved from https://www.verywellmind.com/parenting-styles-2795072

As I sat and listened to the other women talk about their childhoods—some good, some not so good—I felt overwhelmed with fear and sick to my stomach. I knew I didn't have to share, but in the moment, I couldn't help myself.

I told them that I was the oldest of three kids: I love my younger brother and sister very much. I don't have many memories of my parents because they weren't around much. My siblings and I often came home from school to an empty house. Sometimes my parents didn't return for several days.

I felt responsible for my brother and sister, and tried to take care of them even if it meant stealing food from a local market or from a neighbor. I knew stealing was wrong, but didn't feel like I had a choice. At one point, after a few weeks of showing up to school dirty, hungry, and obviously lacking parental care, I broke down. I told my teacher I was afraid my parents were never coming back. My siblings and I entered the foster care system that day.

Although there was not a dry eye among the women listening, I remained emotionally unaffected. I faintly smiled and said, "I hear all of you talk about the way you were raised and I don't think I was raised...I think I just grew up."

Teri

In this brief snapshot of Teri's life, how did the way she was parented affect her as an adult?

One of the most interesting aspects of the parenting style research is the outcome: the overall effect it has on a child's development. Look at some of the common characteristics produced by the different parenting styles:[62,63]

---

[62] Coon, D. & Mitter, J. (2013). Introduction to Psychology: Gateways to Mind and Behavior, (13th ed.). Belmont, CA: Wadsworth, Cengage Learning.

[63] Darling, N. (n.d.). Parenting Style and Its Correlates. Retrieved from https://pdfs.semanticscholar.org/000f/2dc8802e1dad84aa4a2386a6c24f245e96b5.pdf

Authoritarian parents produce children who are or have:

- Obedient
- Self-controlled
- Limited emotional awareness
- Introverted
- Anxious and/or fearful
- Average academic performance
- Independent
- Poor social skills
- Low self-esteem
- Higher levels of depression

Permissive parents produce children who are or have:

- Dependent
- Immature
- Behavioral issues
- Lack of motivation
- Poor academic performance
- High self-esteem
- Good social skills
- Lower levels of depression

Authoritative parents produce children who are or have:

- Competent
- Self-controlled
- Interdependent
- Assertive
- Adventurous
- Excellent academic performance
- High self-esteem
- Good social skills
- Low levels of depression

Uninvolved or neglectful parents produce children who are or have:

- Insecure
- Indifferent
- Introverted
- Suspicious
- Poor academic performance
- Vulnerable to addiction
- Low self-esteem
- Poor social skills
- High levels of depression

While most professionals suggest that we were all raised with a primary parenting style, there can be overlap within the core components.

Based on what you have learned so far, what type of parenting style was used in your childhood environment? Note: the parenting style of your mom could have been different than that of your dad.

What effect did this have on your relationships?

If you are a parent, what parenting style(s) do you use?

While this may be a difficult lesson for many of us, the intent is not to blame our parents. The intent is to help us understand where we come from and how it explains our behavior.

As we process how our environment contributes to who we are today—the good, the bad, and the ugly—contemplate the full extent of what W. Clement Stone was saying:

> **"You are a product of your environment. So choose the environment that will best develop you toward your objective. Analyze your life in terms of its environment. Are the things around you helping you toward success—or are they holding you back?**

What are your thoughts regarding the above quote?

What positive aspects of your current environment are moving you toward success and health?

____

____

____

____

We have discovered the significance of parenting styles: how they contributed to our development and the environment in which we were raised. In so many ways, this created the filter by which we process our life—the filter we use to manage relationships.

FACES EVALUATION

The FACES Evaluation was created to help us identify the way our family of origin contributed to many of our current thoughts, feelings, and behaviors—how it contributes to our personality. This allows us to discern where dysfunctional patterns continue to persist in our relationships.

My husband and I had been married several years and pastored a large church. At some point in our marriage, we took the FACES Evaluation: we were curious—and in denial—about how our past had impacted our relationship. My husband had an addictive personality, seven stepdads, and an alcoholic mom. He scored a one/two on the evaluation. This was the lowest score possible, revealing that his family was highly rigid and disengaged. Most people who struggle with addictive behaviors come from a rigid and disengaged home where there is little emotional connection and firm rules that demand perfection and "trying harder" as a way of life.

My parents had Christian ethics and were married for 50 years before my mom passed away. I was certain I would score much higher on the FACES Evaluation. I was shocked when I also scored a one/two.[64]

The purpose of this evaluation is not to blame our parents, but to discover negative patterns from our past that are inhibiting our relationship with God and others. We can only change the effects of our past through awareness.

Try to be intentional and thorough when taking the evaluation, following all instructions.

[64] Roberts, D. (2016). *Betrayal & Beyond Workbook*. Gresham, OR: Pure Desire Ministries International. 69.

FACES II: FAMILY VERSION[65]

1	2	3	4	5
Almost Never	Once in a While	Sometimes	Frequently	Almost Always

DESCRIBE THE FAMILY IN WHICH YOU GREW UP:

____ **1.** Family members were supportive of each other during difficult times.

____ **2.** In our family, it was easy for everyone to express his/her opinion.

____ **3.** It was easier to discuss problems with people outside the family than with family members.

____ **4.** Each family member had input regarding major family decisions.

____ **5.** Our family gathered together in one room.

____ **6.** Children had a say in their discipline.

____ **7.** Our family did things together.

____ **8.** Family members discussed problems and felt good about the solutions.

____ **9.** In our family, everyone went his/her own way.

____ **10.** We shifted household responsibilities from person to person.

____ **11.** Family members knew each other's close friends.

____ **12.** It was hard to know what the rules were in our family.

____ **13.** Family members consulted other family members on personal decisions.

____ **14.** Family members said what they wanted.

____ **15.** We had difficulty thinking of things to do as a family.

____ **16.** In solving problems, the children's suggestions were followed.

____ **17.** Family members felt very close to each other.

____ **18.** Discipline was fair in our family.

____ **19.** Family members felt closer to people outside the family than to family members.

____ **20.** Our family tried new ways of dealing with problems.

[65] David H. Olson, Joyce Portner & Richard Bell

____ **21.** Family members went along with what the family decided to do.

____ **22.** In our family, everyone shared responsibilities.

____ **23.** Family members liked to spend their free time with each other.

____ **24.** It was difficult to get a rule changed in our family.

____ **25.** Family members avoided each other at home.

____ **26.** When problems arose, we compromised.

____ **27.** We approved of each other's friends.

____ **28.** Family members were afraid to say what was on their minds.

____ **29.** Family members paired up rather than doing things as a total family.

____ **30.** Family members shared interests and hobbies with each other.

DIRECTIONS FOR OBTAINING CIRCUMPLEX TYPE SCORE[66]

FOR COHESION

1. Sum items 3, 9, 15, 19, 25 and 29. ________

2. Subtract that figure from 36. 36 - ________ = ________

3. Sum all other **odd** numbers *plus* item 30. ________ + ________ = ________

4. Add the figures from step 2 and step 3 to obtain a total cohesion score. ________

FOR ADAPTABILITY

1. Sum items 24 and 28. ________

2. Subtract that figure from 12. 12 - ________ = ________

3. Sum all other **event** numbers *except* item 30. ________ + ________ = ________

4. Add the figures from step 2 and step 3 to obtain a total adaptability score. ________

[66] C.H. Olson, C.S. Russell, & d. H. Sprenkle, Circumplex model: Systemic Assessment and Treatment of Families, (The Haworth Press, New York, NY, 1988). Used with permission.

FACES II: LINEAR SCORING & INTERPRETATION

COHESION			ADAPTABILITY			FAMILY TYPE	
8	74-80	Very Connected	**8**	65-70	Very Flexible	**8**	Balanced
7	71-73		**7**	55-64		**7**	
6	65-70	Connected	**6**	50-54	Flexible	**6**	Moderately Balanced
5	60-64		**5**	46-49		**5**	
4	55-59	Separated	**4**	43-45	Structured	**4**	Mid-Range
3	51-54		**3**	40-42		**3**	
2	35-50	Disengaged	**2**	30-39	Rigid	**2**	Extreme
1	15-34		**1**	15-29		**1**	

☐ *Find your total Cohesion score and your total Adaptability score in the chart above. Then look at the number (1 through 8) associated with that range. Write that number (1 through 8) in the space provided.*

Example: If you score a 30 on Adaptability, put a 2 in the blank above Adaptability. If you score a 59 on Cohesion, put a 4 above Cohesion.

☐ *Then add your Cohesion and Adaptability numbers and divide by 2 to get your Type.*

In our example, 4 + 2 = 6, divided by 2 is 3 (Type). If you scored 3 for "Type" you would be in the midrange.

______ + ______ ______ /2 = ______

Cohesion Adaptability Type

☐ *Next, look at the Linear Scoring and Interpretation diagram pictured here to understand what this Type shows about your family of origin.*

LINEAR SCORING AND INTERPRETATION DIAGRAM

As you look at the Couple & Family Map on the next page, notice that the white area in the middle of this scale correlates to the previous page where the Balanced Family Types (8-7-6) are reflected. On this page the Mid-Range Family Types (5-4-3) are light gray, and the Extreme Family Types (2-1) are shown in the dark gray area.

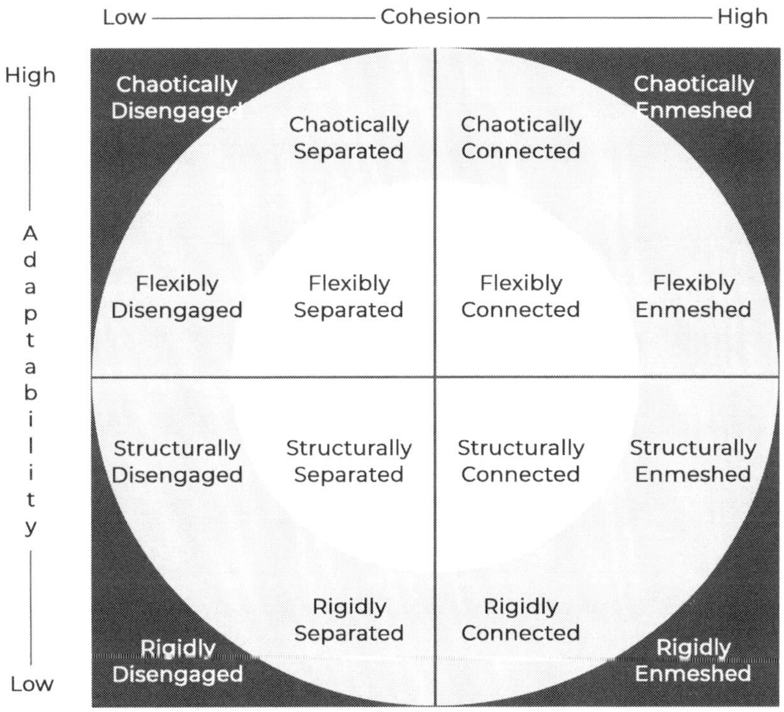

Low ——— Cohesion ——— High

High — Adaptability — Low

Chaotically Disengaged	Chaotically Separated	Chaotically Connected	Chaotically Enmeshed
Flexibly Disengaged	Flexibly Separated	Flexibly Connected	Flexibly Enmeshed
Structurally Disengaged	Structurally Separated	Structurally Connected	Structurally Enmeshed
Rigidly Disengaged	Rigidly Separated	Rigidly Connected	Rigidly Enmeshed

LEVELS OF ADAPTABILITY

CHAOTIC
- Lack of Leadership
- Dramatic Role Shifts
- Erratic Discipline
- Too Much Change

FLEXIBLE
- Shared Leadership
- Role Sharing
- Democratic Discipline
- Change When Necessary

STRUCTURED
- Leadership Sometimes Shared
- Rules Stable
- Somewhat Democratic Discipline
- Change When Demanded

RIGID
- Authoritarian
- Rules Seldom Change
- Strict Discipline
- Too Little Change

LEVELS OF COHESION

DISENGAGED
- **I**
- Little Closeness
- Lack of Loyalty
- High Independence

SEPARATED
- **I**—we
- Low-Moderate
- Little Loyalty
- Interdependent
- More Independence than Dependence

CONNECTED
- I—**We**
- Moderate-High
- Some Loyalty
- Interdependent
- More Dependence than Independence

ENMESHED
- **WE**
- Very High
- High Loyalty
- High Dependency

BALANCED

MID RANGE

EXTREME

Our score is revealing. If our combined average is four or less, we have been negatively affected by our family of origin.[67] Families that reflect low scores are a breeding ground for addictive behaviors; they function with many rules but provide very little relationship.

The good news is that family systems can change, as explained by Diane.

Although my family of origin looked "more put together" than my husband's, both of us came from a rigid and disengaged family system. We decided right then that we didn't want to pass this generational curse onto our children. We looked at all the questions that caused us to have a low score and made a commitment to proactively change how we "did" family. After working on these changes for five years, we gave the FACES Evaluation to both of our children: each scored a six. In one generation, our family went from a one/two score to a six! The generational curse was stopped and God is now pouring out blessings on our family.

[67] Roberts, D. (2016). *Betrayal & Beyond Workbook*. Gresham, OR: Pure Desire Ministries International. 70.

But I lavish unfailing love for a thousand generations on those who love me and obey my commands.

DEUTERONOMY 5:10 NLT

Regardless of our past, God wants the very best for us. He will take all our brokenness and use it for something amazing that will bring glory to our heavenly Father.

After taking the FACES Evaluation, what was surprising about your results?

What was not surprising about your results?

What are two things you could do differently to change your present family and stop the generational curse?

As we continue to learn how our family of origin shaped our current behaviors, we can use this as an opportunity to create new goals through our weekly commitment to change.

Looking Ahead

Complete the FASTER Scale, Group Check-in, Self-Care lesson, Thoughts/Feelings Awareness Log, and Change & Growth Analysis in your *Unraveled: Weekly Tools* before the next group meeting.

LESSON 3: WHERE DOES TRAUMA COME FROM?

The concept of trauma and the impact it has on our life is complex. What is trauma?

Trauma is an overwhelming experience that has a negative impact on an individual's mental and emotional processing ability—in the moment and in the future—because of what they have experienced in the past.[68] **Trauma frequently refers to an experience that is beyond an individual's capability to effectively adapt–an event or series of events that affects our ability to predict an outcome.** This can easily happen during childhood: creating a maladaptive mental system that negatively affects the individual's interpersonal abilities, at the subconscious level, well into adulthood.

The key word is experience. We are born with thousands of neurons, but with few connections between them.[69] We build the operating system of our brain from experience: we are not born with a pre-programmed brain. Comparatively, we are vulnerable and dependent much longer than animals. This vulnerability is the first experience we have in life and it lays the foundation of our mental operating system. A toddler's brain develops so easily in response to stimulation that it absorbs everything uncritically. After age two, the brain starts to rely on the circuits it has developed rather than changing to fit every new input.

This foundational system in our brain is developed very early in life. If we experience trauma in our early childhood, it can significantly influence our perception of our world. As a result, children who have experienced trauma are developing their mental operating system with tainted, faulty circuitry in an attempt to avoid pain and experience some resemblance of pleasure. Later in life, as an adult, we can end up struggling to respond to pleasure and pain in ways that are redemptive. Our mental operating system—our brain—has been programed in a way that has twisted our perception of ourselves, others, and God. In a very real sense, this is one of the main reasons we struggle to manage our relationships.

Choosing to deal with our past trauma can be difficult, but there is hope.

---

[68] Roberts, D. (2016). *Betrayal & Beyond*. Gresham, OR: Pure Desire Ministries International. 93.

[69] Coon, D. & Mitterer, J. (2010). *Introduction to Psychology: Gateways to Mind and Behavior* (12th ed.). Belmont, CA: Wadsworth Cengage Learning. 82.

For I am persuaded that neither death nor life, nor angels nor principalities nor powers, nor things present nor things to come, [39]nor height nor depth, nor any other created thing, shall be able to separate us from the love of God which is in Christ Jesus our Lord.

ROMANS 8:38-39 NKJV

Isn't it interesting that Paul doesn't mention the past? Even though his point is that truly nothing can separate us from God's love—because His love for us is so constant—it is possible to allow our past to make us feel like we are separated from His love. We listen to lies from our past rather than hearing the truth of His love. We may feel that our past behaviors will keep us from relationship with God, but this scripture is very clear: **NOTHING** can separate us from the love of God. Processing our past pain and trauma allows us to develop healthy relationship with God and others.

As a child we had no power to keep ourselves safe. We had to rely completely on the development of our brain to figure out how to stay safe. Today, as adults we have many resources:

- We have a fully developed brain that helps us reason out solutions.
- We have the Spirit of God living in us who gives us power and wisdom.
- We have other women in our group who will not shame us because they understand our pain.

Despite this, the area of our brain that was developing during traumatic times is so powerful, it will override all our resources and logical thought processes. We will find ourselves triggered by the unresolved nature of pain that pulls us back into unhealthy behaviors: leading us to self-medicate and seek pleasure through sex, pornography, masturbation, alcohol, food, spending, and other addictive behaviors.

Describe a time when you were recently triggered by a situation.

____

____

____

____

In what ways were you confused by your reaction?

____

____

____

____

Considering your traumatic experiences, in what ways did your reaction make sense? When do you remember feeling this way in the past?

My mother was hardly ever at home. She worked so hard to provide for us, believing that her work and financial provision was the best way to show us love. My father was an alcoholic and constantly changing jobs, which created anxiety for my mother and only made her work longer hours.

I felt so lonely. Neither of my parents were there when I came home from school. I did my homework, made myself dinner, and often went to bed without even seeing my parents. I felt lonely at school too. My classmates teased me about my darker skin. The other girls at school got so much attention: the boys loved the athletic, blonde-haired, blue-eyed girls. That was not me.

My mom loved treats and often shared with me. These rare moments were so precious. My mom had great taste when it came to quality desserts. I loved when she would say, "Let's go get a treat!" At the same time, she often made negative comments about my body.

"Are you going to wear your hair like that so you stand out so much?"

"Your legs are starting to jiggle, do you want me to get you a gym membership?"

"I bought this fat-free dressing for you."

"What is wrong with your skin? Why do you have acne?"

I began to hate the way I looked. I thought that if I looked different then maybe people would like me more. I bought fashion magazines and scrolled through social media, wishing I looked like someone else. I fantasized about being confident and sexy in my own body. I tried to control my food intake so I wouldn't gain anymore weight, and at the same time, felt like food was my only friend.

Food became a source of comfort when I was home alone. I thought about what I was going to eat as soon as school got out. I was obsessed. After school, I would make a delicious meal and sit in front of the TV, wishing I looked like the actors on the screen. After I finished eating, I hated myself for not having control. I would go to the bathroom and vomit. I was smart: I knew the consequences—that I could die from bulimia—but I couldn't stop myself. I would often think to myself, ***How did I get here? Why can't I stop? God, please help me.***

Adara

While in it, Adara could not recognize the trauma of her environment. What factors were contributing to Adara's behaviors?

____

____

____

____

____

____

What factors caused Adara to become stuck in unhealthy patterns of behavior?

____

____

____

____

____

____

Food became Adara's source of comfort: a way to medicate her pain. What pain was Adara trying to medicate?

____

____

____

____

____

____

When it comes to identifying trauma in our lives, there are three common elements that interfere with our ability to recognize the reality of our trauma.

- We tend to minimize our trauma
- We compare our trauma to others' trauma
- We are protective of our trauma

In many ways, we minimize our trauma. This happens when we experience a life-changing event or series of events but never tell anyone about it. We bury it, stuffing it deep in our soul, with the intent of hiding it from the outside world forever. We move on with life as though nothing happened. We attempt to live as if we are unscathed by the experience.

If we live with a distorted view of our trauma, we fail to see the reality of our trauma, especially compared to others. We tell ourselves, "I've never been..." or "I was never the victim of...," attempting to convince ourselves that our trauma was not as bad as that of the next person. This reinforces the illusion of our trauma, as we continue our mental mantra: *What happened to me wasn't so bad.*

As we work to minimize our trauma, justifying it through comparison, we become protective of our trauma. We keep it hidden from ourselves so we don't have to feel it. We keep it hidden from others so it remains lifeless. We think that protecting our trauma stops it from taking on a life of its own. We're afraid the image we've created to protect us will disappear. We live in fear, knowing that if we tell someone about it and their face emphatically reflects the pain we're trying to hide, we will no longer have the power to keep the effects of our trauma at bay. The floodgates will open. In that moment, we will feel forced to deal with the truth of our trauma.

TYPES OF TRAUMA

There are two types of trauma: trauma of infringement and trauma of abandonment.[70]

Trauma of infringement reflects things done to us, characterized by the intensity of the event. This would include experiences such as combat or natural disaster, rape or sexual assault, extreme physical or verbal abuse, and more. In many cases, these events were infrequent, but intense.

Trauma of abandonment reflects things kept from us, characterized by the frequency of the event. This would include neglect, a lack of support, open rejection, and more. In many cases, these events happened several times, even consistently, but were more mild.

Naturally, we think that infringement trauma would have a greater impact on lives; however, as indicated on the graph below, abandonment trauma can be devastating and have an equally profound impact on our lives.

---

[70] Roberts, T. (2012). *Seven Pillars of Freedom Workbook*. Gresham, OR: Pure Desire Ministries International.

Infringement

- Combat experiences
- Rape
- Sexual abuse
- Punching
- Slapping
- Verbal attacks
- Demeaning nicknames

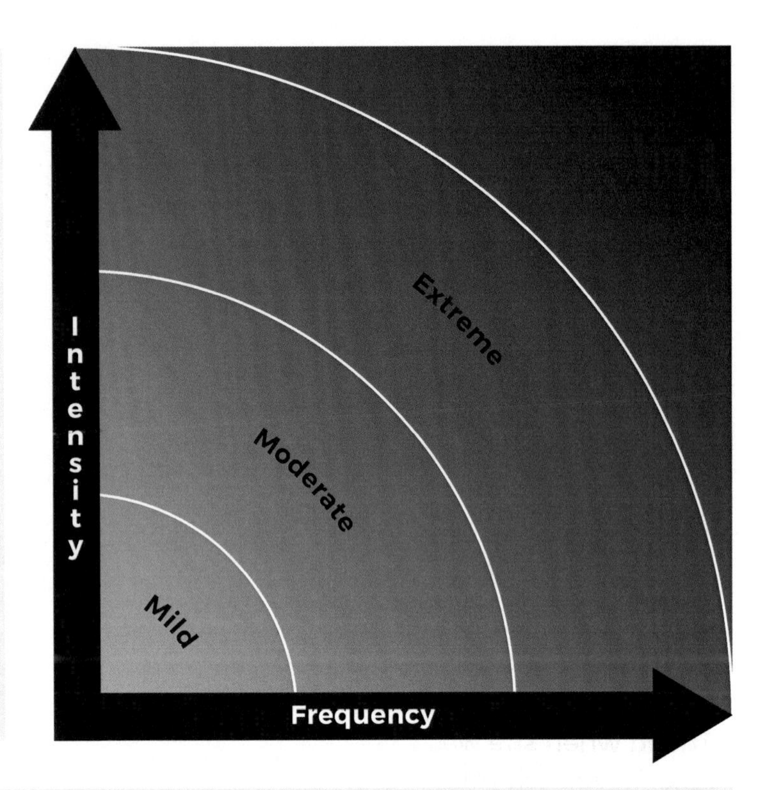

Abandonment · Silence · Neglect · Lack of support · Open rejection

As indicated, an experience of rape or sexual assault can result in extreme trauma; and yet, a consistent experience of neglect can also result in extreme trauma.[71]

Unfortunately, we all experience trauma. In the moment, we may not recognize it as trauma, but it's important to identify the way our traumatic experiences have impacted our lives.

In the following table, indicate whether the traumatic experience was a trauma of infringement or a trauma of abandonment or both. Briefly explain your answer.

TRAUMATIC EXPERIENCE	TYPE OF TRAUMA
Astrid was 7 years old when her dad died in a car accident.	☐ Infringement ☐ Abandonment Why?

[71] Shapiro, F. (2001). *Eye Movement Desensitization and Reprocessing: Basic Principles, Protocols, and Procedures* (2nd ed.). New York: NY; The Guilford Press.

TRAUMATIC EXPERIENCE	TYPE OF TRAUMA
When Pearla came home from school every day, her nanny, Marie, was there to greet her. Her parents' work required extensive travel, but Pearla spoke with them every night via video.	☐ Infringement ☐ Abandonment Why?
Julie loved living down the road from her grandma and stopped by her house on the way home from school to visit for a few minutes, if not hours, every day. During her junior year, her father was transferred and they moved several states away.	☐ Infringement ☐ Abandonment Why?
Ceaira was sexually abused by a family friend when she was 7 years old. She was told, "If you tell your parents, they won't love you."	☐ Infringement ☐ Abandonment Why?
Toni was only 2 years old when her parents divorced. A couple years later, her mom married a man with three kids, which created ongoing relational issues. Several times, her dad married women with kids from previous marriages. Toni liked her step-siblings, but learned to not get too attached: they may not be around for long.	☐ Infringement ☐ Abandonment Why?
Olivia was 10 years old when her oldest brother, Eli, went to live in the "big white house." For several years, she didn't understand why Eli was sick, why he couldn't live at home, and why she could only visit him once a month.	☐ Infringement ☐ Abandonment Why?

Answers: Astrid: Abandonment; Pearla: Infringement & Abandonment; Julie: Abandonment; Ceaira: Infringement; Toni: Infringement & Abandonment; Olivia: Abandonment.

Discussing trauma can be a difficult process and may uncover some buried emotions. If you feel uncomfortable or anxious when answering the following questions, it may indicate an area of deep trauma. In some cases, personal counseling may be required to process past trauma. Please talk with your group leader about a counseling referral if needed or visit puredesire.org/counseling to request a free consultation.

In what ways have you experienced trauma of infringement?

In what ways have you experienced trauma of abandonment?

How have you attempted to minimize your trauma?

How have you compared your trauma to others' trauma?

How have you been protective of your trauma?

When it comes to identifying specific traumatic events in our past, we tend to take a chronological perspective, viewing one event followed by another. While this may be an effective strategy, we often fail to recognize how the specific events are profoundly connected, yielding a much deeper level of trauma. However, when we look at traumatic events happening concurrently—happening at the same time—we gain a more accurate picture of the depth of our trauma.

Look at the following example:

When I was 10 years old my parents divorced.	My mom and I moved to a different city, far away from my dad.	I had to change schools and leave all my friends.	My mom had to work two jobs and was not home much.
When I was 20 years old my boss took advantage of me sexually.	I didn't want to lose my job, so I kept quiet about the sexual abuse.	I started going to bars, drinking a lot, and having sex with strangers.	My family and friends were far away.

In the above example, her parent's divorce and the sexual abuse from her boss were traumatic events, but they put into motion several other events that were equally traumatic and happening at the same time.

If we want to fully understand the impact of our trauma, it is helpful to look at events concurrently—everything that is happening at the same time.

Using the following timeline, indicate four major areas of trauma from your past and the events that were happening concurrently.

Looking Ahead

Complete the FASTER Scale, Group Check-in, Self-Care lesson, Thoughts/Feelings Awareness Log, and Change & Growth Analysis in your *Unraveled: Weekly Tools* before the next group meeting.

chapter five

TOXIC RELATIONSHIPS

LESSON 1: THE CYCLE OF ADDICTION

For those of us who have trouble managing love, sex, and relationships, it can be challenging to accept that we may struggle more than we think. As we have learned, we didn't get here overnight. The mechanisms for how we see ourselves and how our beliefs are shaped were created at an early age. Over the years, through experience, we have developed strategies to push down and ignore the painful feelings that contribute to our negative self-perception. What we believe about ourselves—the negative roadblocks in our thought processes—creates feelings of fear and shame.

As we uncover the hidden elements of our past and raise awareness to where we find ourselves repeating negative behaviors, we can break out of our addictive cycle. It is not enough to simply stop harmful behaviors. That's a good place to start, but if we want to experience true healing, we have to identify the core belief that is driving our unhealthy behaviors, eroding our self-perception. We need to develop new strategies for living in health. Understanding the cycle of addiction helps us recognize our own patterns of thoughts, feelings, and behaviors that keep us stuck in our addiction.

The following stages are not indicative of a single model, but a collaborative representation of the cycle of addiction experienced by those of us who struggle with managing love, sex, and relationships.[72, 73, 74, 75]

STAGE 1: TIME

In this stage, everything is going well. We are enjoying new friendships, attending a self-improvement class, or maintaining consistent physical self-care. This season of "everything seems to be going well" creates a sense of well-being and confidence. However, beneath the surface, we have a nagging sense that something is not right. We ignore this feeling because things really are not bad.

---

[72] Bethesda Workshops. A Place for Healing. Nashville, TN.

[73] Weiss, D. (2012). *She Has A Secret*. Colorado Springs, CO: Discovery Press.

[74] Ferree, M. (2012). *Making Advances: A Comprehensive Guide for Treating Female Sex and Love Addicts*. Royston, GA: Society for the Advancement of Sexual Health (SASH).

[75] Roberts, D. (2010). *Pure Desire for Women: Eight Pillars to Freedom From Love Addiction & Sexual Issues*. Gresham, OR: Pure Desire Ministries International.

There is no fixed duration in this "time" stage. On the outside, things are okay. We are not overly anxious about finding a relationship or maintaining connection in relationship. This stage may seem like the place to live, but as we have experienced, it is not a lasting stage in this cycle. Inevitably, someone catches our attention or if we are in a relationship, we sense they are pulling away, having interests outside the relationship that don't include us. Either of these scenarios raises our level of fear—fear that is created by what we believe about ourselves: are we valued, are we worth it, are we loved? This triggered fear leads to the next stage in the cycle.

How do you feel when everything is going well in your life?

____

____

____

____

____

STAGE 2: FAULTY THINKING

To defend against the fear we're feeling—fear of abandonment or rejection—we may engage in a number of various thought processes.

- Rationalizing: "It's okay that he has outside interests and is less attentive to me."
- Bargaining: "If I were more appealing, I would be loved and accepted."
- Minimizing: "It's okay. It's really not a big deal."
- Excusing: "They didn't mean to hurt my feelings when ____________________."

In this stage, we are vulnerable to seeking out the "perfect" relationship. Faulty thinking takes us out of reality, creating a disconnect from our painful reality: deep inside there is a hurt little girl in need of love, belonging, and nurturing. We want to separate from this emotional pain, so we adopt unhealthy behaviors such as eating, denial, and avoidance. When the pain of our reality becomes too much, we create an altered state or fantasy, which leads to the next stage in the cycle.

Can you think of an event or situation when you felt fearful? How did you defend against this feeling of fear?

____

____

____

____

____

STAGE 3: PREOCCUPATION/FANTASY

During this stage, we take our faulty thoughts and put images to them. We create an alternate reality where we are loved, enjoyed, and pursued. Perhaps we imagine that the new guy at work is "the one." We fantasize about him asking us out, going on dates, romantic walks on the beach, and then he is on bended knee. We snap out of our fantasy only to realize that 30 minutes has passed and we're still stuck in the same painful life we've always had. We feel depressed.

It is easy to get stuck in this stage. We tell ourselves, "I really need to stop," only to find ourselves lost again in our fantasy world. When we build up enough pain without relief, the next stage becomes an appealing way to alleviate the pain.

In what ways do you engage in preoccupation and/or fantasy?

STAGE 4: RITUALS

This is the planning stage. We begin to pursue connection to live out the fantasy. We will seek out someone or something to help us—to rescue us from the pain and loneliness. We plan out ways to get noticed. We find ways to gain attention, which can become obsessive. This creates anxiety, unrealized expectation, and the emotional pain of rejection and loneliness.

The thoughts and emotions that generate our fantasies will activate arousal—a heightened physiological response. This heightened response will cause us to implement our rituals. For those of us who struggle with love addiction, we may excessively flirt, intentionally be "in the right place, at the right time" to catch someone's eye, or dress in a sexually provocative way, with the goal of pursuing a relationship with the object of our obsession. For those of us who struggle with sex addiction, we might plan to entice someone for sex or engage in masturbation. Pornography use or fantasy could also be part of the ritual.

Rituals are not time-sensitive. The time frame can last several minutes to several years. It is important to recognize what we do—our thoughts, feelings, and behaviors—that take us from fantasy to acting out.

What rituals can you identify in your addictive patterns?

STAGE 5: ACTING OUT

There are two distinct ways that we medicate our pain: externalizing or acting out and internalizing or acting in.

Externalizing or acting out: Internet sexual activity—chatting with someone or viewing images while masturbating, hookups, having an affair, masturbation, flirting, or having sex with someone we just met. This would also include following someone to their home, "stalking" a person online, or bumping into someone to get their attention.

Internalizing or acting in: shutting down all sexual desire and sexual awareness. Sexual anorexia. We socially isolate as a means to control our feelings. We reason, "Since I'm not having sex, then I'm not a sex addict." The truth is, we are medicating the pain by not allowing ourselves to feel. We are numb.

In what ways do you externally medicate your pain—acting out?

____

____

____

____

____

____

In what ways do you internally medicate your pain—acting in?

____

____

____

____

____

____

STAGE 6: SHAME/DESPAIR

Feelings of hopelessness, depression, and shame often follow acting out. We make vows to ourselves (and others) that we will stop. We promise ourselves we will never do it again and at the same time feel hopeless—questioning whether we will keep our promise this time or not. Shame conceals our secret: "If others knew, they would reject me. My behavior is too shameful to tell anyone." Once our feeling of shame dissipates, "time" follows as we start the cycle again.

How does shame show up in your cycle of addiction?

____

____

____

____

____

STAGE 7: POWERLESSNESS/UNMANAGEABILITY

This cycle of addiction can be repeated over and over until we realize the unmanageability of our life.[76] We may experience job loss, a crushing low self-esteem, the loss of relationship, and health consequences. There comes a time when we recognize that the way we're living—unable to manage love, sex, and relationship—needs to change, but we may feel powerless to change.

We may feel as though we are living life on autopilot: unable to navigate relationships, resulting in out-of-control behaviors. The consequences of our emotional and physical health may become compromised, allowing the feelings of hopelessness and a loss of control to take their toll.

At this stage, we feel powerless to control our behaviors. This is reflected in our behaviors, thought processes, and emotional health.

- My self-esteem is at its lowest
- I am obsessed with social media
- I use a fake persona online to create relationship
- I masturbate at work
- I have lost all self-respect
- I have lost connection with healthy relationships
- I have accepted money for sex
- I lost my job
- I have lost my reputation and integrity with family and friends
- I hooked up with people whose names I can't remember
- I feel so numb on the inside, I cut myself to feel pain on the outside
- I had an abortion
- I obsessively daydream about the perfect relationship

[76] Carnes, P. (2001). *Out of the Shadows: Understanding Sexual Addiction* (3rd ed.). Center City, MN: Hazelden.

☐ *In what ways do your feelings of powerlessness and lack of control show up in your life?*

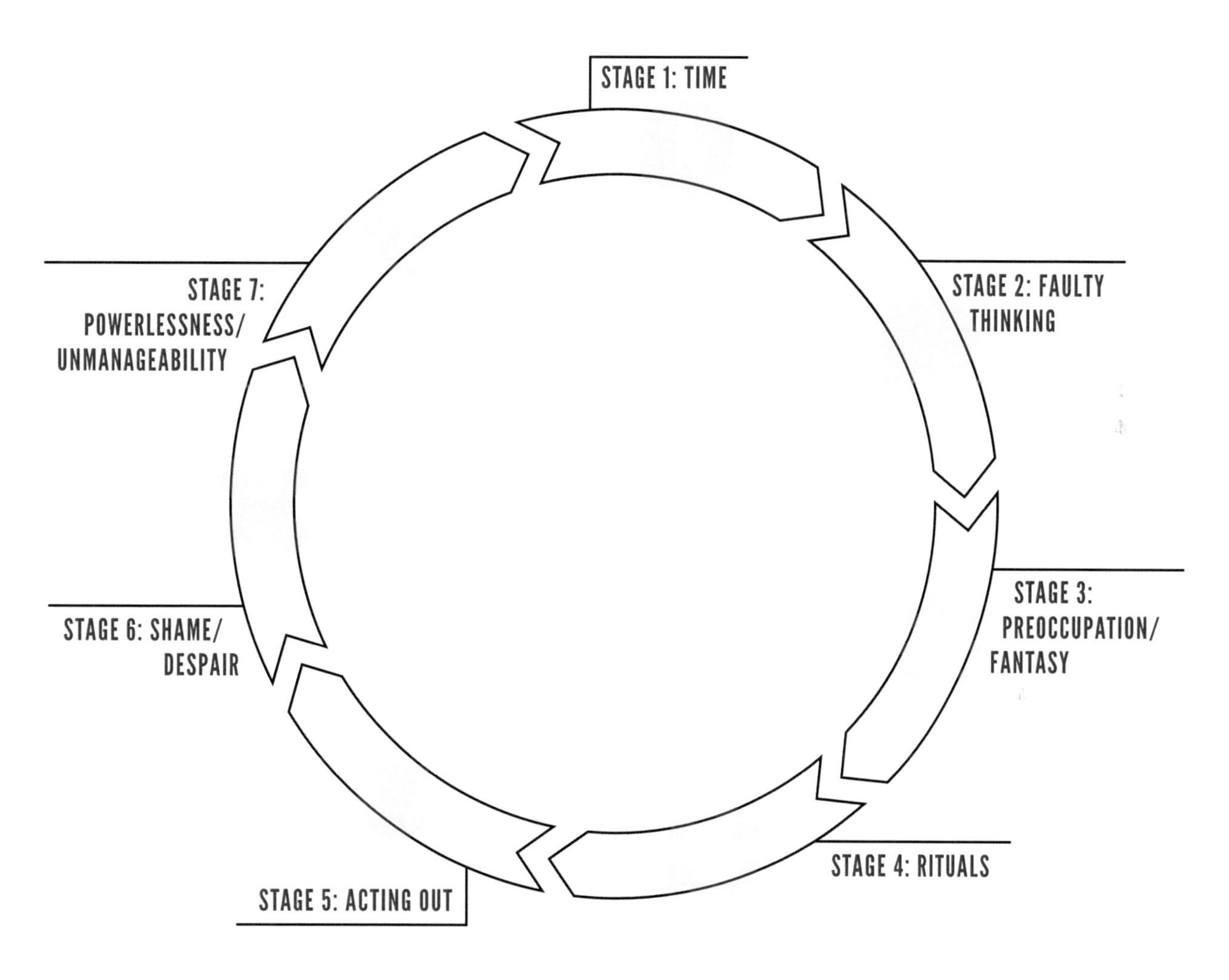

☐ *What is your experience in this cycle of addiction?*

How have you tried to manage your compulsive and/or out of control behaviors?

What consequences have you experienced?

As we take an honest look at how our thoughts, feelings, and behaviors have disrupted our ability to navigate healthy relationships, we may resist and tell ourselves, "I'm not an addict!" This may be true, but we have to ask ourselves, "Why do I have a string of broken relationships in my past?"

Here are a few indicators that might help us gain a new perspective and raise awareness to the reality of our behaviors.[77] We may struggle more than we think if we:

- have tried to stop a behavior, but can't.
- obsess romantically about one person, excluding other interests.
- use sexual seduction to gain power over others.
- use sex as a means to find love.
- think that sex is love.
- fall "in love" repeatedly.
- think the next time will be different.

What indicators—listed above or from your own experience—may suggest that you struggle more than you think?

[77] Carnes, P. (1991). *Don't Call It Love: Recovery From Sexual Addiction*. New York, NY: Bantam Books.

In what way has exploring the cycle of addiction led to a new understanding of your behaviors and areas where you recognize change is needed?

____

____

____

____

____

Unraveling our personal cycle of addiction will be the first step we take toward sobriety and freedom.

MY SAFETY BEHAVIORS

We all want to feel safe: physically, mentally, emotionally, and spiritually. However, when we have experienced trauma in our lives—times when our safety was threatened—it causes us to create behaviors that we feel decrease our fear, pain, and anxiety. Consider the following examples:

As a child, my life was filled with unsafe places and unsafe people. My mom was an addict and often traded sex for drugs. My parents were divorced and my mom didn't want to leave the four of us girls home alone, so she took us with her to the hotels where she met men. I vividly remember being forced into a car at gunpoint and watching as a man hurt my mom. This was one of many similar experiences.

Despite these horrible experiences, I'm an addict too. Not drugs so much, but addicted to romantic relationships. I can't be without a guy. Even when I'm in a relationship, I'm always looking for the next one. Although, I worry about STDs—my mom told me a lot about STDs—in the moment, I can't refuse the affection of a new lover. I try to practice safe sex and tell myself that next time it's going to different, I'm going to be different, but who am I kidding? I'm my own worst enemy.

Samantha

I was raised in a military family, where feelings were not learned or expressed. These things didn't matter. My life was all about following rules and conformity. I didn't really have an opinion about things in my life—the friends I had, who I dated or didn't date, and even where I would go to college. Because of our lifestyle, my parents controlled everything I did and I always did what my parents wanted me to do. I was told this would keep me safe.

Since my parents seemed to insert themselves into all my relationships—with friends and romantic interests alike—I began to seek out relationships online through various chat rooms. This was safe from my parents' prying eyes and finally gave me the freedom to choose for myself. What started as innocent curiosity turned into something I had never before experienced. Initially, I only talked about sexually explicit things, but that quickly turned into fantasy-fueled masturbation. Although I feared my parents would find out, this became a daily pattern.

Lani

I'm divorced. In my previous marriage, everything looked great on the outside: we were the perfect Christian family. It was all a lie. After I discovered my husband's ongoing affair, he left and I initiated a divorce. I never remarried. I read romance novels and watch romantic movies, but nothing with sex in it. I have a strong aversion to anything sexual and feel repulsed by the thought of it. I do fantasize about the perfect husband—one who showers me will love and adoration, but who doesn't want sex. I'm certain this type of man does not exist.

Since my divorce, I am cautious about developing any form of relationship with men. Even at church, I avoid all contact with the men, except the pastor, who is truly a man of God and would never cheat on his wife. I think it's safer to only have relationships with women. I would rather spend my life alone than risk being hurt again.

Deborah

Which of these examples resonates with you most? Why?

In the above examples, each woman created behaviors that supported her feeling of safety, when ultimately, it made matters worse. In each case, the safety behaviors moved the women away from relationship, not toward relationship.

In what areas do you lack appropriate safety measures? (e.g., getting drunk in a bar or at a party, sex with strangers, unable to say "no" when needed).

Briefly describe a situation that caused you to feel threatened, unsafe, or where risk was involved.

As a result of the situation, what safety behaviors did you put in place? What safety behaviors do you need to put in place?

In what ways did your safety behaviors move you away from relationship?

Looking Ahead

Complete the FASTER Scale, Group Check-in, Self-Care lesson, Thoughts/Feelings Awareness Log, and Change & Growth Analysis in your *Unraveled: Weekly Tools* before the next group meeting.

LESSON 2: TRIGGERS AND AROUSAL

Last week, we learned about the various stages in the Cycle of Addiction. Rituals (stage 4) can be subtle and often go undetected for many women. It is important to recognize that our rituals are initiated when we feel triggered and our limbic system is activated. Think of a trigger as a "flashback." It can be almost anything. Some common triggers include:

- Emotions: loneliness, rejection, disappointment, pain, shame, boredom
- Songs
- A specific person
- Smells
- A movie or TV show
- Financial anxiety
- Criticism
- A car: reminds you of a specific time and place
- A place
- Stress
- A person's body type, hair style, or personality

As we learned in chapter 4, whatever triggers us, captures our attention and creates a bump in our awareness: it creates a jolt that focuses our thoughts on a previous experience. This jolt—our trigger—can be positive or negative, putting into motion a process of preoccupation and fantasy. When we are triggered by a painful memory, we use preoccupation and fantasy to make the pain go away—most common for those of us who struggle with love addiction.

When we are triggered by a pleasurable memory, we become preoccupied with good feelings—most common for those of us who struggle with sex addiction. If we have used our computer for sexual activity, we may not recognize how even turning on the computer, the sound it makes and the anticipation it creates, can be a trigger.

This can be a confusing process. We may feel "suddenly" aroused, but cannot understand why. As we continue to pursue health, we will discover that underneath our triggers lies a foundation of emotional pain that was buried by our compulsive and addictive behaviors.

"

The main role of addiction is to push away unwanted thoughts, feelings, and memories from our conscious awareness.[78]

MICHAEL DYE

I grew up in a supportive and loving Christian home. I was very independent and really not interested in my looks or boys until I turned 12 years old. At this point, I began to recognize how good it felt to get attention from boys. This consumed my thoughts. Before I turned 14, I started a relationship with a guy who was a few years older and I knew he was not someone I should be hanging around. My parents did not approve, but I didn't care. I was so drawn to the feeling I got when I was with him. I had never felt anything like it.

I put all my time and energy into thinking about this guy and seeing him when I could. He told me how much he loved me, wrote poems for me, and really cared about me. I wasn't ready to have sex with him, but I know he wanted it. After six months, I discovered that all the emotional energy I was putting into this relationship was for nothing. He was saying the same things, writing the same poems, and going out with two other girls at the same time. I was devastated. I tried to move past the pain but subconsciously vowed to never let myself get hurt like that again. Even though it seemed like a little thing, being led on, manipulated, and lied to for so many months changed me. I felt insecure and struggled with low self-esteem. I had suffered emotional abuse.

Shortly after that relationship ended, I went on to another relationship, and another, and another—all the way through college. I was never without a boyfriend, sometimes dating more than one guy at a time. I never let any guy break up with me and always made sure to have control of the relationship. These relationships were not healthy—physically, sexually, and emotionally. Many of my relationships were manipulative and emotionally abusive. I was so drawn to and aroused by the feelings of love and connection that it didn't matter if the relationships were unhealthy or even unsafe. Ultimately, the patterns of emotional abuse created excessive damage to my self-worth and emotional awareness, driving me further into love and sex addiction.

Katie

[78] Dye, M. (2012). *The Genesis Process: For Change Groups, Book 1 and 2, Individual Workbook.* Ventura, CA: Michael Dye.

When Katie was 14, why didn't she listen to her parents' dating advice?

What factors contributed to Katie's pursuit of unhealthy relationships? What fears were driving her behaviors?

How did Katie's dating experience shape her feelings and arousal?

In what ways do you relate to Katie?

In order to recognize *why* we are feeling triggered, it can be helpful to work through a past situation, walking it out backwards. First, we need to identify our most common form of acting out—it may not be a serious sexual sin, but a behavior that is prevalent or that we consider relapse: angry outbursts, binge eating, isolating, shopping, overspending, misuse of social media, and more.

Next, we need to identify what was happening before we acted out: events, moods, behaviors, and interactions with others. Our weekly FASTER Scale may be helpful in this process. We need to continue to work backwards until we can isolate the trigger, the moment that initiated a chain of events leading to our ritual and ultimately, acting out.

Use the following table to identify this progression. Sometimes, processing out loud with a trusted friend is helpful. Ask your group members for help if needed.

MOST COMMON FORM OF ACTING OUT	PRECIPITATING FACTORS: EVENTS, MOODS, BEHAVIORS, INTERACTIONS WITH OTHERS	POSSIBLE TRIGGER
Yelling at the kids for no reason	Paid bills this morning. Might not have enough money for the month.	Fear of losing my house; not able to take care of family
Pornography and masturbation	Had a fight with my boyfriend. He doesn't like me going out with friends. He wouldn't listen, only lectured me.	Fear of losing this relationship; feeling unheard and unloved

We cannot always avoid feeling triggered, but when we are self-aware, we can control our ritualistic behaviors. Once we recognize how and why we engage in certain behaviors, we can stop the progression that leads to acting out.

For many of us, we recognize when we are feeling triggered by what is happening in our current environment, but we fail to understand why we are so significantly impacted by the situation. Our behavior is often the result of past trauma and abuse. We react to what is happening in front of us, but our limbic brain—the emotional center of the brain—is combining the feelings of a similar past experience with our current experience. This is why, sometimes, our reaction doesn't match the situation.

None of us wants to believe we were abused. Even as we hear the word "abuse," we imagine the worst case scenario of physical or sexual violence. But what comes to mind when we use the following definitions?

- Use for a bad purpose or to effect badly; misuse.
- Treat with intentional cruelty, regularly or repeatedly.
- Use or treat in a way that causes damage or harm.
- Speak to or about in an insulting or offensive way.

If we use the above criteria to define abuse, how many of us would admit to being the victim of abuse? How many of us would begin to develop a new perspective or expand our awareness regarding the abuse we sustained in our past?

The point of identifying past abuse is not to blame anyone or allow ourselves to live in a victim state. Instead, the goal is to gain a realistic view of our past—how it contributes to and shapes our relationships.

Using the Abuse Inventory will help raise awareness to the various ways we have experienced abuse in our past. Facing the truth about our past can feel unnerving, but it is a necessary part of our healing.

ABUSE INVENTORY[79]

Within each category, check any statement that has ever been true for you throughout your lifetime. Then, place a "P" next to any statement that is currently true for you.[80]

PHYSICAL VIOLATIONS:

- ☐ ____ Somebody invading your "space."
- ☐ ____ Being touched in ways that might make you feel uncomfortable, without first being asked.
- ☐ ____ Being told what clothing or make-up you can and cannot wear.
- ☐ ____ Not having freedom to come and go as you please.
- ☐ ____ Being pushed, shoved, slapped, bitten, kicked, hit, punched, or choked.
- ☐ ____ Being tickled without permission.
- ☐ ____ Being threatened with a weapon.
- ☐ ____ Being forced to stay awake.
- ☐ ____ Being raped.
- ☐ ____ Other: ____

EMOTIONAL VIOLATIONS:

- ☐ ____ Being told "you shouldn't feel that way."
- ☐ ____ Having your expressed feelings ignored.
- ☐ ____ Being exposed to uncontrolled anger.
- ☐ ____ Being threatened with abandonment or forced to leave.
- ☐ ____ Being called names.
- ☐ ____ Having affections withheld.
- ☐ ____ Being told you are responsible for someone else's feelings. (e.g. "You make me angry/sad/embarrassed!")
- ☐ ____ Not being allowed to cry or being forced to stuff your feelings out of fear.
- ☐ ____ Other: ____

SPIRITUAL VIOLATIONS:

- ☐ ____ The quoting of scripture to force you to change.
- ☐ ____ Having your relationship with God decided for you.
- ☐ ____ Manipulation using God's authority.
- ☐ ____ Keeping you from church/church people.
- ☐ ____ Other: ____

---

[79] Weiss, D. (2001). *Partners: Healing From His Addiction* (3rd ed.). Colorado Springs, CO: Discovery Press.

[80] Roberts, D. (2010). *Pure Desire for Women: Eight Pillars to Freedom From Love Addiction & Sexual Issues*. Gresham, OR: Pure Desire Ministries International.

INTELLECTUAL VIOLATIONS:

- ☐ ____ Being told you are crazy or stupid.
- ☐ ____ Having your ability to reason things out for yourself discounted.
- ☐ ____ Not being allowed to go back to school or work.
- ☐ ____ Being blamed for your children's failures.
- ☐ ____ Having your parenting abilities discounted.
- ☐ ____ Not being allowed to make everyday choices.
- ☐ ____ Having words put in your mouth or twisted to infer things you didn't say.
- ☐ ____ Other: ______________________________

FINANCIAL VIOLATIONS:

- ☐ ____ Not being allowed to earn or spend your own money.
- ☐ ____ Struggling to pay for necessities when the addict spent money on porn or acting-out behavior.
- ☐ ____ Allowing the addict to take money from you to support his habit.
- ☐ ____ Being forced to account for every cent you spend.
- ☐ ____ Allowing the addict's spending to interfere with your family's welfare or health.
- ☐ ____ Being lied to about finances.
- ☐ ____ Other: ______________________________

SEXUAL VIOLATIONS:

- ☐ ____ Not respecting your right to say "no" to sex.
- ☐ ____ Touching you sexually without permission.
- ☐ ____ Treating you as a sex object.
- ☐ ____ Criticizing you sexually.
- ☐ ____ Withholding affection for sex.
- ☐ ____ Exposing you to pornography.
- ☐ ____ Insisting you wear clothing that you deem inappropriate.
- ☐ ____ Expressing interest in other women while you are with him.
- ☐ ____ Sexualizing affectionate touch from you.
- ☐ ____ Unsolicited comments about your body.
- ☐ ____ Demanding sex or certain types of sexual acts.
- ☐ ____ Minimizing or ignoring your feelings about sex.
- ☐ ____ Having affairs outside your marriage.
- ☐ ____ Exposing you to sexually transmitted diseases.
- ☐ ____ Making sexual jokes.
- ☐ ____ Buying you clothing you are uncomfortable wearing (the gift is really for him).
- ☐ ____ Being physically forced or threatened with harm if you don't perform certain sexual acts.
- ☐ ____ Other: ______________________________

Based on your personal Abuse Inventory outcome, what are your thoughts?

What was surprising or shocking about your results?

Briefly describe a situation where your response didn't match the situation.

In light of what you learned through the Abuse Inventory, how does it explain your response in the previously described situation?

While it is true that many of us have sustained some form of abuse, we don't have to remain the victim. In the safety of this group we can face our past, identify where we have been wounded by others, and continue to move toward restoration and health.

Looking Ahead

Complete the FASTER Scale, Group Check-in, Self-Care lesson, Thoughts/Feelings Awareness Log, and Change & Growth Analysis in your *Unraveled: Weekly Tools* before the next group meeting.

LESSON 3: ENDING THE CYCLE OF ADDICTION

Recovery from compulsive and addictive behaviors starts with recognizing the need to change our behaviors. How do we establish and sustain a life of sobriety? We will need accountability and community through our Pure Desire group, as well as the tools in this workbook. Based on our past trauma, some of us may need additional personal counseling. Through our addiction we learned to stuff down and numb our pain, but sobriety facilitates our ability to access painful emotions and negative self-perceptions. Working through the pain is an essential step to lifelong health and freedom. We must uncover the core issues that perpetuate our shame.

As we pursue a life of sobriety, we must recognize and identify the thoughts, feelings, and behaviors that pull us back into the Cycle of Addiction. We must practically address our triggers. Many of us who struggle with love, sex, and relationships are often blindsided by how easily we are triggered.[81]

Trigger: I received a letter in the mail from my ex-husband's attorney. They would like to schedule a court appointment to discuss changes to the child support agreement.

Avoiding the trigger: I immediately put the letter aside and spent the next four hours vigorously cleaning the house. All I could think was, "My ex-husband used to complain that the house was never clean enough. I'll show him!" Since the kids will be with their dad for the weekend, I made plans with a few girlfriends to go out to dinner and dancing on Friday night.

Acting out: I was feeling especially excited for a girls' night out and wore a super sexy dress. Looking at my reflection in the mirror, I kept thinking, "If my ex-husband saw me tonight, he would have so many regrets." Throughout the night, I danced with many men—absorbing their affectionate words and touch. I felt wanted and loved. These feelings didn't last long; they were replaced with feelings of guilt, shame, and regret when I woke up in bed with a guy I met last night.

Joanne

[81] Triangle SAA Step Retreat (2017). Track 1, 52.

For many of us, this is what it looks like: the trigger causes us discomfort, so we attempt to avoid the trigger and numb our uncomfortable feelings. When our attempts fail, we find ourselves acting out, hoping that it will relieve our uncomfortable feelings, but we find ourselves further ensnared in the Cycle of Addiction.

As we continue to understand how our triggers lead to unhealthy behaviors, we also need to recognize the power we have in stepping off the addictive cycle by putting new healthy behaviors in place. When we are triggered, instead of avoiding the trigger, we confront the trigger head on. This action takes us off the addictive cycle and moves us toward health.

In the previous example, in what ways could Joanne have confronted the trigger?

____

____

____

____

We often feel trapped by our triggers. In the moment, we feel helpless to combat our triggers, unable to think clearly when faced with uncomfortable feelings. This is why it's so important that we understand our unique triggers and how they contribute to our acting out behaviors.

All of us need to experience God's grace in our lives if we are ever going to change our behaviors. Grace is an essential part of lifelong healing. It heals us from the inside out by minimizing the effect of our triggers and helping us break out of the Cycle of Addiction.

Many of us who struggle with sexually compulsive behaviors have often felt like the woman caught in adultery and brought before Jesus. In John 8:1-11, we discover how the Pharisees were trying to trick Jesus by bringing the woman before him, testing whether he will uphold the Law of Moses.

Jesus returned to the Mount of Olives, [2]but early the next morning he was back again at the Temple. A crowd soon gathered, and he sat down and taught them. [3]As he was speaking, the teachers of religious law and the Pharisees brought a woman who had been caught in the act of adultery. They put her in front of the crowd.

The Pharisees were not concerned with this woman's welfare. They were only using her as bait; but Jesus was not falling for it.

[4]"Teacher," they said to Jesus, "this woman was caught in the act of adultery. [5]The law of Moses says to stone her. What do you say?" [6]They were trying to trap him into saying something they could use against him,...

> *...but Jesus stooped down and wrote in the dust with his finger. [7]They kept demanding an answer, so he stood up again and said, "All right, but let the one who has never sinned throw the first stone!" [8]Then he stooped down again and wrote in the dust.*
> *[9]When the accusers heard this, they slipped away one by one, beginning with the oldest, until only Jesus was left in the middle of the crowd with the woman. [10]Then Jesus stood up again and said to the woman, "Where are your accusers? Didn't even one of them condemn you?"*
> *[11]"No, Lord," she said.*
> *And Jesus said, "Neither do I. Go and sin no more."*

Jesus challenged the Pharisees with his reply: *"All right, but let the one who has never sinned throw the first stone!"* In these simple words, Jesus communicates that the law came to show us our need for grace.

As each man dropped his stone of accusation, the only man without sin in His life who could have condemned her asked, *"Where are your accusers?"* Looking around, there was no one left to condemn her. Jesus' next words were life-changing: *"Neither do I. Go and sin no more."* He spoke correction to her without a hint of condemnation. In that moment, Christ gave her the gift of no condemnation *so that* she could go and sin no more.

As we step away from our compulsive and addictive behaviors, and continue to move toward health, we experience an overflow of God's grace.

> *When Adam sinned, sin entered the world. Adam's sin brought death, so death spread to everyone, for everyone sinned.*[82]
> *[15]But there is a great difference between Adam's sin and God's gracious gift. For the sin of this one man, Adam, brought death to many. But even greater is God's wonderful grace and his gift of forgiveness to many through this other man, Jesus Christ.*[83]

We live in a sin-filled world because of Adam's sin; but when we say "yes" to Christ, we are made righteous—not by our performance, but by Christ's obedience. No matter how hard we try to do what is right, we will never be good enough on our own. We need the life-changing blood of Jesus to cover our sin and bring us into relationship with our heavenly Father. When we take hold of God's restorative grace, our lives will forever change. This is the only way we will experience lifelong healing and transformation.[84]

---

[82] Romans 5:12 NLT

[83] Romans 5:15 NLT

[84] Roberts, D. (2010). *Pure Desire for Women: Eight Pillars to Freedom From Love Addiction & Sexual Issues*. Gresham, OR: Pure Desire Ministries International.

What aspects of John 8 are most impactful to you?

As you think about your past, who extended grace—unmerited or unearned favor—to you?

How has this group experience been a source of grace and healing?

MY AROUSAL TEMPLATE: PART ONE

Simply put, the word "arouse" means to evoke or awaken a feeling, emotion, or response. It is a physical reaction to a specific stimulus. Between the ages of five and eight, our arousal template is formed.[85] There are many factors that contribute to our arousal template: family of origin, childhood environment, early abuse and trauma, early sexual experiences, church influences, and the media—television, magazines, movies, and the Internet. All of these elements work together to create our sexual arousal.

Arousal is our brain reacting to something in our environment that triggers us to a heightened state of awareness.[86] When we feel triggered, it creates an emotional response: a limbic response (chapter 2, lesson 2). What we find arousing is a combination of both nature and nurture: what we are born with, our upbringing, and experiences. In many ways, our core beliefs—what we believe about ourselves and others—drive our compulsive and addictive behaviors, and are foundational to our arousal template.

[85] Carnes, P. (2015). *Facing the Shadow: Starting Sexual and Relationship Recovery* (3rd ed.). Carefree, AZ: Gentle Path Press. 329.

[86] Stumbo, N. (2018). Pure Desire University: Establishing Sobriety. Gresham, OR: Pure Desire Ministries International.

Since our arousal template is formed so early in life, almost anything can become a trigger for arousal: sights, sounds, smells, locations, objects, and feelings. It is important to remember that our arousal template is not fixed.[87] While our previous sexual behaviors may have reinforced our arousal template, we may notice shifts in what we find arousing as we continue to pursue lifelong healing.

Understanding our arousal template will help us identify our triggers. When we recognize our triggers, we become more self-aware, and are more likely to intervene when our triggers are leading us toward unhealthy behaviors.

Use the following table to identify your unique arousal template. Don't leave anything out—be thorough and specific. Throughout the week, if you become aroused, stop and think about what happened just before the arousal. Add it to your list if it's not already listed.

MY AROUSAL TEMPLATE: PART ONE[88]

TRIGGER CUES	MY AROUSAL TRIGGERS OR SIGNALS
Locations (hotels, malls, parties, beaches, bars, gym, home computer, being home alone	
Sensory Input (cologne, drugs, music, alcohol, certain smells)	
Physical Characteristics (tall, short, blonde, muscular)	
Perceived Personality (unavailable, vulnerable, dominant, professional, laborer)	

[87] Carnes, P. (2015). *Facing the Shadow: Starting Sexual and Relationship Recovery* (3rd ed.). Carefree, AZ: Gentle Path Press. 329.

[88] Roberts, D. (2010). *Pure Desire for Women: Eight Pillars to Freedom From Love Addiction & Sexual Issues*. Gresham, OR: Pure Desire Ministries International. 49.

TRIGGER CUES	MY AROUSAL TRIGGERS OR SIGNALS
Feelings (danger, risk, fear, pain, loneliness, rejection, shame)	
Culture (older men, Hispanic, French)	
False Beliefs (sex=love, sex=power)	

What are your thoughts after completing the Arousal Template: Part One?

____

____

____

____

MY AROUSAL TEMPLATE: PART TWO

If we want to break free from our sexually compulsive and addictive behaviors, we have to be proactive. We have to be aware of the things that trigger and arouse us, before we become limbically charged and ritually motivated. These next steps in the Arousal Template: Part Two will help us expand our awareness and develop realistic recovery strategies.

Please note: There may be legal ramifications for any information about inappropriate sexual contact or behavior that involves minor children that is shared within your Pure Desire group. Please review the Memo of Understanding.

Step One

A. *List ALL romantic and sexual behavior that are arousing for you.*

Examples: compulsive masturbation, pornography, dirty talk, hookups, cybersex, seduction, exhibitionism, flirtation, romance novels, office romance, affairs, high-risk sexual behavior.

🔖 ***B.*** *Add some specific details for the behaviors listed in part A.*

Examples: type of pornography sites you visit, types of men and women you view, specific sexual acts you find exciting (e.g. romantic, couples having intercourse, more than two people involved, rape, violence, ages, sexual orientation).

What do the individuals you view have in common? Do you pursue them or do you like to be pursued? Do you see yourself dominating the individual or being dominated? Do you like to exhibit images of yourself?

STEP TWO

🔖 *List all early painful sexual and relational experiences in your life. Pay particular attention to traumatic, abusive, and neglectful experiences.*

Examples: rigid or disengaged family experiences; inappropriate exposure to sexually explicit information in your home; parent or parents having affairs or multiple marriages; boundary violations; spanked while naked; punished for normal childhood sexual exploration; no respect for your privacy when dressing or in the bathroom; your body's development being ridiculed; exhibitionism by parent or parents.

STEP THREE

🔖 *Identify childhood feelings and emotions or themes related to abuse or neglect. Pay close attention to sexual or romantic themes.*

Examples: being violated or having sexual boundaries intruded upon; getting something only when you were good (performance); seeing sexual images prematurely (voyeurism); being flirted with (seduced); being subjected to abuse by a powerful parent (exploitive); experiencing abuse from a stranger (anonymous); being spanked while naked (pain); having no privacy (intrusive).

Remember: trauma or pain in the form of an intense one-time experience or numerous small experiences can become a hyper-accelerator for sexual arousal. This is why individuals who have experienced abuse and/or neglect exhibit altered brain function.

STEP FOUR

🔖 ***A.*** *Identify emerging overall themes and core beliefs.*

🔖 ***B.*** *List possible coping skills: disassociation, control, perfectionism, being passive, narcissism, silence, anger/rage.*

🔖 ***C.*** *How have these coping skills become embedded themes or patterns in your life?*

🔖 ***D.*** *How have these patterns expressed themselves romantically and/or sexually in your life?*

🔖 ***E.*** *What triggers you to react romantically and/or sexually?*

STEP FIVE

☐ *Identify your arousal patterns, triggers, and recovery strategies.*

☐ *Place your responses to steps one through four in the following chart. You will fill in step five after completing The Three Circles exercise. A completed Arousal Template is in the appendix.*

MY AROUSAL TEMPLATE: PART TWO

STEP ONE All sexual behaviors that are arousing & problematic	STEP TWO Early painful sexual relational experiences	STEP THREE Childhood feelings and themes	STEP FOUR Your overall themes and core beliefs	STEP FIVE Arousal patterns, triggers and recovery strategies
				Inner Circle **Middle Circle** **Outer Circle**

5

THE THREE CIRCLES

In our pursuit of lasting health, we need to construct a road map for healing. The arousal template identifies the specific behaviors we need to avoid and creates guardrails around, as well as helping us understand what healthy behaviors keep us on the right path. We often presume the sequence of transformation:[89]

changed feelings = changed thinking = changed behavior

However, when it comes to developing a mindset for healing from addictive behaviors, the practical truth is the reverse:

changed behavior = changed thinking = changed feelings

When it comes to changing behavior, we tend to focus more on the behaviors we don't want to do, rather than focusing on the behaviors that will keep us healthy. Using The Three Circles is a great way for us to evaluate the full extent of our behaviors: recognizing the behaviors that keep us stuck in our addiction, the behaviors that serve as boundaries or guardrails to protect us, and the behaviors that continue to move us toward health.[90]

THE THREE CIRCLES CONTAINS THE FOLLOWING COMPONENTS:

The center circle includes the behaviors that reinforce our addictive patterns. These are actions, not ideas or intent. The center circle indicates behaviors that constitute a relapse or violation of our sobriety. For many of us who struggle with sex, love, and relationship addictions, this could include:

- Anonymous hookups
- Online sex
- Pornography use
- Masturbation
- Binge eating
- Uncontrolled anger or rage
- Dating during the first year of recovery
- Sex with boyfriends
- Getting drunk or using drugs
- Cutting
- Self-inflicted pain
- Sexting or sending nude pictures

Remember: these are bottom-line behaviors—they do not support our goals and purpose. If we engage in these behaviors we are not living in health.

---

[89] Roberts, D. (2010). *Pure Desire for Women: Eight Pillars to Freedom from love addiction and sexual issues.* Workbook 1. Gresham, OR: Pure Desire Ministries International. 127.

[90] Carnes, P. (2001). *Facing the Shadow: Starting Sexual and Relationship Recovery* (3rd ed.). Carefree, AZ: Gentle Path Press.

The middle circle includes the behaviors that lead to relapse—the behaviors that we know will take us back to our center circle. Our middle circle behaviors are the warning signs, triggers, or concerning issues that indicate we are headed for trouble. We cannot underestimate our middle circle behaviors. They are more than a temptation. This could include:

- Spending too much time on social media
- Boredom
- Flirting
- Lack of self-care
- Fantasy
- Staying too busy—not saying "no"
- Isolating
- Ignoring feelings
- Distracted from priorities
- Too much TV
- Using food to cope
- Not making time for God
- Being home alone in the evening
- Watching movies with sex scenes or romance
- Sleeping with my phone by my bed
- Not making or staying within my budget
- Shopping online
- Delays in paying the bills
- Drinking alcohol
- Lying, blaming, rationalizing, justifying, and minimizing the desire to act out
- Going to parties where alcohol and drugs are used

The outer circle includes the behaviors that keep us sexually and relationally healthy. To stay on the path toward lifelong healing, our outer circle behaviors are the most important. This is where life happens. Outer circle behaviors are about self-care and should be specific. This could include:

- Taking time for family
- Spending time with spouse
- Learning to set boundaries
- Healthy eating
- Spending intentional time with the kids
- Learning to deal with anger
- Exercising regularly
- Keeping commitments to group/church
- Developing relationship with positive role models
- Spending time with God
- Spending time with friends
- Being present
- Getting seven or eight hours of sleep each night
- Being honest with spouse—no secrets

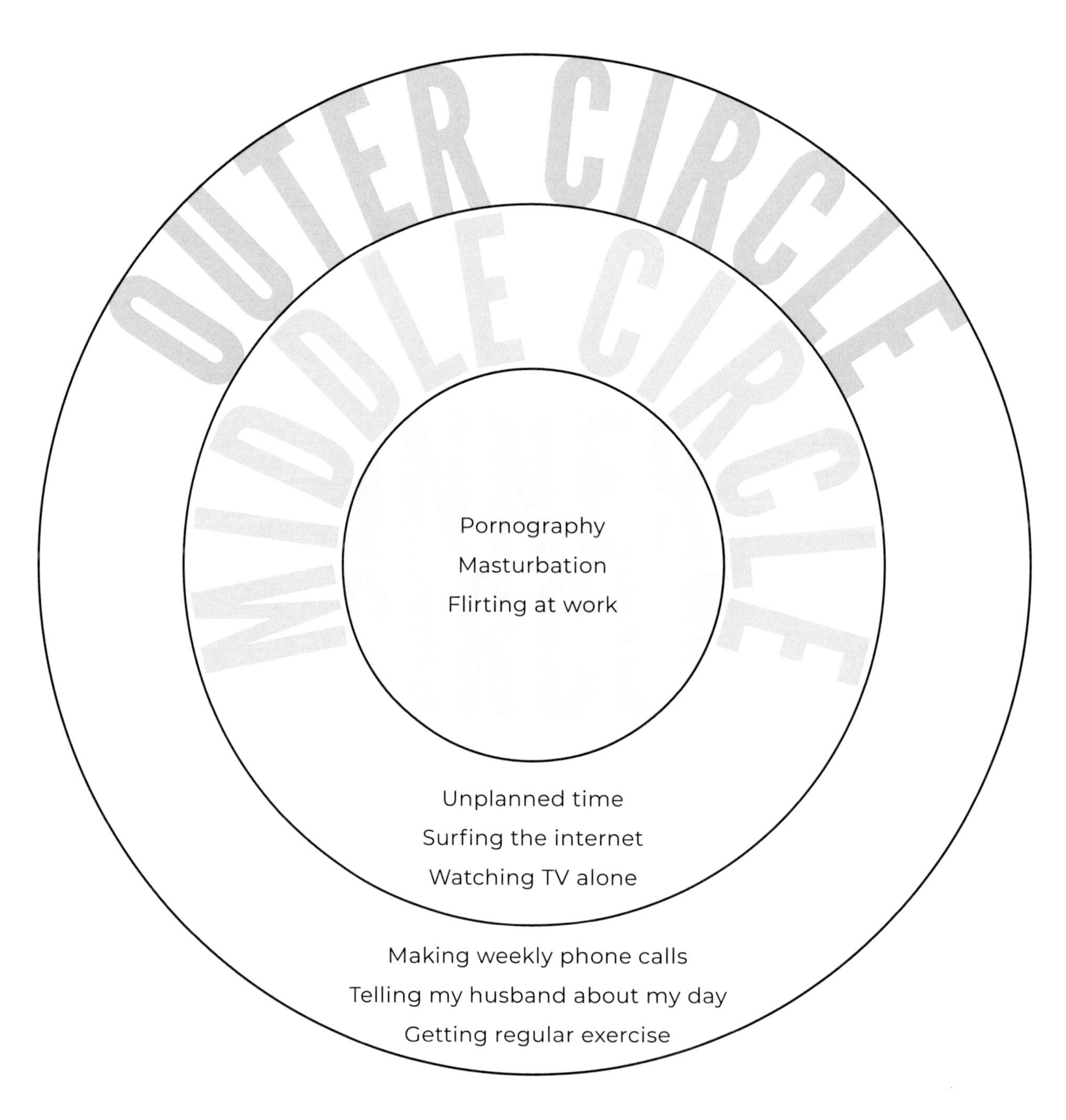

In the space provided, evaluate what you need to include in your personal Three Circles.

My center circle needs to include:

____

____

____

____

My middle circle needs to include:

My outer circle needs to include:

Fill in The Three Circles diagram on the next page based on your evaluation of your personal needs. When completed, add these behaviors to step 5 of the Arousal Template: Part Two.

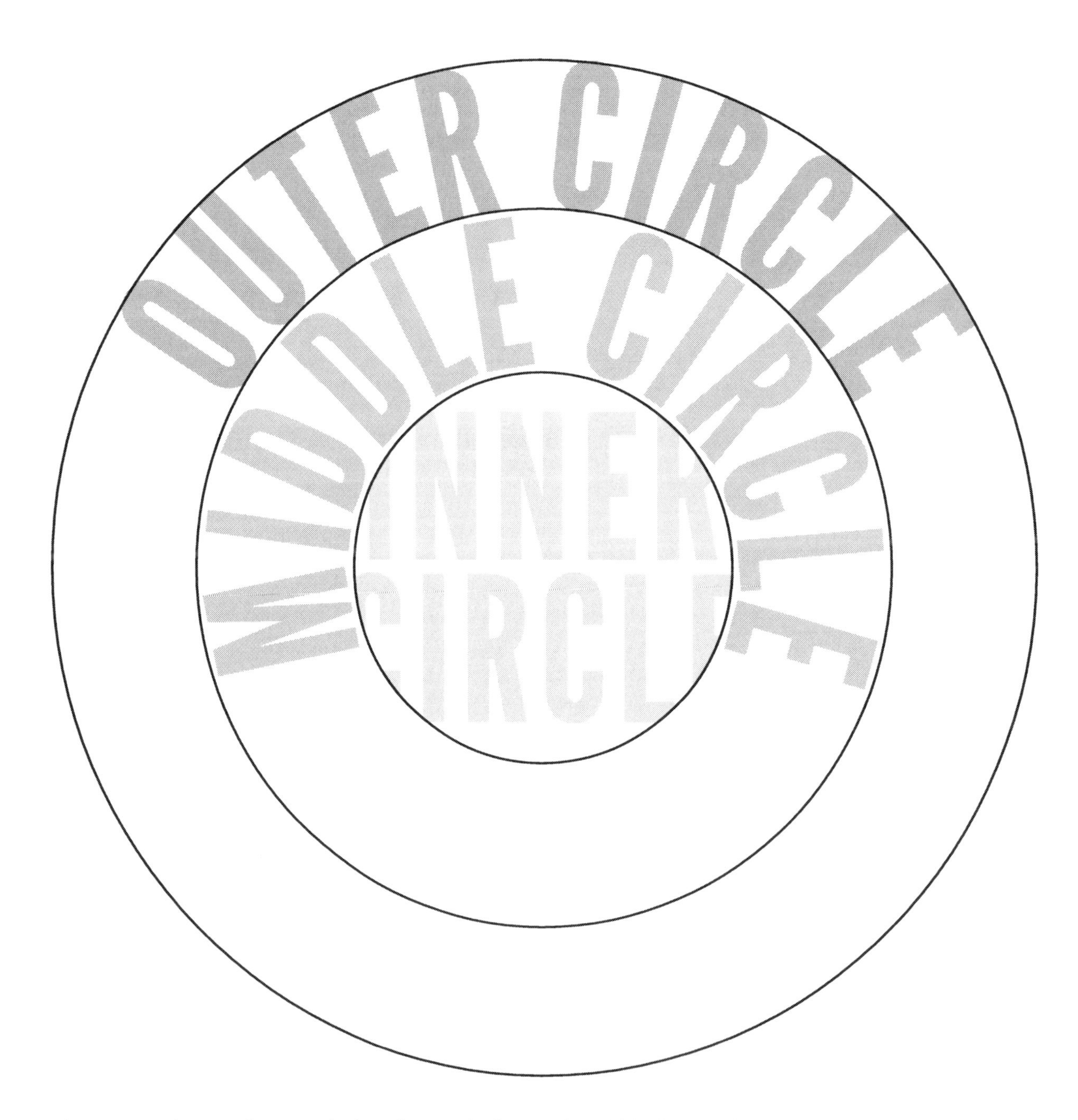

The Arousal Template and The Three Circles tools will help reinforce and support our recovery. Together, we are creating the steps we need on our path to healing and freedom.

Looking Ahead

Complete the FASTER Scale, Group Check-in, Self-Care lesson, Thoughts/Feelings Awareness Log, and Change & Growth Analysis in your *Unraveled: Weekly Tools* before the next group meeting.

chapter six

IN LOVE WITH LOVE

LESSON 1: GENUINE CONNECTION

If we want to experience genuine connection in relationship we have to begin doing things differently. We have to change our needs, behaviors, core beliefs, and expectations in relationship. We have to change our thinking. It can't be about us. We can't seek to have relationship on our terms. We have to evaluate not only where we have failed in relationship, but why we have failed in relationship.

I love being in love. The delicate mix of fear and exhilaration when my eyes lock with a handsome stranger across the room. The warmth and anticipation of a first touch. The nervous excitement that flows through my body during the first kiss. It's insatiable. I crave it!

I've been this way since grade school. I could always find the perfect boy on the playground to give me special attention. I developed my knack for flirting in junior high, which started out as more of a game but resulted in the physical affection from many guys that only left me wanting more. During high school, I perfected my "love" skill, seeking out the most popular guys to tease and please, to make them fall in love with me. By college, I was a pro: engaging in multiple love interests at the same time, never having any relationship last too long.

I wasn't really looking for a husband. When my friends asked about my dating intent, I simply replied, "Any guy that can fill my veins with 'love juice' longer than two months can have me." I knew that my attitude was a bit cavalier, but it was what I wanted. I didn't want a relationship, I wanted to be in love. I wanted to feel in love.

Jenna

What concerns do you have with Jenna's approach to relationships?

____

____

____

____

If Jenna was your friend, how would you express your concerns for her?

____

____

____

____

Developing genuine connection with others takes time and intention. It's not going to happen over night. It will take a deeper understanding of ourselves and others to cultivate successful relationships. While it may be difficult to imagine what this process could look like, a perfect place to start is found in John 13:34.

> *"A new command I give you: Love one another. As I have loved you, so you must love one another."*

Loving others can be tricky. How do we balance a godly version of loving others without it turning into a codependent, compulsive, or addictive behavior? How do we create a proactive approach to genuine connection?

While our past experiences contribute to how we relate to others, we have to work at cultivating relationship in a way that continues to move us toward health. This can feel even more challenging with our technology-saturated society and social media use. While many of us think that social media gives us an even greater opportunity to connect, we have to be careful that it does not give us a false sense of connection.

Keep in mind that the Internet and social media are not inherently bad. As with every area of our life, it's all about balance. The Internet and social media use are not any different. They require the same level of understanding and responsibility we give any other area that has the potential to pull us back into unhealthy behaviors. Keep in mind, many of us who struggle with sexually compulsive and addictive behaviors struggle with addictive tendencies in other areas too. We have to be aware of any behavior that has the potential to facilitate our compulsive needs.

Too often, we unknowingly assign meaning to a thought, feeling, or behavior that then dictates our future behaviors. In the moment, we don't recognize the control it has in our lives—how quickly we can become compulsive or even addicted to it.

I could feel the blood rushing to my head; my heart was pounding; and I was short of breath. I started panting and walking around in circles. I knew I was having a panic attack. I've had them before but never over something like this. I started looking under the couch, in the couch cushions, behind the chair, and in all the drawers. I knew it had to be around here somewhere. I couldn't find it anywhere!

Then I remembered I could use my laptop to locate it. I grabbed my laptop and within a few moments heard the familiar "ding-ding" in the other room. I followed the sound and finally, my phone was back in my hand. I breathed a sigh of relief and plopped down on the couch.

Immediately, I unlocked my phone and opened Facebook. I scrolled and scrolled, liked a few photos, and then opened Instagram. I scrolled for longer on Instagram and followed a few new people. After what seemed like no time (actually 45 minutes), I heard my son awake in the next room, so I grabbed my phone and went to get him.

He looked so cute as he waited for me! I left him in the crib and snapped about 20 pictures, then flipped through them to pick the best one. I heard him start to fuss, but I really wanted to post his cute photo. I picked a filter, wrote a short post, added a couple hashtags, and posted it. I thought to myself, "I can't wait to see what people say about my cute boy." I picked up my screaming son and went to the other room.

As I watched him play with his toys, it wasn't long before my phone chimed with likes and comments. I felt so happy! Just then my son was trying to stack blocks, so I turned the phone around and took a quick selfie with him in the background. I posted the selfie with the words, "Another fabulous day doing the amazing stay-at-home mom job."

I waited and waited. Only a couple people liked it. I wondered, "Why aren't people commenting on my post? It's probably because I'm in the picture. People like photos of babies so much more. People are so irritating!" Feeling frustrated, I walked to the kitchen—ignoring the six feet of dirty dishes on the counter and a sink filled to the brim with an awful smell—and went straight to the pantry. I grabbed a bag of chips, went back to the couch, and started eating.

As I reached the bottom of the bag, I noticed my baby boy crawling for the first time! I grabbed my phone again and went to video this momentous event. I couldn't believe I captured it on video! I was so excited to post it. He was young to be crawling and I wanted the world to know.

I started the post, but before I could finish it, my phone died. I was so irritated. I hate not posting stuff in real time. I plugged my phone into charge, but it had to do an update, so I wouldn't be able to use it for 30 minutes. What will I do while waiting?

I felt so disconnected and out of touch with my friends not being able to use my phone. At least I could see it! I would hate to go into another panic attack from losing the use of my phone.

Yesenia

In what way do you relate to Yesenia's story?

What about Yesenia's behavior seems unhealthy?

In what way does social media give us a false sense of connection?

UNHEALTHY BELIEFS

Too often, our unhealthy behaviors are attached to an unhealthy belief. Our beliefs about life and ourselves are formed early in our childhood. Since our prefrontal cortex was not fully developed, we processed our world through a limbic filter—a highly emotional filter where lies were created, lies the enemy uses against us to keep us in isolation. But there is hope.

> *When I was a child, I talked like a child, I thought like a child, I reasoned like a child. When I became a man, I put the ways of childhood behind me.*
>
> **1 CORINTHIANS 13:11**

As a child, we thought like a child; but now we have to learn to put our childish thinking behind us. We have a choice to either believe the warped view of life and ourselves or believe what God says about us. To break free from our unhealthy beliefs we first have to identify the lie that is holding us hostage.

- "People will only love me if I do what they say."
- "There is something wrong with me."
- "If I'm vulnerable, I'll get hurt."

- "My life on social media defines me."
- "Men only want one thing."
- "If they really knew me, they wouldn't like me."
- "I can't be friends with pretty women."
- "I only have value if I'm needed, especially sexually."
- "I can't trust anyone."
- "My value is based on my appearance."
- "If I get pregnant, he'll marry me."
- "Flirting is harmless and doesn't hurt anyone."
- "I'm responsible for the feelings and happiness of others."
- "I've always had more guy friends than girl friends."
- "I can keep the relationship if I have sex with the guy."
- "If I only date unavailable men, I'll be the one in control and won't get hurt."
- "God won't be there when I really need Him."
- "I can't change ______________________."

We become trapped in a vicious cycle of distorted thinking and negative feelings. Our distorted thinking comes from an unhealthy belief. If we are going to change our unhealthy beliefs, we have to identify where these lies come from. We have to investigate when these thoughts were first planted in our brain.

Use the following questions to help identify how you developed an unhealthy belief. Choose one unhealthy belief that contributes to an area of distorted thinking. Use that same unhealthy belief throughout this entire exercise.[91]

The first time I remember thinking (unhealthy belief) ______________________________
was ____.

The people who reinforced my thinking were (list who and how):

Family members: ____
____

Friends/Peers: ____
____

[91] Riggenbach, J. (2013). *The CBT Toolbox: A Workbook for Clients and Clinicians.* Eau Claire, WI: PESI Publishing & Media.

Other significant people: ______________________________

____

Experiences during my:

Elementary school years: ______________________________

____

____

Junior high years: ______________________________

____

____

High school years: ______________________________

____

____

College/young adult years: ______________________________

____

____

Adult years: ______________________________

____

____

Other significant experiences: ______________________________

____

____

When we work to identify the source of our unhealthy beliefs, it raises awareness. We can then begin to develop strategies that will help us combat our negative thought patterns and create new, positive beliefs that draw us into relationship with God and others.

Looking Ahead

Complete the FASTER Scale, Group Check-in, Self-Care lesson, Thoughts/Feelings Awareness Log, and Change & Growth Analysis in your *Unraveled: Weekly Tools* before the next group meeting.

LESSON 2: ADULT ATTACHMENT

The theory of attachment continues to be an interesting area of research into human behavior: from John Bowlby's pioneering work and Mary Ainsworth's *Strange Situation* research (1969), to more recent research suggesting that a child's temperament and a parent's sensitivity to their child's needs are variables that cannot be ignored.[92]

Like many of the behaviors we learn through interaction and experience with others, our ability to form healthy attachment and relationship is learned at an early age. From infancy, as our needs are met in a healthy, predictable, and safe environment, we develop secure attachments. However, if our needs go unmet—if we are neglected or forced to figure out how to survive on our own—we develop insecure attachments.[93]

I am constantly in and out of romantic relationships. Even when we've formed an amazing sexual connection, at some point, they lose interest in me. My most recent relationship with Bruce ended when he wanted to spend a day alone with his brother who was on military leave. *Why doesn't he want to include me in everything he has planned with his brother? Why doesn't he love me?* There is no excuse! I don't need to be with someone who doesn't love me as much as I love them!

Even when I don't have a boyfriend, I always have Stephen. We've worked together for years. We definitely have times when our relationship is a little out of balance: one minute questionably close, and the next, it borders on hostility. For some reason, with us, there is no in-between. I know Stephen gets frustrated with me sometimes, threatening to stop working with me. When he gets this way, I know exactly what to do: I bring him his favorite coffee, shower him with praise, and act more friendly and flirty with him. He finally comes around.

I always have my family relationships to fall back on. I love them so much! Recently, when I received a promotion, we all went out to dinner. Well, only my brother and parents showed up. They must not have realized that we were

---

[92] McLeod, S. (2014). *Mary Ainsworth*. Retrieved from www.simplypsychology.org/maryainsworth.html.

[93] Cozolino, L. (2016). *Why Therapy Works: Using Our Minds to Change Our Brains*. New York, NY: W. W. Norton & Company, Inc.

celebrating my accomplishment because they didn't even bring me a gift. I offered to pay for dinner, even though I thought my parents would pay. They didn't. I've always felt like they loved and accepted my siblings more than me. I'll give them a few days of the "cold shoulder" to think about how they've hurt me.

After several days, when they didn't call to apologize, I called to see if everything was okay. I immediately told them I had forgiven them and that it was all "water under the bridge."

Abigale

What problems does Abigale have in navigating relationship?

____

____

____

____

Have you ever known someone who exhibited behaviors similar to Abigale? Briefly explain.

____

____

____

____

____

ATTACHMENT STYLES

When it comes to the research done in determining attachment styles, the primary caregiver is often the mother; however, the following descriptions can apply to either or both parents, or any person who serves as a primary caregiver.

Children who are raised in an environment where their parents are available and attentive to their needs tend to be **securely attached**. In this environment, parents monitor and respond to their child's needs, recognizing when help is needed, but disengaging appropriately. They step back and observe, allowing the child to explore their surroundings. When feeling distressed or frightened, the child quickly seeks comfort from the parent, is easily soothed, and returns to play. They expect their parents to be present, helpful, and encouraging as they develop their individuality and independence. A secure child learns that their physical and emotional needs will be met in a safe environment.

When parents are inattentive and neglectful of their child's needs, the child becomes **avoidantly attached**. This causes a great deal of stress for the child, but they ignore or become disengaged with their parent. The parent-child relationship is not safe. The child has no expectation that their parent will meet any of their needs, resulting in an insecure attachment. An avoidant child learns to be self-reliant for their physical and emotional needs.

When a child is raised in an environment where parents are inconsistently available, this results in an **ambivalent attachment**. In many cases, the parent is present but distracted by their own stress and anxiety; therefore, they are not responsive or supportive of the child's needs. The child becomes easily distressed, but is not soothed by a parent's efforts to provide comfort. This results in an insecure attachment. An ambivalent child learns that the world is a scary place, where their physical and emotional needs will not be met in a safe environment.

Children who form a **disorganized attachment** have experienced conflict and stress with their parent, resulting in confusion about the safety of the environment. When distressed, they want comfort from their parent, but are equally reluctant to engage. The child will often move toward the parent, stop, and move away. They do not receive comfort from their parent and are not able to self-soothe. This results in an insecure attachment. A disorganized child learns that their parent and environment is frightening. They have resolved that their needs will not be met.

While many of us can identify our primary attachment style, our ability to attach is influenced by our childhood environment.[94] Since our attachment style is learned behavior, we can develop a different style of attachment based on the relationships and influences we have throughout our lifetime.

For example, if a person was raised with a secure attachment, but spends years in an abusive, unsafe relationship, their attachment style will change—they will feel insecure in the relationship, which will impact their overall attachment style with others.

In a similar way, if a person was raised with an insecure attachment and then spends years in a healthy, loving, and safe relationship, their attachment style will change—they will feel secure in the relationship, which will influence the way they develop and attach to others.

The significance of understanding our attachment style—how well we bonded with our parents or other caregivers—is key to developing healthy relationships.[95]

---

[94] Cozolino, L. (2016). *Why Therapy Works: Using Our Minds to Change Our Brains*. New York, NY: W. W. Norton & Company, Inc.

[95] Coon, D. & Mitter, J. (2013). *Introduction to Psychology: Gateways to Mind and Behavior* (13th ed.). Belmont, CA: Wadsworth, Cengage Learning.

Based on what you have learned, what type of attachment style(s) do you observe in Abigale's behaviors?

What type of attachment style(s) do you observe in your own relationships?

KNOW YOUR ADULT ATTACHMENT STYLE MINI-QUESTIONNAIRE[96]

Instructions: When completing this questionnaire, please focus on one significant relationship—ideally a current or past partner since the focus here is on adult relationships. This does not necessarily need to be a romantic relationship but must be the individual with whom you feel the most connection. Who is your primary "go to" person if you're sick, in trouble, want to celebrate, or have news to share? This questionnaire is designed to be an interactive learning tool. Please highlight, circle, or comment on any statements that are particularly relevant to you or that you'd like to revisit for exploration at a later time. When responding, consider how strongly you identify with each statement. Using the scale below, respond in the space provided

PLEASE UNDERSTAND THAT THIS IS NOT MEANT TO BE A DIAGNOSTIC TOOL, but it's a good starting point to begin your personal exploration into your attachment styles.

[96] Heller, D. (2014). *Know Your Adult Attachment Style Mini-Questionnaire*. Retrieved from dianepooleheller.com.

0	1	2	3
Disagree	Sometimes Agree	Mostly Agree	Strongly Agree

SECURE

____ **1.** I feel relaxed with my partner most of the time.

____ **2.** I find it easy to flow between being close and connected with my partner to being on my own.

____ **3.** If my partner and I hit a glitch, it is relatively easy for me to apologize, brainstorm a win-win solution, or repair the misattunement or disharmony.

____ **4.** People are essentially good at heart.

____ **5.** I attempt to discover and meet the needs of my partner whenever possible, and I feel comfortable expressing my own needs.

____ **6.** It is a priority to keep agreements with my partner.

____ **7.** I actively protect my partner from others and from harm and attempt to maintain safety in our relationship.

____ **8.** I look at my partner with kindness and caring and look forward to our time together.

____ **9.** I am comfortable being affectionate with my partner.

____ **10.** I can keep secrets, protect my partner's privacy, and respect boundaries.

Section Total: ____________

AVOIDANT/DISMISSIVE

____ **1.** When my partner arrives home or approaches me, I feel inexplicably stressed—especially when he or she wants to connect.

____ **2.** I find myself minimizing the importance of close relationships in my life.

____ **3.** I insist on self-reliance; I have difficulty reaching out when I need help, and I do many of life's tasks or my hobbies alone.

____ **4.** I sometimes feel superior in not needing others and wish others were more self-sufficient.

____ **5.** I feel like my partner is always there, but I would often prefer to have my own space unless I invite the connection.

____ **6.** Sometimes I prefer casual sex instead of a committed relationship.

____ **7.** I usually prefer relationships with things or animals instead of people.

____ **8.** I often find eye contact uncomfortable and particularly difficult to maintain.

____ **9.** It is easier for me to think things through than to express myself emotionally.

____ **10.** When I lose a relationship, at first I might experience separation elation and then become depressed.

Section Total: ____________

ANXIOUS/AMBIVALENT

____ **1.** I am always yearning for something or someone that I feel I cannot have and rarely feel satisfied.

____ **2.** Sometimes, I over-function, over-adapt, over-accommodate others, or over-apologize for things I didn't do, in an attempt to stabilize connection.

____ **3.** Over-focusing on others, I tend to lose myself in relationships.

____ **4.** It is difficult for me to say NO or to set realistic boundaries.

____ **5.** I chronically second-guess myself and sometimes wish I had said something differently.

____ **6.** When I give more than I get, I often resent this and harbor a grudge. It is often difficult to receive love from my partner when they express it.

____ **7.** It is difficult for me to be alone. If alone, I feel stressed, abandoned, hurt, and/or angry.

____ **8.** At the same time as I feel a deep wish to be close with my partner, I also have a paralyzing fear of losing the relationship.

____ **9.** I want to be close with my partner but feel angry at my partner at the same time. After anxiously awaiting my partner's arrival, I end up picking fights.

____ **10.** I often tend to "merge" or lose myself in my partner and feel what they feel, or want what they want.

Section Total: ______________

DISORGANIZED/DISORIENTED

____ **1.** When I reach a certain level of intimacy with my partner, I sometimes experience inexplicable fear.

____ **2.** When presented with problems, I often feel stumped and feel they are not resolvable.

____ **3.** I have an exaggerated startle response when others approach me unexpectedly.

____ **4.** My partner often comments or complains that I am controlling.

____ **5.** I often expect the worst to happen in my relationship.

____ **6.** Protection often feels out of reach. I struggle to feel safe with my partner.

____ **7.** I have a hard time remembering and discussing the feelings related to my past attachment situations. I disconnect, dissociate, or get confused.

____ **8.** Stuck in approach-avoidance patterns with my partner, I want closeness but am also afraid of the one I desire to be close with.

____ **9.** My instinctive, active self-protective responses are often unavailable when possible danger is present – leaving me feeling immobilized, disconnected, or "gone."

____ **10.** Because I am easily confused or disoriented, especially when stressed, it is important for my partner to keep arrangements simple and clear.

Section Total: ______________

Scoring: For each section, add up your responses and record your total number. The section with the highest number will likely correspond to your unique attachment style. You may discover a dominant style or a mix of styles.

This questionnaire is not meant to be a label or diagnosis. It is only intended to indicate tendencies and prompt more useful, precise personal exploration.

After completing the attachment assessment, what did you learn about yourself?

What attachment style is strongest for you? What attachment style do you need to work on?

We all have areas within our attachment styles where we are strong as well as areas that need improvement. Look at this as an opportunity to explore what we can learn about ourselves and how to build healthy relationship with God and others.

Looking Ahead

Complete the FASTER Scale, Group Check-in, Self-Care lesson, Thoughts/Feelings Awareness Log, and Change & Growth Analysis in your *Unraveled: Weekly Tools* before the next group meeting.

LESSON 3: CODEPENDENCY

No one likes being considered "codependent." It's a word that has been overused and carries a negative connotation, especially in Christian circles. On one hand, as Christians we should want to help and support others. What's wrong with wanting to please others, to help them become better, or to show them the correct way of doing things? Of course, being helpful is good, but when that helpfulness becomes a compulsion, when we become enmeshed in relationships, or when we strive to rescue someone from the consequences of their own behavior, we have swerved into an unhealthy relational dynamic that is often referred to as codependency.

When talking about codependency, we are really talking about behaviors that come from a trauma response. These behaviors usually begin at a point in our lives when we felt unsafe—when the safety and security of our environment was reinforced by our behaviors. The problem comes when the unsafe situation passes and we are still stuck in our protective behaviors, keeping us from healthy relationships.

Those of us who struggle with codependent behaviors tend to demonstrate a lack of objectivity: an inability to see the reality of a situation.[97] Additionally, we have a warped sense of responsibility, which makes us think we need to control those around us. In the moment, we may feel as though we are motivated by love, but in reality, this is a form of manipulation, fueled by fear. This can come from a need to feel safe and take control.

It is important to realize what is motivating our need for control. Are we obsessing over another's behavior because we need to feel safe or do we want to control the outcome of their behavior? If safety is the motive, then we are probably reacting out of a sense of trauma. However, if the danger has passed and control is now the motive, then codependency is probably the root.[98]

It is common for women who struggle with compulsive and addictive behaviors to exhibit codependent symptoms; however, not all women with codependent symptoms have an addiction. As we continue to move toward health, it is important for us to recognize and address issues related to codependency, such as early childhood trauma and abuse.

Recognizing our own unique codependent behaviors is only half the battle. We need to change our behaviors—not only for ourselves, but for those around us. We need to understand in a practical way what it looks like to manage our relationships.

---

[97] Springle, P. (1993). *Untangling Relationships: A Christian Perspective on Codependency*. Merritt Island, FL: Rapha Publishing.

[98] Roberts, D. (2016). *Betrayal & Beyond Workbook*. Gresham, OR: Pure Desire Ministries International.

Codependency is also known as a "relationship addiction."[99] People who struggle with codependency often form and maintain relationships that are one-sided, emotionally destructive, and/or abusive. Codependency is learned behavior, often modeled or perceived through a dysfunctional family system.

Codependency is a byproduct of low self-esteem. We look for external validation by helping others. We rely on feeling "needed" by others. Although we often enable those around us, we develop a sense of satisfaction and self-worth by our compulsive caretaking behaviors. We have good intentions, but our codependent behaviors have some very strong characteristics:[100]

____ An exaggerated sense of responsibility for the actions of others

____ A tendency to confuse love and pity, with the tendency to "love" people we can pity and rescue

____ A tendency to do more than our share, all of the time

____ A tendency to become hurt when people don't recognize our efforts

____ An unhealthy dependence on relationships—a codependent will do anything to hold on to a relationship to avoid the feeling of abandonment

____ An extreme need for approval and recognition

____ A sense of guilt when asserting themselves

____ A compelling need to control others

____ Lack of trust in self and/or others

____ Difficulty knowing who we are—becoming who others want us to be.

____ Fear of being abandoned or alone

____ Difficulty identifying feelings

____ Rigidity/difficulty adjusting to change

____ Problems with intimacy/boundaries

____ Chronic anger

____ Lying/dishonesty

____ Poor communication

____ Difficulty making decisions

None of us plans to become codependent. In fact, most of us don't even realize how codependent behaviors become such a strong part of our life. Understanding and

---

[99] Mental Health America (2018). *Co-Dependency*. Retrieved from http://www.mentalhealthamerica.net/co-dependency.

[100] Kleffner, T. (n.d.). *Co-dependency*. St. Louis Counseling and Wellness. Compiled from www.mentalhealthamerica.net/go/codependency.

recognizing the core characteristics of codependency is the first step in changing our codependent behaviors.

On the list on the previous page, put a "T" next to the behaviors you think are a trauma response. Put a "C" next to the behaviors you think are codependent.

I am married with four kids and work a part-time job three days a week. Every morning, after the kids and I are ready to go, I quickly get them in the car, drive through my favorite coffee shop, and drop them off at school. Three days a week, I go to work and the other two days I run errands and clean house.

I look forward to seeing my husband each night when he comes home from work. We were best friends long before we got married and always have fun together. I tend to set high expectations for myself and one of my goals is to always have a home-cooked meal on the table when my husband gets home at 5:30 p.m. Occasionally, he calls to say he is running late and that we should eat without him. This makes me angry.

Immediately, my mind fills with negative thoughts: *"I can't believe he values his work more than his family! Doesn't he know how hard I work so we can all have family time? We set a schedule and we stick to it, to make the most of the time we have together. How could he devalue the work that I put in each day? How am I supposed to explain to the kids why their dad isn't here? This is all my fault."* These thoughts repeat over and over in my mind, but I never tell my husband how I feel.

When he comes home late from work, I always put on a smile but remain distant. It really doesn't matter why he is late—I was depending on him to be home on time and he wasn't. Although I feel frustrated, as I fall asleep, I remember to be grateful: he came home and he has not abandoned me to raise our four kids alone.

Maura

What codependent behaviors do you see in Maura?

____

____

____

____

____

____

Why do you think Maura becomes so angry with her husband?

IDENTIFYING SIGNS OF CODEPENDENCY[101]

As with many behaviors, codependency appears in various degrees, ranging from mild to severe symptoms, not necessarily on an all-or-nothing scale. The following statements are designed to identify symptoms of codependency; however, only a qualified professional can make a diagnosis of codependency.

Place a check mark next to the statements that are true of you and your behaviors. If the statement is true now or has ever been true in your lifetime, mark it. Don't spend too much time evaluating or overthinking each statement.

- ☐ 1. I keep quiet to avoid arguments.
- ☐ 2. I'm worried about others' opinions of me.
- ☐ 3. I have lived with someone with an alcohol or drug problem.
- ☐ 4. I have lived with someone who hits or belittles me.
- ☐ 5. The opinions of others are more important than my own.
- ☐ 6. I have difficulty adjusting to changes at work or home.
- ☐ 7. I feel guilty setting limits on my time.
- ☐ 8. I doubt my ability to be who I want to be.
- ☐ 9. I am uncomfortable expressing my true feelings to others.
- ☐ 10. I often feel inadequate.
- ☐ 11. I feel like a "bad person" when I make a mistake.
- ☐ 12. I have difficulty taking compliments or gifts.
- ☐ 13. I feel humiliated when my child or spouse makes a mistake.
- ☐ 14. I think people in my life will go downhill without my constant efforts.
- ☐ 15. I frequently wish someone could help me get things done.
- ☐ 16. I have difficulty talking to people in authority, such as the police or my boss.
- ☐ 17. I overextend myself, then feel upset that I have to do everything.
- ☐ 18. I have trouble saying "no" when asked for help.

---

[101] Ibid.

- ☐ 19. I have trouble asking for help.
- ☐ 20. I have so many things going at once that I can't do justice to any of them.
- ☐ 21. I feel rejected when my significant other spends time with friends.
- ☐ 22. I often feel confused about who I am or where I'm going with my life.

_____ **Total number of true statements**

What do you think about the number of statements that are true for you?

____

____

____

Of the statements marked above, which one do you struggle with most?

____

____

____

What is the motivation behind your codependent behaviors: safety or control? Explain.

____

____

____

____

In what ways are your codependent behaviors contributing to unhealthy relationships?

____

____

____

____

Now that we are aware of our behaviors, we can take proactive steps to change our future behaviors.

Choose one codependent behavior that you struggle with and devise a plan. This will require a double bind exercise. Start by asking yourself, "What behavior do I want to change; what fear do I have to face?" Then work through the process: "If I don't change, I will continue in my codependent behavior. If I change, I will have to face my fear of..." This will help you determine what change is needed.

Then, identify a new behavior you can implement that will keep you moving forward on the path toward health. If you cannot think of a new behavior to implement, ask your group for help.

EXAMPLES:

Codependent behavior: *I have trouble asking for help. I fear that others will think I'm not perfect. New behavior: When I feel overwhelmed with household chores this week, I will ask my husband and kids for help.*

Codependent behavior: *I fear what others' think of me, so I don't share my thoughts and opinions. New behavior: In my college class, I'm going to share my thoughts and opinions during class discussion.*

____

____

____

____

____

____

In the moment, how did you feel when implementing your plan?

____

____

____

____

____

____

____

Change doesn't happen overnight. It takes raising awareness to the behaviors that keep us stuck in our compulsive and addictive behaviors. It takes a process of unraveling the messiness of relationships, one day at a time, one step at a time.

Looking Ahead

Complete the FASTER Scale, Group Check-in, Self-Care lesson, Thoughts/Feelings Awareness Log, and Change & Growth Analysis in your *Unraveled: Weekly Tools* before the next group meeting.

chapter seven

FACING LOSS

LESSON 1: HEARTBREAK, BETRAYAL, DIVORCE, ABORTION

At some point in our life, we all have been there: unexpected news at the doctor's office; the call in the middle of the night; the secret discovered or exposed; a decision made. In that moment, we are left feeling lost, broken, and empty. Unsure if our life will ever be the same. Paralyzed by the fear of what lies ahead. We didn't choose what is happening to us. We can't control it. We don't want it—we don't want to face the unknown.

Our fear causes us to react. Some of us may react in our stubbornness, digging in our heels, resistant to life pulling us forward. Others of us will freeze, crippled by the experience, feeling powerless to move in any direction. However, the majority of us will want to run: run from the pain, run from our unknown future, run from connection with others, run from our relationship with God.

Only two pages of scripture are designated to telling Jonah's story, but these two pages reveal the heart of those who run from God and God's heart toward the runner.

God asked Jonah to do something that would be a stretch for any of us. "Go to the great city of Nineveh and pronounce judgment on the wicked people there."[102] Jonah knew God well enough to know what God was really saying: *"I want to give your enemy a second chance."*[103]

Not many of us want our enemy to receive a second chance. Jonah probably responded like most of us would. *A second chance? Not on my watch. They deserve to die.* We might feel the same about someone who has inflicted pain in our life or in the lives of those we love. *Give them a second chance? Are you kidding? God, the only thing they deserve is Your wrath.* When God asked Jonah to do something beyond his capacity to comprehend, he ran.

Throughout the countless generations, two categories of runners exist. The first category includes those of us who do not want God's involvement in our life. For instance, some of us grew up in a Christian home and got to an age where we had to decide for ourselves if we wanted to follow God or not. Some of us leave our parents' home wanting nothing to do with God. We are determined to have full control over our lives.

---

[102] See Jonah 1:1-3

[103] See Jonah 4:2

The second category includes those of us who love God but want to control a particular decision. For example, let's say we meet an individual we would like to date. He is not a Christ-follower, but he's cute. We reason that it would be far easier to help a guy become a Christian than become cute, so we run from God and begin the relationship of our own choosing.[104]

Regardless of the personal reasons we run, our fellow runner, Jonah, offers a few lessons from his experience with running. Immediately following God's instruction to go to Nineveh, Jonah boards a boat headed for Tarshish, a boat headed in the opposite direction from where God had asked him to go. Life is full of boats waiting to distance us from God's purpose. This boat headed toward Tarshish provides a great parallel to the things we run toward when we're running from God. *"There will always be a boat headed for Tarshish. If we want to gossip, there will always be someone to talk about. If we want to hang on to bitterness and resentment, there will always be someone we can blame. If we want to mismanage our sexuality, there will always be a site. If we want to compare, there will always be something new to fuel the fire."*[105]

We can run from God, but we can never outrun God. He didn't lose sight of Jonah. God never loses track of our lives even when we think we've outwit and outrun him. The psalmist declared, *"Where can I go from your Spirit? Where can I flee from your presence? If I go up to the heavens, you are there; if I make my bed in the depths, you are there. If I rise on the wings of the dawn, if I settle on the far side of the sea, even there your hand will guide me, your right hand will hold me fast."*[106]

God's legs are longer than ours. We will never outrun him. In Jonah's story, we discover that running from God is costly: not only for us but for those who are in close proximity to us. God hurled a powerful storm on the sea that threatened to destroy the ship, the crew, and all their cargo.[107] The crew was not to blame for the storm, but they suffered the effects of Jonah's sin.

We believe the lie that as long as no one knows about our sin, we're not hurting anyone. We might justify and defend our actions. *It's not a big deal. It's just a little compromise!* However, when we run, we are incapable of controlling the ripple effect.

Sin will take you farther than you want to go, keep you longer than you want to stay, and cost you more than you want to pay.[108]

---

[104] Stanley, A. (2005). *Lessons from the Runner*. Northpoint Church. Message Series.

[105] Stuart, B. (2018). *Running and Chasing*. Passion City Church. Podcast Audio. April 13.

[106] Psalm 139:7-10. NIV

[107] Jonah 1:5. NLT

[108] Zacharias, R. (n.d.) Retrieved from https://www.goodreads.com/quotes/746709-sin-will-take-you-farther-than-you-want-to-go

What does God do with the runner? If it feels like our life is on a downward spiral, Jonah's story gives us hope. Mercy often shows up greatly disguised—possibly in the form of a scary, man-swallowing fish. Being swallowed by that huge fish wasn't God's punishment on Jonah. It was his rescue mission. God was in the midst of the circumstances that stopped Jonah from running. He will be in the midst of the circumstances that stop us from running.[109]

God's discipline is incredibly thorough. It probably took Jonah about three seconds to repent inside the belly of the fish, but God kept him there three days and nights. It was from the belly of the fish that Jonah prayed, "From now on I will fulfill my vows."[110] That prayer is amusing: from now on? Jonah was being digested in the belly of a fish. There is no, "From now on!" One would not have much leverage with God from the belly of a fish.[111]

This looks like a hopeless situation from all vantage points. Perhaps our situation looks just as hopeless. However, Jonah's story gives us an opportunity to see God's heart toward the runner. He listens to the sincere cries of the runner and rescues him.

Then the Lord ordered the fish to spit Jonah out onto the beach. The Lord spoke to Jonah a second time: "Get up and go to the great city of Nineveh, and deliver the message I have given you." This time Jonah obeyed the Lord's command and went to Nineveh.[112]

God is a God of second chances. He has a purpose for our life beyond our running. Just because we ran in the past or are running now does not mean He is finished with us. He knows how we will run and yet the hand that keeps reaching for us is a hand of mercy.[113] Our healing begins when we choose to put on the brakes and stop running. The prophet Isaiah records a promise from God to those willing to stop running.

Let the wicked change their ways and banish the very thought of doing wrong. Let them turn to the Lord that he may have mercy on them. Yes, turn to our God, for he will forgive generously.[114]

As we turn toward God, He breaks the chains that entangled us beneath the waters of sin. His resources are unlimited. He will go as far as turning a tuna into a taxi to get our feet back on the pathway of His purpose for our life.

---

[109] Stanley, A. (2005). *Jonah Series*. Northpoint Church.

[110] Jonah 2:8

[111] Stanley, A. (2005). *Jonah Series*. Northpoint Church.

[112] Jonah 3:1-3. NLT.

[113] Stuart, B. (2018). *Running and Chasing*. Passion City Church. Podcast Audio. April 13.

[114] Isaiah 55:7. NLT.

What is your purpose?

In what ways are you running?

In what way has the ripple effect of your running impacted those around you?

What would it take for you to stop running? What have you learned through this process that will help you stop running?

How has Jonah's story been an encouragement to you?

All of us will experience loss; there is no way around it. What we do in the midst of that experience—how we respond to our circumstance—is important. It will either drive us away from relationship with God and others, or toward a deeper love relationship with God and others.

> *I have told you all this so that you may have peace in me. Here on earth you will have many trials and sorrows. But take heart, because I have overcome the world.*
>
> **JOHN 16:33 NLT**

In the midst of your circumstance, how does this scripture give you hope?

____

____

____

____

____

____

Over the course of our eight-year marriage, my husband struggled with pornography use and had affairs. Even when he wasn't acting out, he was disengaged and lacked the motivation and drive that my parents instilled in me. As our connection and intimacy faded, I felt invisible, unvalued, and unwanted. I tried to be the perfect wife and would do anything to make my husband feel loved and appreciated. With nothing in return, I eventually turned to movies and romantic books as a way to escape. I fantasized about a husband who wanted, desired, pursued, and fought for me. I desperately wanted a take-charge type of man and found myself growing more bitter toward my unmotivated, addicted husband.

An old high-school friend began to connect with me through text and social media. He made me feel so special and loved. I got such a rush when he sent me a message. I started masturbating and fantasizing about being with him and the way he would care for me. He was educated and driven, a real man's man. The more I thought of him, the less I cared about my marriage.

My friend finally asked me to lunch, which started our secret relationship and affair. It felt invigorating to be wanted, passionately pursued, and physically touched. Although my husband and I were already headed toward divorce, I felt so much shame.

When our divorce was finalized, I thought everything would be okay—that I would go about my single life and raise my two kids. After a while, I felt lonely, but knew my ex-husband was not healthy. The pain of his pornography addiction and affairs were too much for me to bear.

I ended up dating several men over the next year, trying to fill the deep ache in my soul. On my 30th birthday, I sat in my dark house and cried. I couldn't believe what my life had become. I loved my kids so much, but felt like I had failed them. Why didn't anybody want to fight for me? I am educated, have friends and coworkers who love me, but I couldn't make a relationship work.

I was in and out of relationships, searching for something better than what I had with my ex-husband. I felt out of control but couldn't stop my behaviors. Nighttime would come and the pain of being alone was too much. I desperately wanted connection and love, but continued to search for it in all the wrong places.

I got pregnant: the result of a one-night stand. My heart felt like it had stopped. How would I explain this to my kids? They already missed their dad and begged for him to come home. I wrestled with the idea of having another baby. I had always viewed pregnancy as a life, but now I couldn't bear the thought of having this baby. My two kids meant the world to me and I knew this would wreck them. My son was already struggling with anxiety and anger because of the divorce. I couldn't do this to my kids.

As my heart pounded and I fought back the tears, I called the local women's center and scheduled an abortion. As I entered the clinic, I felt like I was living someone else's life. The procedure itself was quick. The medical professionals assured me it was safe and very common.

In the months following the abortion, I felt an ache and pain in my heart—a pain so deep that, at times, I thought it would break me. Oftentimes, several glasses of wine helped to dull the pain. That was my baby. I felt stuck between protecting my unborn baby and protecting my other two kids, who had already endured so much.

A year later, my ex-husband and I got back together. Our kids felt safe again. I told my husband about the abortion and the pain still has a place in my heart. At times, I wonder if I am the only one who has ever made this choice. I pray that God will forgive me, even if I can't forgive myself.

Svetlana

What part of Svetlana's story do you resonate with most?

How does it feel to read Svetlana's story? Why?

Why did Svetlana think her best option was to have an abortion?

MY TRAUMA STORY

How did we get here? How did we get to this place, unable to manage love, sex, and relationships? How did we become so entangled with our compulsive and addictive behaviors? What went wrong? These can be difficult questions to answer, but foundational to our healing.

We live in a fallen world, so all of us have a trauma story.[115] We have been wounded, mistreated, neglected, and hurt. Since childhood, we have experienced pain and trauma that continues to influence our behavior. In many ways, our trauma has become part of our existence, yet we are oblivious to it—unable to recognize its presence in our lives, but we feel it. We feel the way it impacts us emotionally—the way it controls us on a limbic level.

Over the past few months, we discovered how our family of origin contributes to our behaviors and continue to raise awareness through processing our trauma timeline. While we can pinpoint various life events and circumstances that may have fostered our

[115] Roberts, D. (2010). *Pure Desire for Women: Eight Pillars to Freedom from love addiction & sexual issues*. Gresham, OR: Pure Desire Ministries International.

addictive choices, we are not blaming others. In a very practical way, we are trying to identify the source of our trauma and grieve our losses, so we can begin reconstructing our limbic system. We need to understand the pain of our past so we can reclaim God's blessing and purpose in our lives.

Identifying the source of our trauma is only part of this process. We have to grieve our losses. We have to feel the loss. This is not so we can feel like a victim, but it is a process that allows us to release the feelings that we have buried deep in our soul—the feelings that are keeping us in isolation, unable to cultivate healthy relationships.

Grieving our losses can be fearful. It requires unpacking the pains of our past and facing the pain head-on. It requires a realistic look at our life. We can no longer ignore the pain and think it will go away. We have to face our fear and grieve our losses.

I'VE LOST...

- ☐ my job
- ☐ my reputation
- ☐ relationship with family and friends
- ☐ feelings of joy and contentment
- ☐ my innocence/virginity
- ☐ financial security
- ☐ the life I planned
- ☐ knowing who I am—my identity
- ☐ a sense of community
- ☐ self respect
- ☐ a close relationship with God
- ☐ my ability to trust others
- ☐ ____________________
- ☐ ____________________

Which losses do you identify with most?

____
____
____
____
____

How have these losses contributed to where your life is now?

____
____
____
____
____
____

7

As we grieve our losses and continue to process the pain of our past, it is important to identify significant events, recurring situations, and relationships that created trauma in our lives. We need to write out our trauma story. Put it all down on paper, where we can see it—where it becomes real. We need to recognize how our traumatic experiences shaped our core beliefs, forming the negative messages that often drive our compulsive and addictive behaviors.

In the space provided, write your trauma story. Write your story in third person, as though you are telling a story about someone. Be thorough and specific. Write your story from the beginning of your life. This exercise is intended to help you answer some of the questions previously asked, specifically, "How did you get here, right now, to this point in your life?"

ONCE UPON A TIME...

☐ *Be prepared to read your story out loud to your group.*

Looking Ahead

Complete the FASTER Scale, Group Check-in, Self-Care lesson, Thoughts/Feelings Awareness Log, and Change & Growth Analysis in your *Unraveled: Weekly Tools* before the next group meeting.

LESSON 2: GRIEF AND ANGER

In the midst of grief, we experience feelings we've never known. We feel hollow, trepidation, deserted, and invisible. We want others to recognize and acknowledge the depth of our pain, and at the same time, we seek isolation: we know they can never fully understand our pain. It is too big and too deep for us to fully grasp, how could we expect others to know how we feel? This is a very common response to grief.

With empathy, others offer condolences. They want us to know that they care. They want to help us, but they don't know how. With love and compassion they provide what they think is encouragement: "I know how you feel" or "God allowed this to happen for a reason." Their intent is pure. They are honestly trying to help. However, in the moment, it doesn't help.

There is no way anyone can know exactly how we feel. We are uniquely fashioned by our temperament, personality, and life experience. Even if we have experienced a similar life event as someone else, our feelings are distinct. The way we process grief will look different based on our individual experiences. Some of us will spend a lifetime processing our grief, while others may process grief in a few years. Despite how we process the unexpected events that happen in our lives, our pain is real. Our grief is real. Knowing how to live in the midst of our grief is the challenge.

It has been said, 'time heals all wounds.' I do not agree. The wounds remain. In time, the mind, protecting its sanity, covers them with scar tissue and the pain lessens. But it is never gone.[116]

ROSE KENNEDY

As we will learn, anger accompanies grief. When we feel pain and loss, we are experiencing a complex mix of thoughts, feelings, and actions that, when put together, culminate as anger.[117] In our anger we may have hurt ourselves or others. In the moment,

---

[116] AZ Quotes (n.d.). Retrieved from https://www.azquotes.com/quotes/topics/time-heals-all-wounds.html.

[117] Eifert, G., McKay, M., & Forsyth, J. (2006). *ACT on life not on anger: The New Acceptance & Commitment Therapy Guide to Problem Anger.* Oakland, CA: New Harbinger Publications, Inc.

the explosive power of our anger has caused us to become the worst version of ourselves: lost in a hurricane of feelings that have taken control.

It is important to recognize that anger is not one thing. It's not the result of one incident or one conversation. In fact, it's basis is much deeper than the circumstance that brought it to the surface. It contains a multitude of experiences, filtered by our thought process, and laid over a lifetime of trauma, woundedness, and pain.

We have all experienced grief and loss in some form. The details of our stories and the extent of the offense against us may be different, but the relational wounds we suffer have common denominators: they run deep, are very personal, and feel gravely unjust.[118]

"

We cannot solve our problems with the same thinking we used when we created them.[119]

ALBERT EINSTEIN

At some point, even in the midst of our pain, many of us will run toward our heavenly Father to receive comfort from his grace. Although we still feel grief and anger, we may gladly receive grace, but it is often a far greater challenge to extend grace to others. God is not content to simply pour his grace into our soul. The grace that flows *to us*, must flow *through us*, or our soul becomes stagnant and all God's good gifts die within us.

Nature provides a riveting illustration of this: two famous bodies of water shape the land of Israel—The Dead Sea and the Sea of Galilee. They are called seas but, in reality, they are freshwater lakes. The waters of the Jordan River flow into both bodies of water.

The Sea of Galilee is known for its rich diversity of underwater plants and fish life. The Dead Sea, however, contains no life. The mineral count is so overindulgent, the waters become toxic and everything dies. Only one factor distinguishes these two bodies of water: one has an outlet and the other does not.

The Dead Sea represents a life without an outlet of grace. We may receive an abundance of God's love, attend weekly church services, a women's Bible study, memorize Scripture, and even participate in regular prayer gatherings or group dynamics. All of these thing are wonderful, but can ruin us if we dam up the grace and life freely given to us: we become self-righteous. The waters of our soul reflect waters as toxic and lifeless as the Dead Sea.

---

[118] Smedes, L. (1984). *Forgive and Forget: Healing the Hurts We Don't Deserve*. New York, NY: Harper Collins.

[119] Marlin, D. (2017). *27 Quotes to Change How You Think About Problems*. Retrieved from https://www.entrepreneur.com/article/288957.

The Sea of Galilee, however, represents a life respondent to the grace received. The current, created from the inflow and outflow, invigorates the waters of our life. This abundant grace that flows to every one of us is constantly searching for an outlet to flow from us.

In what way does your life reflect the Dead Sea?

In what way does your life reflect the Sea of Galilee?

How can you begin to let the grace you've received flow from you to others this week?

I remember everything about that day: the feeling of the crisp fall air, the sound of the fallen leaves rustling on the ground, a faint smell of smoke hanging in the air from a nearby fire. Since I left work everyday at the same time, it was no surprise to see my husband waiting by my car. As our eyes met, in that moment, I saw an expression never before seen on his face: I knew something was wrong.

Our oldest child, Justin, was dead—killed instantly when his motorcycle rear ended a truck in front of him. He was 20 years old. After high school, he moved to the city and pursued several dead-end jobs. Justin recently moved back in with us: enrolled in the local community college, ready to take life more seriously, and get an education.

The next couple weeks were a blur. My husband and two daughters helped with the funeral arrangements. Relatives came and left. I had taken a couple weeks off from work, but was expected back. How could life just go on?

As weeks turned into months, I went through the motions of life, but internally withdrew. I minimally engaged with my husband and daughters—we were all suffering the loss in our own way. Although I continued to get calls from my friends at church, my attendance was sparse. I didn't want to hear another person say, "I'm so sorry for your loss" or "How are you feeling?" I didn't want to hear the pastor preach about how God works everything out for good, how God loves us, and has a plan for our lives.

I was angry: angry that my passion for life was gone; angry that I felt distant from my husband and daughters; angry that I would never again see my son or hear his voice; angry that my life would never be the same; angry at God for taking my son.

On the one-year anniversary of Justin's death, I came home and found flowers on my doorstep. There was a simple card that read, "I remember." The floodgates opened: in that moment, I allowed myself to feel the overwhelming grief and agony of losing my son. I let myself cry. As I cried off and on for the next week, I felt the weight in my chest begin to lift. For the first time in a year, I felt like I could breathe.

That day changed my perspective. I was still hurting, distant from my family, and angry at God for taking my son; but I felt something new. On the anniversary of my worst day, someone remembered—someone remembered my son and remembered my pain. In two words, someone extended to me a measure of grace unlike anything I had ever experienced. Although my heart was still broken and needed to heal, I was able to grasp the Father's love for me.

Olivia

In what way does Olivia's grief and anger make sense?

___

___

___

___

Why does trauma rob us of relationship with God and others?

___

___

___

___

___

When we experience such tragedy, is life ever the same? Explain.

____

____

____

____

Satan desires to make our worst day our defining day; yet God offers us a new beginning. His redemption is not a one-time gift—the saving grace that brought us eternal life is the same grace he offers us daily. He longs to step into every one of our stories, any moment of any given day. He will write a new ending to any situation we allow him to touch.

OUR RESPONSIBILITY

If we are going to experience true healing, we have to unpack some of the trauma from our past—the trauma we have caused. It is challenging to take responsibility for the pain we have caused in the lives of others. While this may not have been our intent, it happened—we responded in a manner that put into motion a sequence of events that we never intended. Nonetheless, we are responsible for our part.

Many of us have made split-second decisions that set our lives on a course we never anticipated. To this day, we feel immense guilt and shame for the choices we've made. If asked, many of us could easily answer this question: "I wish I never would have...

- broke up with the love of my life."
- started having sex when I was 15."
- cheated on my boyfriend."
- had so many sexual partners."
- experimented with a same-sex relationship."
- had an affair with a married man."
- yelled and threw something at my daughter."
- had an abortion."
- neglected my kids because of my addiction."
- cheated on my husband."
- lashed out at my son."
- gave up custody of my kids."
- filed for divorce."
- exposed my husband to an STD."

And the list goes on and on.

How would you answer this question? "I wish I never would have..."

However difficult, taking responsibility for our part—in causing pain and trauma to others, and ultimately to ourselves—moves us one step closer to health. As we think about the people we have harmed in our lifetime, it is never too late to make amends.

In the space provided, take the opportunity to write a letter of apology to someone, expressing the regret you feel for causing them pain and trauma. This is not a letter you will send, but a letter-writing process: an experience of putting words and feelings on paper, so that you can relinquish your feelings of guilt and shame.

No one is going to see what you write. This does not have to be well written or pretty, but intentional and thoughtful in the process.

What are your thoughts after completing this letter?

What new feelings were brought to the surface as a result of this exercise?

SELF-MONITORING

As we continue to move toward health, we need to understand our anger. Some of us may go from "0 to 60 in 2 seconds," while others may gradually steam and then boil into anger.[120] Many of us are not fully aware of when our anger ignites or the behaviors we turn to when feeling angry. Our anger, like many other emotions, exists on a continuum—a range that is always present, each stage not obviously different than another, but having distinct extremes. We have to recognize the slightest change in our thoughts, feelings, and behaviors that contribute to our anger. We cannot discount or minimize times when we think, "That doesn't count. I wasn't that angry."

Watch out for justifications. When we are dieting and we have a bite of cake, we tell ourselves, "That doesn't count. It was only one bite." The same is true when dealing with anger. We convince ourselves that because this outburst is not as bad as it's ever been or we were only slightly angry, that it doesn't count.

If our goal is to learn how to stay in relationship, despite our circumstance and the struggles we face, we have to take a proactive approach to managing our anger. We have to recognize not only our angry behaviors, but our angry feelings.

Raising awareness to how and why we react in anger is an important step on the path toward lifelong healing. It takes time and intention. It takes recognizing that our anger if fueled by fear—the true feeling our anger is covering.

---

[120] Riggenbach, J. (2013). *The CBT Toolbox: A Workbook for Clients and Clinicians*. Eau Claire, WI: PESI Publishing and Media.

Use the following tables to keep track of your angry behaviors and angry feelings this week.[121] Write down any time you experience an angry behavior: the day of the week, the number of times you experienced this behavior, and how long the behavior lasted. Also, write down any time you felt angry: the day of the week, the event or trigger that created the feeling, the intensity—on a scale of 1-10: 1=mild, 10=extreme—and how long the feeling lasted. On both tables, try to identify the fear that is driving your anger.

ANGRY BEHAVIOR

DAY	BEHAVIOR	FEAR	FREQUENCY	DURATION
Thursday	Yelled at the kids	I'm a horrible mom.	2 times	5 min, 2 min

[121] Ibid.

ANGRY FEELINGS

DAY	EVENT/TRIGGER	FEAR	INTENSITY	DURATION
Monday	Received a manipulative text from my mom	I don't like being controlled, but I don't want to confront my mom	8	30 min

As we monitor our angry behaviors and feelings this week, it is important that we track accurately when they occur. We need to be vigilant with this process. Once we become more aware of our anger—when it happens and why—we will be better equipped to recognize when we need to initiate self-care and other practical tools.

Example in the above chart: *I'm in Ticked Off on the FASTER Scale. Using the double bind exercise will make the best choice obvious. If I don't confront my mom, I will continue to feel angry and take it out on those around me. If I face my fear and confront my mom, she may reject me.* When we choose to face our fears and make the difficult choice, it leads us back to a place of restoration.

Looking Ahead

Complete the FASTER Scale, Group Check-in, Self-Care lesson, Thoughts/Feelings Awareness Log, and Change & Growth Analysis in your *Unraveled: Weekly Tools* before the next group meeting.

LESSON 3: FORGIVENESS

The process of forgiving others can be extremely difficult. However, holding onto unforgiveness can keep us stuck in a victim role. Finding a holistic balance to forgiveness—physically, mentally, emotionally, and spiritually—can make a huge difference as we continue on the path toward lifelong healing. When we forgive, it gives us the opportunity to imagine a brighter future, a future that is no longer based on the hurt we've experienced.[122]

I was blindsided by my husband's resignation as lead pastor of our church. I was invited to a meeting he called with the board of elders. There, surrounded by friends who loved and believed in us, my husband confessed to crossing boundaries that put our family in a very vulnerable place. Though this confession would cost him dearly, he wanted to bring into the light what was hidden in the dark.

As the glass doors of our loving church closed behind us, I had no idea if our marriage could survive. Two bleeding and broken lives walked toward our car, the offender beside the offended. I felt as if I had been plunged into an inky blackness and couldn't see my next step. I had no lofty prayer or theological explanation to bandage this mess. My soul was shattered. I doubted whether the pieces would ever be retrieved.

Over the next few months and years of our recovery, I saw evidence of Jesus' involvement in the stench and slime of our mess. We began to experience peace that transcended our pain. We surrounded ourselves with counselors and friends who showed us how to press the full weight of our lives into the chest of Christ. We were given the courage to choose a daily walk of humility, repentance, and forgiveness. Although I didn't see it at first, we were both in need of forgiveness.

I discovered that as long as I held on to unforgiveness toward my husband, I was bound with chains to a painful past. The wounds that initially tore into my soul, threatened to mutilate my life over time. I began to understand that if I didn't learn how to release my pain to God, I would not only suffer from the original offense, I would also suffer from the continual pain of not releasing that offense to God.

It took years of deep soul-digging, a willingness to lay a new foundation, and a determination to build protective boundaries for our fractured souls. By His

---

[122] Carnes, S., Lee, M. & Rodriguez, A. (2012). *Facing Heartbreak: Steps to Recovery for Partners of Sex Addicts*. Carefree, AZ: Gentle Path Press.

remarkable grace, God has used our experience to chisel us into who we are today. In our utter brokenness, God disclosed the richness of His character, His infinite care, and limitless power.

Hillary

During her recovery, what things did Hillary learn about herself?

___

___

___

___

Briefly describe a time when your soul was shattered and you did not know if the pieces would ever be retrieved.

___

___

___

___

___

___

___

___

What gave you the strength to move forward in your healing?

___

___

___

___

As we begin to develop new healthy thoughts, feelings, and behaviors, it is important that we recognize the truth of forgiveness. For example, forgiveness does not mean we have to stay in relationship with a person who continues to hurt us and doesn't want to change. If married and in an abusive situation, we do not have to stay in an unsafe environment. If we choose to stay in relationship, forgiveness allows an opportunity to build a more solid foundation. If single and choose to leave the relationship, forgiveness allows us to be emotionally available and more healthy in our next relationship.

Another thing to consider is that although many of us have experienced betrayal in relationship, it doesn't mean we have to remain a victim. Forgiveness helps us understand that whatever happens, we have the power to heal.

> **Everyone says forgiveness is a lovely idea until they have something to forgive. We always have plenty of virtue when we don't need it. It's when we need it that we discover how little of the virtue we really have.**[123]

Forgiving others is a process—a process that cannot be rushed. If it is rushed, it may result in premature forgiveness, which is usually short-lived.

We can still forgive, even if we can't forget. As we practice forgiveness, we will eventually be able to recall the experience without feeling triggered. When the painful memory resurfaces, we acknowledge the pain, remind ourselves that it happened in the past, and that we have forgiven the offender.

Forgiveness is something we do for ourselves. We do not forgive for the offender; instead, we forgive to free ourselves of the resentment, pain, and anger that we experience because of the offense.

God's grace is so beyond what we can fathom or experience in our own strength. This is evident through Corrie ten Boom's story—a holocaust survivor who faced unprecedented forgiveness.[124] Years ago, on a radio program, she shared how God opened doors for her to spread the message of forgiveness all over the world. Yet, one evening she found herself unable to forgive. After listening to her compelling message on forgiveness, a German man stepped forward, asking for God's forgiveness.

The man standing before her was the guard who abused both Corrie and her sister in the German concentration camp. Obviously, he didn't recognize her. She thrust her hand deep within her pocket unable to respond. She prayed to God silently, "Oh God, you must recognize forgiveness has its limits." It was at that moment the Holy Spirit reminded her of His promise in Romans, "God's love has been poured into your heart, Corrie, through the Holy Spirit who has been given to you." God's voice thundered through her spirit, "My love in you is stronger than the hate in you. Offer your pain to Me and receive My love!" By faith, Corrie extended her hand toward her enemy.

---

[123] Lewis, C.S. (1952). *Mere Christianity*. New York, NY: Harper Collins.

[124] Guideposts (1972). Corrie ten Boom on Forgiveness. November.

The essence of her next words speak to the heart of forgiveness: "We never experience the endless depths of God's love in greater measure than when we forgive. In that very moment when my hand clasped the hand of my enemy, an ocean of God's love swept over me."

What part of Corrie ten Boom's story is most meaningful to you?

____

____

____

____

____

How does this story change or expand your view of forgiveness?

____

____

____

____

____

Forgiveness isn't easy. It may include forgiving ourselves, for any part we may have played in the offense.

Forgiveness does not mean:

- excusing a person's deception.
- tolerating further betrayals.
- allowing someone to escape the consequences of their actions.
- looking the other way and pretending nothing happened.
- continuing to stand in the victim role.

The more we understand about the process of forgiveness, the more we recognize how much forgiveness has to do with our relationship with God.

> *[14]For if you forgive other people when they sin against you, your heavenly Father will also forgive you. [15]But if you do not forgive others their sins, your Father will not forgive your sins.*
>
> **MATTHEW 6:14-15**

When we stay in relationship with our heavenly Father, He will guide our steps, directing the decisions and choices we make when it comes to forgiving others.

Think of a specific relationship where you have been stuck in an unhealthy place due to a lack of forgiveness. Briefly describe the situation.

In what area of the forgiveness process are you struggling?

How has this discussion helped you identify where you are in the forgiveness process and what steps you need to take to keep moving forward on the path toward health?

ACCEPTING HELP

So often, our needs go unmet because our fear of asking for help, or fear of rejection, gets in the way—we keep trying to look like we have it all together. Not only is it awkward to ask for help, but it can feel uncomfortable accepting help.[125] To make matters worse, we might not know the best person(s) to ask for help with a specific need.

[125] Riggenbach, J. (2013). *The CBT Toolbox: A Workbook for Clients and Clinicians*. Eau Claire, WI: PESI Publishing and Media.

I normally have no problem asking for help. I typically flaunt my "womanly wiles" and get whatever I want. It's just part of my natural charm. I've been pulled over for speeding dozens of times and have never received a ticket.

When I need help around my apartment, I quickly find a suitable neighbor who will carry in a new piece of furniture or hang a picture. Sometimes, I don't even have to ask for help. Every time I start to wash my car, in my shorts and tank top, several male tenants offer to help me. It's so nice.

The only time I've struggled with finding help is when I need help from women. One time, I needed help in my biology class because I wasn't sure how to get into a study group. When I approached some of the other female students in class, using my same natural charm, the women were dismissive and wouldn't help me. They were so rude. I felt frustrated and embarrassed.

This was not the first time I experienced this response from women. In fact, this is most often the response I get from other women. I was never close to my mom and spent most of my childhood following my older brothers and their friends around. I never really learned how to develop a friendship with other girls. I would love help with this, but I'm not sure how or who to ask.

Jasmine

What part of Jasmine's story do you relate to most?

___

___

___

If Jasmine asked you for help, how would you respond?

___

___

___

___

For many of us who have struggled with unhealthy relationships, this will be a huge area of growth. We cannot continue to use our sexuality as a means to get what we want. We can't charm and manipulate others to get our way. We also cannot use previous patterns of passive-aggressive behaviors: sighing, avoiding eye contact, slamming doors, or giving others the silent treatment. We have to use our words. We have to figure out what healthy relationships look like. We have to be intentional.

UNDERSTANDING MY COMMUNICATION STYLE

The way we communicate with others is an essential part of managing relationships. Communication involves two distinct processes: sending and receiving information.[126] We have to learn how to effectively speak in a way that is understandable, and also listen in a way that allows us to grasp the meaning of what others are saying. This can be challenging. So much of our communication process runs through our filter—our wounded, traumatized, victimized, emotional filter. This influences how we interpret what we hear others say and also the way we respond. It is difficult to communicate effectively when our emotions are on high alert.

When it comes to how we communicate and how we use our words, look at what Paul writes:

Do not let any unwholesome talk come out of your mouths,
but only what is helpful for building others up according to their needs,
that it may benefit those who listen.

EPHESIANS 4:29

According to scripture, how are we supposed to use our words?

____

____

____

____

There are three basic communication styles: aggressive, assertive, and passive. Each communication style reflects attributes of personality, temperament, social development, and more. So much of who we are and where we've been is exhibited in our communication style.

Gloria is **aggressive** in her communication style. She reacts instantly and uses her words to dominate and intimidate others. She expects to get her way—she has no problem violating the rights of others or verbally "walking" on others to get what she wants. Gloria's communication is often loud, bossy, and pushy.

Sarah is **assertive** in her communication style. She speaks clearly and concisely. She is respectful of the rights of others, allowing them to equally express their opinion. Sarah's communication style reflects a confidence in herself and her life choices. Her communication is firm, direct, and honest.

---

126 Riggenbach, J. (2013). *The CBT Toolbox: A Workbook for Clients and Clinicians*. Eau Claire, WI: PESI Publishing and Media.

Penny is **passive** in her communication style. She is unable to stand up for herself and is unclear about her personal rights. She is often taken advantage of and verbally "walked" on by others. Penny's communication style is soft-spoken, submissive, and accommodating.

☐ *How would you describe your communication style?*

☐ *When have you noticed changes in your communication style? Does your style of communication change based on the person you're speaking to or the situation?*

☐ *Describe a situation where your communication style—either in the sending or receiving process—contributed to a breakdown in relationship.*

☐ *What is one change you need to make in the way you communicate?*

Assertive communication is the goal. Working to create healthy communication takes time and practice. Set aside time this week to practice assertive communication with a trusted person in your life.

I will practice assertive communication with ______________________________.

We cannot develop lasting health on our own. We need others. We need community. God designed us for relationship: with Him and with others. This often requires asking for help.

Share each other's burdens, and in this way obey the law of Christ.

GALATIANS 6:2 NLT

If we want to learn to manage relationships, we have to be willing to ask for and receive help from others. We have to recognize the areas in our life where we need help and who we should ask. Keep in mind, our areas of need change over time. Some of our needs may be practical and physical, while others may be emotional and spiritual. Some of our needs could be work-related, but others could be for entertainment and connection. Asking for help requires a delicate balance of recognizing when we honestly need help without imposing our needs and expectations on other people.

Raising an awareness to our own personal needs and figuring out healthy ways to get our needs met is foundational in finding health in all our relationships.

All of us need help. Sometimes that help comes from people we know, but often it comes from people God has not yet brought into our lives. Allow God to bless you and those around you by asking for help.

Use the following table to identify the areas where you could use some help. Then, list at least one person who could potentially help meet that need.

EXAMPLE:

MY NEEDS	PERSON WHO COULD HELP ME
Discuss past trauma	Counselor, pastor
Parenting advice	Mom with healthy grown kids
Lawn and yard work	Students in church youth group
Spiritual growth	Women's ministry leader
Consistent exercise	Family members

The example is very general. In your table, identify specific people who could help you with your needs.

MY NEEDS	PERSON WHO COULD HELP ME

Based on the needs you listed above, what one need are you going to address this week? Who will you contact to help you meet that need?

Forgiving those who have caused us pain takes time. As we continue to pursue healing and discover what healthy relationships look like—through effective communication and asking for help when needed—we are gaining a new perspective of God's plan and purpose for our lives. As we grow in our relationship with Him, we will uncover the blessing that comes with forgiveness.

Looking Ahead

Complete the FASTER Scale, Group Check-in, Self-Care lesson, Thoughts/Feelings Awareness Log, and Change & Growth Analysis in your *Unraveled: Weekly Tools* before the next group meeting.

chapter eight

BEYOND YOURSELF

LESSON 1: LEARNED BEHAVIOR

Our behaviors are learned throughout our lifetime. Some behaviors are automatic and have a biological basis while many other behaviors are learned through experience.[127] As a child, we pick up on mannerisms, language usage, and emotional responses from those around us. We learn through reinforcement. Our behaviors are shaped by positive and negative reward. We also learn from the experiences of others, observing the positive and negative results of others' experiences.

Our ability to engage in healthy relationships is learned through experience. We learn to trust or mistrust those around us. We learn positive emotions such as love, support, and encouragement. We also learn negative emotions like anger, disappointment, guilt, and shame. We learn to tell the truth or that it's okay to lie. Unfortunately, we don't get to choose how our early experiences are going to affect the rest of our life.

At five years old, I was adopted. Compared to my previous impoverished environment and drug-addicted mother, I thought my new home would be amazing! However, it wasn't long before I recognized some behaviors in my new parents that frightened me, especially with my new mom.

My new family consisted of a mom and dad, two younger brothers, and an older sister. My new mom was very controlling and yelled at us kids a lot. She made us clean the house and take care of the pets while she sat on the couch, watched daytime television, and ate snacks. My new dad worked two jobs to support the family and wasn't home much. I loved spending time with him and felt safe when he was around. However, it wasn't long before my mom's crazy, chaotic behaviors drove him away.

I was confused. Although there were no drugs, alcohol, or strange men coming and going from the house, I still felt anxious—the way I felt in my last family. Many times, my new mom would make us go through the neighborhood collecting cans or door-to-door collecting money for a local charity, but it was all for my mom. There was no charity. I learned that using lies and manipulation was okay to get what you want. When we came home with a good amount of money, we were praised; but when we came home with little or no money, we were punished. I learned that love was conditional and given based on behavior.

[127] Duffy, K. & Atwater, E. (2008). *Psychology For Living: Adjustment, Growth, and Behavior Today* (9th ed.). Upper Saddle River, NJ: Pearson Prentice Hall.

This played a significant role in my relationships. I was manipulative and controlling with my siblings, friends, and even more so with men. I began having sex during junior high and got pregnant with my first child in eighth grade. My boyfriend and I, and our baby lived with my mother. I had four children with two different men by the time I turned 20 years old.

I married the father of my two last children and moved away from my mother to live near his family. I was shocked at the difference between my husband's family and mine. His family didn't yell at each other, lie, or manipulate to get their way. They were kind and loving to one another. They were supportive and helpful when it was needed. I had never seen anything like it, but knew I wanted to raise my kids in this type of environment. But was it too late?

Raelyn

What were some of Raelyn's unhealthy learned behaviors?

____

____

____

____

____

How did Raelyn's learned behaviors contribute to her relationships?

____

____

____

____

The best part of learned behavior is that it can be unlearned. Despite the negative behaviors we may have learned from our childhood environment, we can learn new, healthy behaviors to replace unwanted or unhealthy behaviors.

> *So the trouble is not with the law, for it is spiritual and good. The trouble is with me, for I am all too human, a slave to sin. [15]I don't really understand myself, for I want to do what is right, but I don't do it. Instead, I do what I hate. [16]But if I know that what I am doing is wrong, this shows that I agree that the law is good. [17]So I am not the one doing wrong; it is sin living in me that does it.*
>
> **ROMANS 7:14-17 NLT**

Making changes to our behaviors and living in health is challenging, especially when we continue to do what we don't want to do. We have to continue to work on our awareness: what is driving our behaviors; what fear are we not willing to face?

None of us were raised by Jesus, which means that all of our parents made mistakes. They were not perfect and neither are we. If we think we can change our behaviors on our own, then our pursuit of lifelong health will be in vain. Alone, we don't have what it takes to be healthy. What we need comes from the Lord.

As we strive toward replacing our unhealthy behaviors with new healthy behaviors, it is important that we take every opportunity to learn. Not just from God's Word but from others who are also working toward health. This is why being in this group is so crucial—we cannot do this alone. We need to be dedicated to this process, not just for ourselves, but for the other women in our group. This is where we will learn to develop authentic relationships. We will practice learning new behaviors by living in community.

> *And so, dear brothers and sisters, I plead with you to give your bodies to God because of all he has done for you. Let them be a living and holy sacrifice—the kind he will find acceptable. This is truly the way to worship him. [2]Don't copy the behavior and customs of this world, but let God transform you into a new person by changing the way you think. Then you will learn to know God's will for you, which is good and pleasing and perfect.*
>
> **ROMANS 12:1-2 NLT**

Which of the above scriptures is most impactful to you? Why?

___

___

___

What learned behaviors are you looking forward to unlearning?

___

___

___

How have negative learned behaviors influenced your capacity for relationship?

___

___

___

___

If you have children, what negative behaviors are they learning from you?

____

____

____

____

RECOGNITION OF CONSEQUENCES

For many of us who struggle with compulsive and addictive behaviors, our awareness of consequences is limited. We tend to be more spontaneous, in-the-moment people, making decisions without much thought. We act impulsively without considering the consequences. Although we keep our coping behaviors close—our automatic responses to stressful situations—we don't always recognize how our decisions impact our future.

If we want to change our behavior, we have to become more aware of what we're doing and why, as well as the role our behaviors play in the consequences we experience. When we are stuck in our coping behaviors, the consequences we experience can take many forms: our relationships suffer; we create financial hardship; it affects our mood; it impacts our physical, mental, emotional, and spiritual health.[128]

Vera has a great job. She is very productive and efficient. She strives to make her boss look good, which earns her compliments and approval in return. During Vera's performance evaluation, her boss spent most of the time reflecting on all the things she does well; however, there were a couple areas he suggested she could improve. Vera sat there with a smile on her face, but was internally mortified. Feeling overwhelmed by this "horrible" evaluation, Vera impulsively went shopping after work and spent more than $700.

A couple days later, Vera realized that after spending so much money in the heat of the moment, she didn't have enough money for rent. She could return the clothes she bought, but that would be embarrassing; she didn't want the sales clerk to judge her. She could ask her mom to borrow money, which would result in a long lecture about responsibility and money management. Their relationship is a bit strained, but her mom would probably still give her the money.

[128] Riggenbach, J. (2013). *The CBT Toolbox: A Workbook for Clients and Clinicians*. Eau Claire, WI: PESI Publishing and Media.

Nancy has many friends and is very active on social media. She prides herself in her ability to keep up with so many friends. She is constantly on her phone or iPad, checking in with friends and commenting on posts. Taylor, one of Nancy's good friends, has spent the past several months losing weight and recently posted a before and after photo to show her progress. Without thinking, Nancy replied with, "It must be nice to go shopping and find clothes that actually fit!" (Smiley face, thumbs up, heart emoji)

A short time later, Taylor sent a text to Nancy. She was not expecting Taylor's response: "I can't believe you said such a horrible thing! I thought we were friends! Why would you embarrass me like that? I have never been so humiliated!" Taylor was very upset. Nancy would have apologized, but Taylor has blocked her on social media and is not responding to Nancy's calls or texts. Nancy meant her response to be encouraging and supportive, not hurtful. In the moment, she didn't realize how her comment could seem offensive.

For Vera, what coping behaviors and consequences can you identify? What fear is she avoiding?

COPING BEHAVIOR	WHAT FEAR IS SHE AVOIDING?	CONSEQUENCE(S) IF SHE DOESN'T CHANGE

For Nancy, what coping behaviors and consequences can you identify? What fear is she avoiding?

COPING BEHAVIOR	WHAT FEAR IS SHE AVOIDING?	CONSEQUENCE(S) IF SHE DOESN'T CHANGE

Sometimes our behaviors result in immediate consequences that can be short-term and resolved quickly. However, there are times when the consequences of our behaviors can become long-term and stay unresolved.

Raising awareness is key. If we want real change, we have to take an honest look at how our behaviors shape and influence relationship. We cannot avoid the difficulty of analyzing our past behaviors—this takes time and intention. We have to address the fear we are avoiding. Even when we recognize our unhealthy coping behaviors, putting new behaviors in place is equally challenging. As we continue to gain new insights into our past behaviors, we become better equipped to develop strategies for creating and maintaining healthy relationships.

Use the following table to analyze and evaluate any of your past behaviors and consequences that contributed to a disruption or breakdown of relationship. Work to uncover the fear you are avoiding. If needed, do a double bind exercise to expose the underlying fear.

COPING BEHAVIOR	WHAT FEAR AM I AVOIDING?	CONSEQUENCE(S) IF I DON'T CHANGE

As we continue on the path toward healing, we may come face to face with an astonishing truth: despite our past learned behaviors, it is never too late to learn how to develop healthy relationships with others.

Looking Ahead

Complete the FASTER Scale, Group Check-in, Self-Care lesson, Thoughts/Feelings Awareness Log, and Change & Growth Analysis in your *Unraveled: Weekly Tools* before the next group meeting.

LESSON 2: UNRELIABLE LOVE

It would be easy to presume that when we think of love, we all think of the same thing—this could not be further from the truth.

In previous chapters, we learned about love.

- In chapter 3, we learned how God created love and wants a love relationship with us.
- In chapter 4, we learned how our family of origin, family dynamics, and trauma shape our perception of love.
- In chapters 5 and 6, we learned how our addictive behaviors interfere with genuine relationship, contributing to a lack of attachment and/or codependent behaviors.

All of this is helpful for gaining a better understanding of love, but practically applying this to our lives is challenging. How do we develop a healthy perspective of love? What does this look like in our daily lives?

If we were to think of one word to describe love, what would it be? Beloved, romantic, caring, intimate, devoted, adored, passionate, desired? For many of us, these are the words that come to mind. But what about these words: disappointed, hurt, abandoned, abused, betrayed, deceived, lonely, unreliable? Are these the words we naturally think of when we think of love? For some of us, yes. This is how love was modeled for us.

Our view of love, like everything else, is shaped by experience. There are many variables that influence our expectation of love: our biology, family of origin, attachment, trauma, emotional intelligence, and more. We can't possibly discuss everything that played a role in our love-learning process, but there are several factors that are key contributors. Understanding how they impact our view of love is vital to our healing.

I can't understand why men treat me poorly, even when I try to do everything for them. This had been a pattern in many of my relationships. In my current relationship, with José, I work hard to appease him, yet cry myself to sleep night after night.

When I got pregnant, José asked if I really thought we would be together forever. He demanded that I abort our unborn child, called me names that cut through my soul, then blocked my number on his phone. The day I decided to move closer to my family so they could help me raise my baby, José reached out. If I was going to have his baby, he wanted to be involved. I was so excited! I quickly moved in with him and worked harder than ever to keep the peace. I let him take control, making all the decisions, hoping to avoid any conflict. I thought, *This will make him truly love me.*

When our baby arrived, I spent tireless evenings alone with the baby, then would get up for work. So sleep-deprived, I began to feel crazy. I loved my daughter more than anything but also recognized that I needed a break. José went out with friends all the time, so I didn't think it was a big deal when I wanted to go out with friends, without the baby. José should stay home with HIS daughter. To make things easier on him, I made sure our daughter was sleeping when I left. While I was out with friends, I received a stream of manipulative texts:

You are a horrible mother for leaving your baby.

If you wanted to party then why did you have a kid?

I'm leaving you.

When I came home that night, José had moved out of our room. I cried myself to sleep, wondering why this continued to happen. Over the next couple weeks, I kept quiet, did extra loving things for José, and everything went back to normal. I didn't want my daughter to come from a broken home.

Three months later José got sick. I was sure it was allergies—everyone around me had been suffering from allergy season—but José insisted it was my cat. This didn't make sense; the cat hadn't bothered him in the two years we had lived together, so why now? I've had the cat for 15 years. It gave me so much joy to see my daughter playing with the cat.

I pleaded with José to give it time, to see if he was just experiencing a common cold or allergies. Within a week, José had all of the cat's things by the door and told me not to come back with the cat. He again moved his things out of our room, into the second bedroom. I desperately wanted this relationship to work, for me and my daughter. With a broken heart I took the cat to my mom's house, until I could find him a good family.

I just don't understand why José continues to treat me poorly when I do everything to make him happy. I wonder what I should say or do differently to avoid all the conflict with José. All I want is to make José happy with me again—make him love me again.

Blanca

Based on her relationship with José, what words would Blanca use to describe love?

____

____

____

In your opinion, what factors are contributing to the conflict in their relationship?

Why is Blanca loyal to José, even when he hurts her? What unhealthy behaviors is Blanca exhibiting?

If Blanca stays in this relationship, in its current condition, what will her daughter learn about love and relationship?

In chapter 6, we learned about our attachment style and how it contributes to our ability to form relationship—how it trained us to be in relationship. Of the four attachment styles discussed, only one type developed a secure attachment. The other three developed an insecure attachment style.

If we were not raised to understand relationship—to understand love—we will continue to struggle in relationships, making the same mistakes over and over again, and still never recognize what went wrong.

For many of us with an insecure attachment style, when we begin a new relationship, it becomes our only focus. It becomes our world. Let's say we meet a person, a potential love interest, and then start dating that person. We are enamored. We quickly become emotionally attached to this relationship—not just to the person, but to the relationship. We clear our calendar so we're available to this person. We minimize our other relationships to make this new relationship a priority.

We spend endless hours fantasizing about how the relationship is going to develop "perfectly" and how this person—the love of our life—is going to make us eternally happy.[129] We neglect our other responsibilities. We become consumed by this relationship. We convince ourselves that this person is going to love us forever—they hold the key to our happiness.

Now an emotionally healthy person—a securely attached person—recognizes that personal happiness is not solely based on another. However, a person who is emotionally unhealthy—an insecurely attached person—cannot comprehend this idea. In many ways, we have created a delusion around this relationship, attaching any hope of lifelong happiness on this other person. The "perfect" life we've created through fantasy, has been projected onto this unsuspecting individual.

Even when the relationship begins to deteriorate, we find ourselves clinging to the fantasy we've created in our mind, clinging to the relationship as though our life depends on it. We become desperate. We will do ANYTHING to keep the relationship, to keep the other person from falling out of love with us. We devote ourselves to the preservation of this relationship. We become codependently committed to the relationship. We become increasingly obsessed.

To make matters worse, as the other person pulls away, our grasp becomes tighter. We hang on with all our strength. We use manipulation. We use deceit. We are in complete denial. We hold on as though this person—the relationship—is our oxygen; and without it, we will die.

We are addicted. We are addicted to love. We are addicted to relationship.

When we struggle with love and relationship addictions these patterns are consistent, and not just in romantic relationships. This is how we behave in all our relationships. Why? Because we were never taught how to be in relationship. We immediately attach all our weaknesses, insecurities, hopes, dreams, and identity on to others. We make them responsible for our happiness.

This is why we are continually disappointed by love. We think that love is unreliable because it never turns out like we plan. From our perspective, we give and give to make others happy, but we can't seem to find anyone else who "gives as much as we give."

Have you ever been in a relationship like the one described above? Explain.

____

____

____

____

____

[129] Peabody, S. (2005). *Addicted to Love: Overcoming Obsession and Dependency in Relationships.* New York, NY: Random House, Inc.

In what ways do you relate to the above scenario?

What behaviors can you identify that make it challenging for addicts in relationship?

FACING MY FEARS

So many of our behaviors surrounding love, sex, and relationships contain elements of fear. We fear that no one will love us. We fear that everyone will leave us. We fear that we will be alone. The impact of fear in relationship is endless. To some degree, we allow our fear to control our behaviors, to control our relationships.

Although some of our fears have a basis in reality, many do not. So often our fears become our main focus, paralyzing us and making us ineffective. We are unable to move toward health when we are so consumed by fear. Our feelings of fear are generated in the limbic system of our brain (see chapter 2, lesson 2). In many ways, the enemy of our soul uses our fear against us—using our fear to keep us stuck in our addiction, using our fear to keep us in isolation.

When it comes to facing our fears and changing our behaviors, it starts with awareness. What fears are keeping us from cultivating relationship with God and others? Which of our fears are creating a prison from where there is no escape?

Then, how would we prove to ourselves that our fears are irrational or not based in reality? How do we convince ourselves that change is needed? What steps will we take to move from living in fear to living in freedom?

The only way for this to happen is through new experiences and support of scripture. We cannot get beyond ourselves if we don't know who God has called us to be. We have to change our thinking. We have to change our core beliefs and the way we see ourselves so we can understand the way God sees us. We have to allow God's Word—His personal promises to us—to permeate our limbic system, diffusing our fears. This is how we will discover lasting freedom.

This week, use the following table to identify some fears that are keeping you from moving toward health. Complete a double bind exercise. This is one of the best ways to face your fears and evaluate what change is needed. Then, find a Scripture that supports God's personal promise to you, combating the fear. This is how to create practical, lifelong healing from the inside out.

Remember, you can't change everything at once—lifelong change takes time. Be patient with yourself as you practice relieving the fear in your life.

FEAR	DOUBLE BIND	PERSONAL PROMISE/ SUPPORT SCRIPTURE
	If I don't change?	
	If I change?	

FEAR	DOUBLE BIND	PERSONAL PROMISE/ SUPPORT SCRIPTURE
	If I don't change?	
	If I change?	

FEAR	DOUBLE BIND	PERSONAL PROMISE/ SUPPORT SCRIPTURE
	If I don't change?	
	If I change?	

CONFIRMATION OF PERSONAL PROMISES:

Be strong and courageous. Do not be afraid or terrified because of them, for the Lord your God goes with you; he will never leave you nor forsake you.

DEUTERONOMY 31:6

The Lord is my light and my salvation—whom shall I fear? The Lord is the stronghold of my life—of whom shall I be afraid?

PSALM 27:1

Take delight in the Lord, and he will give you the desires of your heart.

PSALM 37:4

Trust in the Lord with all your heart and lean not on your own understanding; in all your ways submit to him, and he will make your paths straight.

PROVERBS 3:5-6

Even youths grow tired and weary, and young men stumble and fall; but those who hope in the LORD will renew their strength. They will soar on wings like eagles; they will run and not grow weary, they will walk and not be faint.

ISAIAH 40:30-31

> *For I am the Lord your God who takes hold of your right hand and says to you, Do not fear; I will help you.*
>
> **ISAIAH 41:13**

> *Though the mountains be shaken and the hills be removed, yet my unfailing love for you will not be shaken nor my covenant of peace be removed," says the LORD, who has compassion on you.*
>
> **ISAIAH 54:10**

> *"For I know the plans I have for you," declares the LORD, "plans to prosper you and not to harm you, plans to give you hope and a future."*
>
> **JEREMIAH 29:11**

> *And my God will meet all your needs according to the riches of his glory in Christ Jesus.*
>
> **PHILIPPIANS 4:19**

Many times, change requires that we face our fears—face the consequences if we don't change and also face the unknown if we decide to change. Embracing change may be one of the most challenging and most rewarding things we choose to do. Be brave. Let the women in your group support you through this change.

Looking Ahead

Complete the FASTER Scale, Group Check-in, Self-Care lesson, Thoughts/Feelings Awareness Log, and Change & Growth Analysis in your *Unraveled: Weekly Tools* before the next group meeting.

LESSON 3: BREAKING GENERATIONAL CYCLES

At some point, all of us wrestle with the question: "Who am I?" We think there is some absolute answer to this question, something that will validate our existence and make us feel whole. We want our life to have meaning, but we cannot shake the fact that our past, in every way, contributes to who we are today.

Whether we were raised in the church or not, many of us have heard the idea of "the sins of the father" being passed down to his children. We could spend time in a theological debate between the Old Testament doctrine of the "generational curse" and the New Testament teaching of individual salvation.[130] We could discuss whether the "sins of the father" refers to our own father or our first father, Adam.

A simple definition of generational curse is the way we have been taught to react through our family of origin—how we emotionally, limbically respond to what is happening to us and around us.

For example, if we come from a family where a parent is controlling or angry, and there is no input from us as a child, we learn what to do. We may try to hide our feelings of anger but eventually end up yelling when angry, just like we were taught. We might shut down or freeze in response to anger and try to keep the peace or appease others. It's possible that when faced with anger, we run away, attempting to physically avoid our feelings of fear.

Generational curses are learned behaviors. If we want to pursue lifelong healing, we have to recognize how we have been limbically programed through our experiences. We have to reprogram our limbic system, based on who God says we are, otherwise we will pass on the same unhealthy limbic responses to future generations.

What generational curses are exhibited in your family of origin? What role did addiction play in your family?

____

____

____

[130] Focus on the Family (2012). *Understanding The "Generational Curse" of Exodus 34:7*. Retrieved from https://www.focusonthefamily.com/family-q-and-a/faith/understanding-the-generational-curse-of-exodus-347.

What generational behaviors continue to impact your life and relationships?

____

____

____

____

____

Our family of origin doesn't have to dictate our future. There is a way to change our story.

The story of Ruth provides an excellent example of generational change. She was a Moabite woman, who was widowed and living with her mother-in-law, Naomi. Since Naomi's husband and sons had died, she planned to return to the land of Judah. Naomi encouraged Ruth to return to her mother's home, but after experiencing a relationship with Naomi, Ruth replied,

> *"Don't urge me to leave you or to turn back from you. Where you go I will go, and where you stay I will stay. Your people will be my people and your God my God."*
>
> **RUTH 1:16**

In going to Bethlehem, Ruth experienced a new culture and a new relationship. This was a huge generational change. Ruth let go of her old way of thinking and embraced a new way of thinking—and a new way of living.

When Ruth said to Naomi, "Your people will be my people and your God will be my God," this was her personal promise from God. Even though it required great change, she faced her fear, acted on this promise, and moved to a foreign land. She experienced a life-change that she never could have imagined.

> *You shall not bow down to them or worship them; for I, the Lord your God, am a jealous God, punishing the children for the sin of the parents to the third and fourth generation of those who hate me, [6]but showing love to a thousand generations of those who love me and keep my commandments.*
>
> **EXODUS 20:5-6**

In choosing to follow God's leading in her life, Ruth literally experienced the blessings to the thousandth generation. She became part of the lineage of David and Jesus.

As we continue to change and grow, our children will reap the benefits. It's never too late to start breaking down negative generational behaviors and replacing them with new generational blessings. As we learn what it looks like to live in health, we teach what we are learning to our kids. This happens practically, through relationship with God and others.

> *These commandments that I give you today are to be on your hearts. [7]Impress them on your children. Talk about them when you sit at home and when you walk along the road, when you lie down and when you get up.*
>
> **DEUTERONOMY 6:6-7**

I was in the kitchen when my 14-year-old son, Chet, came in to show me his "broken toe." I checked his toe and could see that it was a bit swollen but probably not broken. I told Chet to ice and elevate it for the night. Chet turned red, became very angry, and started yelling at me about how I didn't care about him.

I was surprised by Chet's reaction. I tried to assure him that I did care, but that his toe was not broken and I wouldn't take him to the doctor until a few days had passed. Chet stormed to his room, slamming the door. This was a common reaction when Chet was hurt.

I took a few breaths and asked God, "What just happened? Please help me." I headed to Chet's room to talk. Chet was sitting on his bed, steaming. I sat next to him, looked him in his eyes, and told him, "I think you're reacting to old trauma. There was a point in my life—after I divorced your dad, was going to school, and working three jobs—where I couldn't take care of you because I couldn't even take care of myself.

"I was so heartbroken and overwhelmed during those years that I developed an eating disorder and OCD, was over-serving in church, and had a few failed relationships. Although I have experienced years of healing, in those early years of your life, I was so absent minded that I lacked the ability to nurture and care for you the way you needed."

Chet's eyes flooded with tears as I told him how sorry I was for the pain that his dad and I caused him. I told him, "Even though you don't remember me being this way, your brain remembers. Your brain remembers all of the pain I caused you through my anger and neglect: when you feel like 'Mom doesn't care about me,' you can't help but react."

I asked Chet to forgive me for hurting him when I was reeling with pain and living in my addiction. I reminded him that Jesus can heal anything. Chet's breathing slowed. With tear-soaked cheeks he looked at me and forgave me. Chet had no memory of the life I described and only knows me as "the Christian mom who read her Bible all the time and didn't curse or party." I gave him a hug and left his room.

I felt very sad in realizing how my unhealthy choices hurt my son so deeply, even though he was just a toddler. At the time, he didn't need to know what was going on with me, but even as a baby, he could feel it. I cried and prayed that God would cover the gaps and protect the son I loved so much.

A week later, Chet told me about a writing assignment that was a big chunk of his grade. He was supposed to choose someone he admired to write about. He told me that he was going to write about me—all I had been through and my struggle to care for him the best I could. My heart melted into a puddle as I hugged Chet.

Chet never again displayed an overreaction the way he did that night. Sadly, our sinful behavior harms more people than we know. It is never too late to enter into those wounded areas to offer an apology and allow the Holy Spirit to heal.

Lang

In what way do you resonate with Lang's part of the story?

____

____

____

____

____

____

In what way do you resonate with Chet's part of the story?

____

____

____

____

____

____

You can't go back and change the beginning but you can start where you are and change the ending.[131]

C. S. LEWIS

[131] C. S. Lewis. (n.d.). AZQuotes.com. Retrieved from AZQuotes.com Web site: https://www.azquotes.com/quote/1334084.

When we choose to pursue lifelong healing, it not only changes us, but it also changes those around us. It's true: we cannot change our past, but we can change our future. As we follow God's leading in our lives, we can make tomorrow better than today.

> *Today I have given you the choice between life and death, between blessings and curses. Now I call on heaven and earth to witness the choice you make. Oh, that you would choose life, so that you and your descendants might live!*
>
> **DEUTERONOMY 30:19 NLT**

How does this scripture empower you to pursue lifelong health?

____

____

____

____

____

____

How do you think your healing will affect your relationships?

____

____

____

____

____

____

____

How has God worked to restore blessings in your family—your family of origin or your current family?

____

____

____

____

____

____

____

What area would you like to see become a generational blessing in your family? Will it take a huge change like what Ruth experienced or a few smaller changes like Lang experienced with her son?

____

____

____

____

____

____

FIGHT WITH ME!

Most people don't like conflict. In fact, most people will avoid conflict at any cost. Too often, because we don't know how to handle conflict, we walk away from relationship. This is not our intent. In the moment, we are trying to avoid the negative feelings that accompany conflict. We also don't want to hurt the other person involved. We think that avoiding conflict—not saying what needs to be said—is the best way to maintain the relationship. This thinking is distorted and ultimately creates bigger problems in the relationship.

We need to change our perspective regarding conflict. When we experience friction in a relationship—especially with a spouse, family member, or close friend—we initially feel anxious, fearful, stressed, and more. This array of negative emotions can feel so overwhelming that we will do almost anything to make them stop. We will apologize without reason. We will appease with words of affirmation and praise. We will even give gifts, hoping to restore the relationship to its previous status.

We think that by avoiding conflict the relationship will continue on the same path, but that is not the truth. When we neglect our feelings, when we keep our pain hidden, when we fail to say the hard things or have the difficult conversation, we are hurting the relationship. Our feelings—the feelings that initiated the conflict—will remain with us, festering into an ugly wound, infecting our soul. Like every other type of infection, without the proper treatment, it will spread and infect every area of our life.

For our own health and for the health of the relationship, we have to engage in healthy conflict. We have to create a safe place where disagreements can happen in a healthy way. We have to be willing to wade through the uncomfortable feelings to get to the other side, where we experience appreciation and growth in the relationship. Conflict is the price of growing in intimacy: being uncomfortably close.[132]

---

[132] Roberts, T. & Roberts, D. (2010). *Sexy Christians: The Purpose, Power, and Passion of Biblical Intimacy*. Gresham, OR: Pure Desire Ministries International.

Think of it this way: in a relationship, when we walk away from an argument or disagreement, we are telling the other person, "You're not worth it." It may sound strange, but think about it. Essentially, we are telling them that our feelings are more important than the relationship. We so badly want to avoid the negative feelings of conflict that we will abandon the relationship to save ourselves. We may not completely walk away from the relationship, but this action alone changes the relationship. The things that need to be said out loud in an agreeable way, are left unspoken. It won't be long before the infection seeps into the relationship in ways we could never imagine.

If we want healthy relationships, we have to develop a healthy approach to conflict. We have to stay in—have the difficult conversations—so that we can experience the irreplaceable benefit of true relationship. We will never know true relationship without conflict. We have to "feel" the process and effects of restoration. We have to experience the positive feelings that come from resolved conflict, moving past the discomfort into a place of vulnerability, contentment, and peace.

Healthy conflict resolution starts with communication, using your words to proactively contribute to a resolution. Here are a few things to keep in mind as you develop a mindset for healthy conflict.[133]

- **Resolution is the goal:** When we experience conflict, in the heat of the moment, we may feel overwhelmed by our emotions: anger, disappointment, fear, and more. It is easy to lose sight of the goal. **Keep in mind that resolution does not mean both people completely agree; instead, it means they are purposeful in achieving a healthy outcome where both have been heard and understood.** Remember to stay calm and breathe. We can't allow our emotions to get the best of us.
- **Stick to the current issue:** It's important to identify the problem and stay on topic. Deal with issues involved in the current conflict and don't get derailed by unresolved past issues.
- **Listen:** Relationship is a two-way street. It is important that we express our feelings, but we need to consider the other person's feelings too. We need to listen to their perspective.
- **Protect the relationship:** The language we use during conflict can either tear down or build up the relationship. We need to make sure the other person knows how much we value the relationship. Avoid using language that contributes to blame, shame, and criticism. We can say, "I'm so thankful for our relationship and want to protect it. Last night, when you were dismissive of my opinion, it made me feel unappreciated and unloved."

The intent of healthy conflict is to bring about a new understanding and a solution that benefits both individuals—a solution that promotes growth and continuity in the relationship.

---

[133] Yerkes, M. (2008). *Tips and Tools for Healthy Conflict Resolution*. Retrieved from https://www.focusonthefamily.com/lifechallenges/relationship-challenges/conflict-resolution/tips-and-tools-for-healthy-conflict-resolution.

> *Do nothing from selfishness or empty conceit, but with humility of mind regard one another as more important than yourselves; [4]do not merely look out for your own personal interests, but also for the interests of others.*
>
> **PHILIPPIANS 2:3-4 NASB**

Recognizing the benefit of healthy conflict can be useful in all our relationships. It's not easy. There will be times when we want to walk away, when we want to avoid the uncomfortable feelings of conflict. But, we have to remember what healthy conflict brings to our relationships. Healthy conflict requires humility, trust, and vulnerability. Developing and practicing healthy conflict is essential to managing our relationships.

Briefly describe a time when you walked away from conflict and it remained unresolved.

What was the result of the unresolved conflict?

In the situation described above, explain how engaging in healthy conflict would have contributed to a better relationship.

What do you think the benefits are when engaging in healthy conflict?

God wants to do amazing things through our healing—not just for us, but for future generations. As we learn to be in relationship with God and others, find hope in the One who can do immeasurably more than we ask or imagine (Ephesians 3:20).

Looking Ahead

Complete the FASTER Scale, Group Check-in, Self-Care lesson, Thoughts/Feelings Awareness Log, and Change & Growth Analysis in your *Unraveled: Weekly Tools* before the next group meeting.

chapter nine

MY VALUE

LESSON 1: REDUCING SHAME

Shame can be a challenging emotion to recognize. We struggle not only with identifying this feeling, but also with understanding the impact it has on our behaviors and potential for healing. **Shame is a feeling that takes us beyond guilt–past the feeling that suggests we did something bad, to a deeper feeling that tells us we *are* bad.**[134]

It happened again. As I snuck out of his apartment, unable to remember many details from the night before, I was overwhelmed with guilt. I didn't even know his last name. He was handsome and charming and said all the right things in all the right ways. Over drinks and in the moment, I was valued, adored, and loved. I was happy.

As I drove home, I tried to put the pieces together. How did this happen again? Work had been especially challenging this past month. As part of a team, I was working on a big proposal and our presentation was yesterday. All week long, although I was doing my best, I had endured negative comments from a female coworker—comments belittling and demeaning my work. Despite the fact that my supervisor was happy with my work, I felt intimidated and unsure in my abilities.

When I thought about my feelings of guilt and shame, I was immediately reminded of my childhood. My family home was very chaotic. I was the third child of five, which made for a very busy home. Both my parents worked full-time jobs, so after school I was home with my siblings.

Most of the time, my older two siblings fought with each other while the younger two watched TV or stayed in their room. However, there were some days when my older two siblings turned their aggressiveness toward us younger three and made us participate in cruel or inappropriate behavior with one another. They threatened, "If you ever tell Mom or Dad, they won't believe you. They will know you're lying and they won't love you anymore."

I remember feeling so much shame and guilt from what I was forced to do with and to my younger siblings. At times I felt angry—angry that my parents didn't protect me and angry that my older siblings got away with such cruelty. I believed their threats and was fearful that if I ever told anyone about this, my family would reject me.

---

[134] Golden, B. (2017). *Overcoming the Paralysis of Toxic Shame*. Retrieved from www.psychologytoday.com/us/blog/overcoming-destructive-anger/201704/overcoming-the-paralysis-toxic-shame.

> Anonymous sex with strangers was becoming part of a disturbing pattern. I recognized that when I was feeling undervalued and unappreciated at work I would often go to the bar looking for a hookup. Although it left me feeling overwhelmed by shame, I became more desperate for connection and validation through sex when I was feeling harassed at work or fearful that my job was in jeopardy. Fearful that I would be rejected. Fearful that if anyone knew the truth about me, they wouldn't love me.
>
> *Lisa*

What was happening in Lisa's current environment that contributed to her behavior?

____

____

____

____

____

What unprocessed trauma was at the core of Lisa's behaviors?

____

____

____

____

____

____

When we are controlled by shame, it becomes the lens through which all self-evaluation is viewed. It not only affects our self-perception, it affects the way we engage in relationship with God and others. When we feel shame, we isolate. We think such negative thoughts about ourselves, fueling the shame, but also creating a negative feedback loop in our head: "They can never know what I've done. If they knew, they would reject me. They would hate me. They would abandon me."

This thought pattern plays over and over and over in our mind. In our distorted thinking, we believe that we have committed an unforgivable sin. Not just one, but many. So many unforgivable sins that if anyone ever knew the truth about us—the whole truth—they would certainly reject us. We would be forced to live a life of isolation. So, as a means of self-preservation, we impose this life of isolation on ourselves, allowing our feelings of shame to hold us hostage, keeping us from ever experiencing true relationship with God and others.

Shame can convey many meanings. From a clinical perspective, "shame means being exposed and feeling diminished by that exposure."[135] When we feel we have done something wrong or bad, many of us will experience guilt. Dr. Brené Brown suggests that guilt can be a beneficial emotion, motivating us to make a change in our behavior that moves us toward health.[136]

For example, all of us have experienced times where we lied, or perhaps we said something or did something hurtful to another. When we feel guilty about our behavior, we immediately work to restore the relationship. We confess. We apologize. We make things right. We take responsibility for our sin and work toward health in relationship.

However, what would happen if we didn't take the opportunity to make things right, if we didn't confess or apologize—if we didn't work to restore the relationship? In many ways, we would begin to feel the consequences of our sin. By its very nature, unresolved sin in our lives creates a condition of shame: we hide; we keep secrets; we seek isolation. We may not recognize it in the moment, but shame propelled by sin is toxic.[137]

When we live in a constant state of shame, it contaminates and permeates all areas of our lives. We deceive ourselves into believing that if others knew the truth, they would reject us. We believe that the only way to stay in relationship is through an illusion we create, allowing others to only see what we want them to see. Our illusion creates a barrier to keep others at a distance, and at the same time, continues to perpetuate our shame.

In your own words, how would you describe guilt? How would you describe shame?

____

____

____

____

____

Briefly describe a time when you felt guilt.

____

____

____

____

---

[135] Roberts, T. (2009). *Seven Pillars of Freedom Workbook*. Gresham, OR: Pure Desire Ministries International.

[136] Golden, B. (2017). *Overcoming the Paralysis of Toxic Shame*. Retrieved from www.psychologytoday.com/us/blog/overcoming-destructive-anger/201704/overcoming-the-paralysis-toxic-shame.

[137] Roberts, T. (2009). *Seven Pillars of Freedom Workbook*. Gresham, OR: Pure Desire Ministries International.

In the above situation, were you able to use the feeling of guilt to restore relationship, or did the situation lead to shame? Explain.

____

____

____

____

____

In what ways have you allowed shame to hold you hostage and keep you from experiencing true relationship with God and others?

____

____

____

____

____

____

Guilt is a feeling that tells us, "I did something bad," so we feel guilty about it.[138] When the guilt we feel remains unaddressed, it morphs into shame. Shame misleads us further, providing the basis for *why* we did something bad. Shame produces a feeling that tells us, "I did something bad because I AM bad." Shame convinces us that, "There is something wrong with me."

Shame and guilt impact our lives in many ways, and no one knew this better than the woman at the well (John 4:4-29).

> *He had to go through Samaria on the way. [5]Eventually he came to the Samaritan village of Sychar, near the field that Jacob gave to his son Joseph. [6]Jacob's well was there; and Jesus, tired from the long walk, sat wearily beside the well about noontime. [7]Soon a Samaritan woman came to draw water, and Jesus said to her, "Please give me a drink." [8]He was alone at the time because his disciples had gone into the village to buy some food. [9]The woman was surprised, for Jews refuse to have anything to do with Samaritans. She said to Jesus, "You are a Jew, and I am a Samaritan woman. Why are you asking me for a drink?"*

[138] Stumbo, N. (2017). *Safe: Creating A Culture Of Grace In A Climate of Shame*. Gresham, OR: Pure Desire Ministries International. 88.

> *[10]Jesus replied, "If you only knew the gift God has for you and who you are speaking to, you would ask me, and I would give you living water."*
> *[11]"But sir, you don't have a rope or a bucket," she said, "and this well is very deep. Where would you get this living water? [12]And besides, do you think you're greater than our ancestor Jacob, who gave us this well? How can you offer better water than he and his sons and his animals enjoyed?"*
> *[13]Jesus replied, "Anyone who drinks this water will soon become thirsty again. [14]But those who drink the water I give will never be thirsty again. It becomes a fresh, bubbling spring within them, giving them eternal life."*
> *[15]"Please, sir," the woman said, "give me this water! Then I'll never be thirsty again, and I won't have to come here to get water."*
> *[16]"Go and get your husband," Jesus told her.*
> *[17]"I don't have a husband," the woman replied.*
> *Jesus said, "You're right! You don't have a husband—[18]for you have had five husbands, and you aren't even married to the man you're living with now. You certainly spoke the truth!"*

Jesus was intentional about His journey through Samaria. Most Jews and rabbis would have avoided this geographical area, but Jesus had a divine appointment.[139] As Jesus rested beside Jacob's well, a Samaritan woman came to draw water. In this desert region, most women would draw water from the well in the early morning or late evening, but this woman came to the well around noon. The woman was surprised when Jesus said to her, "Please give me a drink," for Jews did not associate with Samaritans. Puzzled by Jesus' behavior, she asked, "Why are you asking me for a drink?"

Jesus' reply is so profound: *"If you only knew the gift God has for you and who you are speaking to, you would ask me, and I would give you living water."* Even more confused, the woman takes this statement literally. But Jesus says,

> *"Anyone who drinks this water will soon become thirsty again. [14]But those who drink the water I give will never be thirsty again. It becomes a fresh, bubbling spring within them, giving them eternal life."*

At this point, the conversation takes an interesting turn. When the woman says, "...give me this water!" Jesus changes the subject. He asks the woman to go get her husband, already knowing that she doesn't have a husband, has been married five times, and is not currently married to the man with whom she is living. Jesus needed her to know that He was the real deal. He was the only one who could give her living water.

---

[139] Bradley, R. & Roberts, D. (2012). *Behind the Mask: Authentic Living for Young Women*. Gresham, OR: Pure Desire Ministries International. 23.

> *"Sir," the woman said, "you must be a prophet. [20]So tell me, why is it that you Jews insist that Jerusalem is the only place of worship, while we Samaritans claim it is here at Mount Gerizim, where our ancestors worshiped?"*
> *[21]Jesus replied, "Believe me, dear woman, the time is coming when it will no longer matter whether you worship the Father on this mountain or in Jerusalem. [22]You Samaritans know very little about the one you worship, while we Jews know all about him, for salvation comes through the Jews. [23]But the time is coming—indeed it's here now—when true worshipers will worship the Father in spirit and in truth. The Father is looking for those who will worship him that way. [24]For God is Spirit, so those who worship him must worship in spirit and in truth."*
> *[25]The woman said, "I know the Messiah is coming—the one who is called Christ. When he comes, he will explain everything to us."*
> *[26]Then Jesus told her, "I am the Messiah!"*
> *[27]Just then his disciples came back. They were shocked to find him talking to a woman, but none of them had the nerve to ask, "What do you want with her?" or "Why are you talking to her?" [28]The woman left her water jar beside the well and ran back to the village, telling everyone, [29]"Come and see a man who told me everything I ever did! Could he possibly be the Messiah?"*

This woman was ecstatic to discover that despite her current and past behaviors—married multiple times and currently living with a man to whom she wasn't married—Jesus was offering her eternal life. He was offering her a genuine, life-giving relationship. She ran back to her village, thrilled to tell others what happened at the well, wanting them to experience the same freedom she found in Christ.

☐ *In what ways do you relate to the woman at the well?*

____

____

____

____

____

☐ *Describe your thoughts and feelings toward Jesus' response:* ***But those who drink the water I give will never be thirsty again. It becomes a fresh, bubbling spring within them, giving them eternal life.***

____

____

____

____

How does this story help to reduce shame in your life?

____

____

____

____

A WAY OUT

"If we want to battle shame at the root, we have to know how it relates to God.[140]

The effects of shame in our life can be so paralyzing that we fail to look for a way out. We have lived in a state of shame for so long, we are resolved to remain captive. We cannot begin to imagine what life would look like without shame. This is what the enemy of our soul wants for us: to feel hopeless, isolated, and alone. But God has already given us a way out. He gave us Jesus. He gave us grace.

It would be amazing, if once we received God's grace—through the saving knowledge of His Son, Jesus—we fully understood grace. That is often not the case. For many of us, we will spend our entire lives developing an understanding of God's grace—not because we get hung up on God's part, but because we feel so undeserving. We fail to comprehend and recognize how God's grace plays out in our life. At our core, we struggle with receiving grace—when God gives to us what we don't deserve. Our shame keeps us blinded to grace, but we don't have to stay this way.

The power of God's grace is invincible! Even with our strongest shame-shield in place, when we experience the depth of God's grace, it transforms our life. The blinders fall away. For the first time, we see ourselves from God's perspective—as His dearly loved daughter.

If we want to reduce the shame in our lives, we have to experience God in our lives. We don't have to be afraid. We can let go of our secrets. We can allow God's abundant grace to pour over us and fill our wounds with his love.

Removing our shame-shield requires risk. We don't know what it looks like to step into a place of grace. We want it and fear it at the same time. We want to experience and live in freedom, but we will have to risk vulnerability to get there. This will take time. We have to

[140] Piper, J. (1988). *Battling the Unbelief of Misplaced Shame*. Retrieved from www.desiringgod.org/messages/battling-the-unbelief-of-misplaced-shame.

be intentional. We have to begin by strengthening our understanding of grace. We must embrace grace.

Use the following scriptures and questions to expand your knowledge of grace.

> *God saved you by his grace when you believed. And you can't take credit for this; it is a gift from God. [9]Salvation is not a reward for the good things we have done, so none of us can boast about it. [10]For we are God's masterpiece. He has created us anew in Christ Jesus, so we can do the good things he planned for us long ago.*
>
> **EPHESIANS 2:8-10 NLT**

What does this verse say about God's grace? What does this verse mean to you?

___

___

___

___

> *Let us then approach God's throne of grace with confidence, so that we may receive mercy and find grace to help us in our time of need.*
>
> **HEBREWS 4:16**

What does this verse say about grace? How does this verse personally speak to you?

___

___

___

___

It is not enough that we *know* of God's grace—that we have a head-knowledge of what the Bible says about grace. We have to *experience* God's grace. Much like the woman caught in adultery (chapter 5, lesson 3), we have to *feel* God's grace.

Imagine what that must have been like: standing before her accusers, men who were ready, willing, and eager to stone her to death, waiting for Jesus to give the go-ahead. When Jesus comes to the woman's defense, her accusers slip away one by one.[141] When they have all gone, Jesus asks her, "Has no one condemned you?"

[141] John 8:9 NLT

"No one," she said. Then Jesus says the greatest words of grace:

> *"Neither do I. Go and sin no more."*

The gift of no condemnation allows us to stop sinning and walk in true relationship with God. When we experience the free, unmerited favor of God—when we accept Jesus as our Lord and Savior—we experience the fullness of God's grace.

Imagine standing before your accusers, humiliated, disgraced, and full of shame. Fearing judgment and rejection, being ostracized, and possible death. All of your worst failures and sins on display for everyone to see.

Then, Jesus steps in and defends you, offering you this same gift of no condemnation.

What would this look like for you? What would this ***feel*** *like for you? Draw your answers in the box below.*

Looking Ahead

Complete the FASTER Scale, Group Check-in, Self-Care lesson, Thoughts/Feelings Awareness Log, and Change & Growth Analysis in your *Unraveled: Weekly Tools* before the next group meeting.

LESSON 2: HEALTHY BOUNDARIES

Boundaries are often the most misunderstood concept in the healing process. Without boundaries, we can't find inner peace—a place of safety. We can't properly regulate our emotions and we frequently hurt others when trying to get our needs met.

Boundaries are taught in childhood and become a natural part of our "space" and individuality. In a functional family system, we are encouraged to express our dreams and opinions, likes and dislikes; and when we do, we are respected and encouraged to be who we are becoming through life experience. Through this healthy family system, when conflict happens, we have learned to stay in relationship and stay connected to those around us.

In a dysfunctional family system, our dreams and opinions are often met with criticism or rejection, resulting in feelings of abandonment. We come to the emotional conclusion that we don't matter and that our feelings aren't important. We grow up with the belief that we are unworthy of love and belonging. This creates an internal narrative that gives way to shame. Without boundaries, the words and behaviors of others—the emotional energy of another—impact our self-perception of worth, further wounding our heart. Our perception is skewed and we either fall into victimhood or become angry at the world.

A lack of boundaries deteriorates our sense of worth, making it nearly impossible to objectively perceive our world and relationships. We live a lifestyle of anxiety, wondering what others think of us, and generally feel disconnected in relationships.

What is your experience with boundaries?

____

____

____

____

____

As we continue on the path toward lifelong health, it is important that we understand how boundaries operate—how they are developed and how they are violated. Most of our current struggles in relationship are due to a lack of effective boundaries. We need to identify our unmet needs and the role they have played in our current struggle with boundaries.

Simply put, a boundary is a perimeter around how others impact us and how we impact others. God created us inherently worthy of His love and belonging. He also wired into our heart a sensitivity to harm—an intuitive sense of self. Even the youngest of children, including those who cannot yet speak, react anxiously to harsh words, sensing danger or harm. This "wired" sense stems from our inherent worth from God.

There are two types of boundaries: external and internal.[142]

External boundaries are perimeters around our physical space. This includes our personal space, the level of comfort we feel when interacting with others. This may fluctuate over time and change from person to person. From an early age, our physical boundaries are shaped through experience.

When it comes to external boundaries, our sexual boundary is probably the one with which we are most familiar. Many of us were raised in an environment where we learned that our body was our own. We learned sexual boundaries from our parents usually at an early age. Our caregivers are instrumental in shaping how comfortable we are with external boundaries.

Internal boundaries pertain to how we think, feel, and behave when interacting with others. This includes how well we listen and talk to others. Internal boundaries are the key to living a life of intimacy with others. It is the "fencing" that holds us intact from the inside.

Our talking boundary governs how we verbally communicate with others, as well as how we feel about and filter what someone is saying to us. It reflects that others have the same inherent worth we have, which is deserving of respect, even when we don't like what they have to say. Listening boundaries govern how we hear and take in information from others objectively, allowing them to have a different opinion than ours.

Our internal boundaries protect how we hear information from others, as well as how and with whom we share information. This helps us determine whether the relationship is safe or unsafe. When we develop healthy internal boundaries, it helps us recognize that we are in control of our thoughts and feelings. We get to decide how the words of others are going to affect us. When we take responsibility for our internal boundaries—our thoughts and feelings—it helps to reinforce our external boundaries.

Based on the family system in which you were raise, what type of boundaries did you develop?

____

____

____

[142] Mellody, P., Miller, A., & Miller, K. (2003). *Facing Codependence: What It Is, Where It Comes From, How It Sabotages Our Lives*. New York, NY: HarperCollins Publishers, Inc.

Developing healthy boundaries is learned behavior. Our first step in this process is to recognize that God will protect us. For some of us, this may require a fresh perspective of God. Those of us who have been betrayed by caregivers or others, or have had our boundaries violated, may struggle with trusting God. We need to examine the truth of who God is and how He intervenes in our life. Gaining a new perspective of God can provide a renewed sense of ourselves and our inherent worth. Healthy boundaries protect our self-worth and self-esteem.

As we begin to develop healthy boundaries, what does it look like?

I entered college with excitement about social life, academics, and life on my own. My high school experience was amazing! During this time, highly influenced by a friend, I was involved in many activities so my college and scholarship applications would stand apart from others. While my friend's advice seemed a bit extreme, I knew what colleges were looking for, so I followed my friend's direction. I was involved in every high school activity I could possibly do and excelled in all my honor courses. All my hard work paid off and I was going to college on a full-ride scholarship. What I didn't realize is that after four years of trying to do everything and saying "yes" to as many things as I could to make myself look good on paper, I now felt the need to say "yes" to everything. I said "yes" all the time, even when I really wanted to say "no."

Within the first few weeks of college, I signed up for a few clubs and joined student government. I was taking 21 credits, trying to maintain my relationship with my high school boyfriend, working four part-time jobs, volunteering for the worship team at church, and participating in several freshman activities in my dorm. I said "yes" again and again and did not know how to say "no." The year continued on a downward spiral. My grades took a turn for the worse; I broke up with my high school boyfriend; I was carelessly spending all the money I made; and the stress from all my classes and hardly getting any sleep was taking a toll on my body. My life clearly reflected that I had no boundaries in place. I had no idea where to start developing healthy boundaries.

Sierra

What type of boundaries does Sierra need to develop? Explain.

____

____

____

____

Where should Sierra start developing healthy boundaries? Provide suggestions.

____

____

____

____

ESTABLISHING HEALTHY BOUNDARIES

Many of us grew up in an environment where boundaries were not modeled or respected.[143] For those of us who struggle with managing love, sex, and relationships, we have problems setting healthy boundaries as well as not recognizing when we violate the boundaries of others.

Establishing and maintaining healthy boundaries is an essential step on the path toward health. It is important to understand that when we develop healthy boundaries to keep us safe in relationship, it helps others recognize that we are safe because they feel more secure and less threatened in the relationship.

When it comes to recognizing differences between healthy and unhealthy boundaries, there are many distinct characteristics that reflect our thoughts, feelings, and behaviors.

PEOPLE WHO HAVE HEALTHY BOUNDARIES:

- Interact with others effectively
- Frequently get what they want in relationship
- Know what they will and will not do
- Know what they will and will not allow others to do
- Can set limits and still love
- Do not violate the personal space of others
- Do not take on responsibilities of others
- Can be responsible to others without feeling responsible for them
- Feel safe and secure
- Create healthy connections

PEOPLE WHO HAVE UNHEALTHY BOUNDARIES:

- Frequently have difficulty in relationships
- Have difficulty getting their needs met in relationships

[143] Riggenbach, J. (2013). *The CBT Toolbox: A Workbook for Clients and Clinicians.* PESI Publishing & Media.

- Trust too easily and overshare with the wrong people
- Trust too little and don't have people to share with
- Violate the personal space of others
- Ask inappropriate personal questions of people they don't know well
- Feel responsible for others' behavior and feelings
- Often live lives driven by guilt
- Choose actions based on what will please others rather than their convictions
- Tolerate unhealthy or inappropriate behaviors from others
- Feel unsafe in relationships
- Create unhealthy connections

From the lists above, which behaviors do you relate to most?

Describe how failing to set healthy boundaries in past relationships has hurt you.

What is your greatest fear with setting boundaries?

After setting healthy boundaries, how do you feel? If you have not set any healthy boundaries, what is stopping you? What double bind are you facing?

What people in your life do you struggle with most when setting healthy boundaries?

What is one healthy boundary you want to set for yourself this week?

EUPHORIC RECALL

When it comes to our pursuit of lifelong healing, we can unknowingly become our own worst enemy. We are unable to recognize how our memory of past events is tainted by euphoric recall.[144] This is the process by which we only remember the positive aspects of an experience, not the negative.

Here's how this works: an alcoholic remembers the fun they had partying with friends, but blocks out the memory of throwing up all night and waking up on the bathroom floor. In the same way, a new mom remembers the immense joy she feels when she holds her baby for the first time, suppressing the memories of morning sickness and the pain of childbirth.

[144] Carnes, P. (2001). *Facing the Shadow: Starting Sexual and Relationship Recovery*. Carefree, AZ: Gentle Path Press.

For those of us who struggle with love, sex, and relationship addictions, euphoric recall keeps us stuck in our unhealthy patterns. We remember the feelings of excitement and pleasure that come from a night of passion but block out the feelings of emptiness and loneliness that follow the next day. This process distorts our memory, disrupting the healing process, and limiting our ability to set healthy boundaries.

Describe a time when euphoric recall distorted your memory of an event—when your memory was formed by focusing on the positive aspects of the experience, not the negative.

____

____

____

____

____

What was the outcome of the above described event?

____

____

____

____

____

Can you identify any patterns of euphoric recall in your life? Explain.

____

____

____

____

____

How has euphoric recall inhibited your progress toward lifelong health?

____

____

____

____

____

Establishing healthy boundaries allows us to live in freedom: having the ability to make choices that continue to move us toward relationship with God and others.

AN IMPORTANT STEP

Many of us who struggle with managing love, sex, and relationships have experienced sex with several partners. Scripture reveals the bond that takes place between two people when they engage in sexual intercourse—the two will become one flesh.[145] This bond is not only physiological, but spiritual.[146] Sex is such a powerful bonding agent, God intentionally designed sex for marriage to bond husband and wife together in a way that is unlike any other relationship.

Think of it this way: anytime we glue two surfaces together and later separate them, what happens? Residue and pieces of the other surface remain affixed to one another. Sometimes the bonding agent is so strong that it takes extensive work to get the surface clean again.

This is what happens when we have sex outside of marriage. We form a sexual, emotional, and physical attachment to another person that becomes part of our soul. Even years later, the enemy can continue to use these experiences against us, creating destructive patterns in our thinking, feelings, and behaviors.

> *Do you not know that your bodies are members of Christ himself? Shall I then take the members of Christ and unite them with a prostitute? Never! [16]Do you not know that he who unites himself with a prostitute is one with her in body? For it is said, "The two will become one flesh." [17]But whoever is united with the Lord is one with him in spirit. [18]Flee from sexual immorality. All other sins a person commits are outside the body, but whoever sins sexually, sins against their own body. [19]Do you not know that your bodies are temples of the Holy Spirit, who is in you, whom you have received from God? You are not your own; [20]you were bought at a price. Therefore honor God with your bodies.*
>
> **1 CORINTHIANS 6:15-20**

When we engage in sex outside of marriage, we not only sin against God, we also sin against the other person involved, our spouse (if we have one), and against our own body. However, we can find sexual freedom through prayer, confession, and forgiveness.

---

[145] Genesis 2:24; Ephesians 5:32.

[146] Roberts, D. (2010). *Pure Desire for Women: Eight Pillars to Freedom from love addiction & sexual issues*. Workbook 2. Gresham, OR: Pure Desire Ministries International. 163.

Use the following steps as a guide to find freedom through prayer.

- Ask forgiveness for sinning against God (Psalm 51:4).
- Ask forgiveness for sinning against your own body (1 Corinthians 6:18).
- Ask forgiveness for sinning against the other person's body (1 Corinthians 6:18).
- Ask forgiveness for sinning against a spouse's body (Matthew 5:23-24).

Use the following space to write out your prayer.

Looking Ahead

Complete the FASTER Scale, Group Check-in, Self-Care lesson, Thoughts/Feelings Awareness Log, and Change & Growth Analysis in your *Unraveled: Weekly Tools* before the next group meeting.

LESSON 3: FORGIVING YOURSELF

As we pursue lifelong healing, our goal is to remove any unhealthy behaviors that interfere with our ability to create relationship with God and others. For many of us who struggle with love, sex, and relationship addictions, this can be especially challenging when it comes to forgiveness—not in our ability to forgive others, but in our ability to forgive ourselves.

Many people think I'm an amazing person. They tell me so. I overhear people say that I am caring, giving, and self-sacrificing. At work, I go above and beyond my job responsibilities, helping wherever there is a need. At church, I help with the children's program, sing in the choir, and volunteer in the kitchen for every social event and potluck.

In my neighborhood, I keep an eye on all my neighbors, taking in trash cans, putting the neighbor's dog back behind the fence when she digs out, and watching the neighbors' homes when they are on vacation. I attend two Bible studies each week. I volunteer at the local hospital. I help with the quarterly bake sale at the women's shelter. I am always busy doing something for someone.

Here's what most people don't know about me: at 16 years old I was pregnant and at 17, I was living out of my car with my baby and the state eventually took my baby away. Desperate for love, I married the first guy who showed the slightest interest in me. My husband was an alcoholic and drug addict. He beat me on a regular basis, which didn't stop when I was pregnant, and continually threatened to leave me. At times, even when my face was bleeding from the abuse, I begged him to stay.

I finally left him when his physical abuse threatened the safety of my son. I was married and divorced two more times before my son turned 18 years old, unknowingly choosing the same type of guy each time: handsome, charming, and attentive until we got married. After each marriage, my husbands became distant and uninterested. When I questioned their behavior, they were abusive and eventually left me. At one point, newly pregnant and about to be divorced again, I had an abortion.

My son blames me for his horrible childhood and left home when he turned 18. We haven't spoken in years.

One evening a few years ago, when feeling lonely, depressed, and suicidal, I was wandering around the city streets contemplating my death. Inadvertently, I ended up at a local church, received the help I needed, and dedicated my life to the Lord. That night, God had a different plan for my life.

I continue to work toward health, but struggle with incredible guilt and shame. I know God has forgiven me, but I cannot seem to forgive myself.

Patricia

What will Patricia need to do to heal from her past?

Why do you think Patricia is struggling to forgive herself?

If Patricia was in your group and you knew the truth about her life, what would you say about forgiveness to encourage her?

While there are no specific scriptures that address self-forgiveness, there are many verses about forgiveness that can be applied to our healing process.[147]

[147] All About God (2018). *Forgiving Yourself - An Important Choice*. Retrieved from https://www.allaboutgod.com/forgiving-yourself.htm.

- God loves all of us and will forgive our sins. He doesn't only forgive His favorite children (Acts 10:34). He forgives all of us.
- When God forgives us, He does not remember our sin any longer—He is not going to hold it over us or use our sin against us (Jeremiah 31:34).
- In Christ we are redeemed. We are forgiven. He lavishes upon us the richness of His grace (Ephesians 1:7-8).

What do these verses tell us about forgiveness?

____

____

____

____

____

How can we apply this to our life?

____

____

____

____

What specific things are you holding on to, the areas in your life where you are not allowing yourself to experience the complete forgiveness God is offering?

____

____

____

____

For several weeks, we have dug into our past—unpacked our trauma—and exposed our wounds. We have revealed the depth of our brokenness. We have said things out loud that we intended to take with us to the grave. We have chosen this process because we long for healing. We want to experience true relationship. We want to be free.

The truth is: we are free. Christ gave us our freedom when He died for us on the cross. We are forgiven by the only One who can pardon us—set free by the One who holds the key.

Why do we struggle with forgiving ourselves when our debt has already been paid? What makes our sin so unique that Jesus' death on the cross cannot cover it? Why can we not accept God's forgiveness?

The enemy of our soul wants us to remain captive, paralyzed by our feelings of fear and worthlessness. We live as though we are still behind bars, hiding in the dark, suffering in isolation, but the door of our cell is open. We can leave anytime we want. We can have relationship with God and others. We can experience life. What is holding us back?

As you contemplate this question, use the following scripture to expand your understanding of forgiveness.

> *When I refused to confess my sin, my body wasted away,*
> *and I groaned all day long. [4]Day and night your hand of discipline was heavy on me. My strength evaporated like water in the summer heat.*
> *[5]Finally, I confessed all my sins to you and stopped trying to hide my guilt.*
> *I said to myself, "I will confess my rebellion to the Lord."*
> *And you forgave me! All my guilt is gone.*
>
> **PSALM 32:3-5**

What does this scripture tell you about God's forgiveness?

____

____

____

____

How does it pertain to you specifically?

____

____

____

____

The torment of David's sin and guilt is evident in Psalm 32. His sin of adultery with Bathsheba and the murder of her husband weighed heavy on his heart. He recognized how his sin and guilt were affecting him mentally, physically, and spiritually. However, when David confessed his sin and stopped trying to hide his guilt, God forgave him! The weight of his sin and guilt was gone.

This act of confession required that David, too, needed to forgive himself so that he could step back into relationship with God. Despite David's sin, God refers to him as "a man after my own heart."[148]

[148] Acts 13:22

How would understanding God's grace and love toward David help you receive God's forgiveness and forgive yourself?

______

______

______

______

______

______

> *Repent, then, and turn to God, so that your sins may be wiped out, that times of refreshing may come from the Lord,...*
>
> **ACTS 3:19**

How does Acts 3:19 apply to David?

______

______

______

______

______

How does Acts 3:19 apply to you?

______

______

______

______

______

Repentance leads to forgiveness. Forgiveness leads to refreshing times with the Lord. This leads to relationship.

WHERE WE WANT TO GO

As we continue to pursue healing, we develop a sense of hope—the hope that our future could look drastically different from our past. We begin to imagine what our life might look like and what our relationships might look like. We consider new goals. We envision our life with meaning and purpose.

"

When we deny our story, it defines us.
When we own our story, we get to write a brave new ending.[149]

BRENÉ BROWN

When we own our story—when we can stand in it unashamed—it's transformative. We are learning what it means to live in freedom, no longer held captive by our guilt and shame. Through our personal promises and experience with God and others, we are changing our thoughts and feelings. We are renewing our mind. Our desire for authentic relationship with God and others has become the driving force of our healing. The anticipation of a brighter future gives us the courage to *write a brave new ending* to our story.

What does your brave new ending look like? What goals do you have for the future? In what ways have you developed a new sense of purpose? How do you want to use your healing to help others? Where do you want to go from here?

Use the space provided to write the rest of your story. Be prepared to share your brave new ending with your group.

As I think about the future...

____

____

____

____

____

____

____

____

____

____

____

____

____

____

[149] Brown, B. (2015). *Own our history. Change the story*. Retrieved from https://brenebrown.com/blog/2015/06/18/own-our-history-change-the-story/.

Looking Ahead

Complete the FASTER Scale, Group Check-in, Self-Care lesson, Thoughts/Feelings Awareness Log, and Change & Growth Analysis in your *Unraveled: Weekly Tools* before the next group meeting.

chapter ten

SECURITY IN CHRIST

10

LESSON 1: MY IDENTITY

Moses is a source of encouragement for many of us who feel we have missed our opportunity to live a life of purpose. His adulthood mistakes included the murder of an Egyptian taskmaster, which became public knowledge and had the potential to cost him his life. Realizing his actions had gone viral, Moses became so terrified; he re-established his life in the distant plains of Midian, picking up a new career path as a shepherd.

This new life was a form of security for Moses. He had run far from the failures of his past and had been given a second chance at a new life as a husband and father. When he got ready for work every day, he grabbed his staff, which represented financial security, emotional security far from his failures, and relational security with his father-in-law.[150] He embraced his quiet, new identity as a shepherd and refused to dream of doing anything else.

One day, while tending his sheep on the backside of Mount Sinai, he noticed a blazing bush that remained completely intact. It was the place he first heard God's voice. As he stepped forward, God called him by name and asked him to take off his shoes. He was standing on holy ground.

It probably felt like a run-of-the-mill day until that moment. The reality is, God can show up anywhere, at any time in our life—in our car, the bathroom while we're getting ready for work, even at the kitchen sink. No place is devoid of His presence, and He wants us to acknowledge His presence with us. For Moses it required taking off his shoes.

God told Moses He had been listening to the cries of His people and was intent on delivering them from their bondage. Of all the people God could choose, He announced to Moses, "I am choosing you to deliver them."

Moses came up with every reason he could think of that would disqualify him from this God-sized invitation. God didn't agree or disagree with him. He simply responded, "I will be with you."[151]

So many of us carry dreams and a sense of God's purpose for our life. Yet, when we look in the mirror, we know who we are in the light of our God-sized destiny. Much like Moses, we find ourselves severely lacking. God's words to Moses reflect His heart to us today: *I will be with you*. He is not impressed with our accomplishments or deterred

---

[150] Batterson, M. (2008). *Wild Goose Chase: Reclaim the Adventure of Pursuing God*. Colorado Springs, CO: Multnomah Books.

[151] Exodus 3:12

by our failures. He wants us to realize it's never been about who we are, but it is about *whose* we are.[152]

The author of Hebrews reminds us that God is the One who will accomplish His purposes through our lives.

> *Now may the God of peace...equip you with all you need for doing his will. May he produce in you, through the power of Jesus Christ, every good thing that is pleasing to him. All glory to him forever and ever! Amen.*
>
> **HEBREWS 13:20-21 NLT**

Moses chose to lay down his security and identity as a shepherd to pick up his new identity found only in God. The same hand of grace extended to Moses on Mount Sinai is extended to each of us today. All we have to do is receive it.

How does Hebrews 13:20-21 personally speak to you?

___

___

___

Moses received a God-sized invitation. Have you received a God-sized invitation? Explain.

___

___

___

We may sense God's nearness in the most obscure places and during the mundane moments of our life. We may feel the need to kick off our shoes just to acknowledge our awareness of that holy moment in His presence.

Describe a time when you have sensed God's nearness in an unexpected way. How did this experience make you feel?

___

___

___

___

___

10

[152] Batterson, M. (2008). *Wild Goose Chase: Reclaim the Adventure of Pursuing God.* Colorado Springs, CO: Multnomah Books.

Like Moses, many of us think that God can't use us—that our past experiences disqualify us from being useful for the Kingdom of God. We don't want to think this is true, but it *feels* true. Fighting against the pain and stress of our past will only drive us deeper into unhealthy behaviors. We need to lay down our wounded and broken identity and pick up the new identity we have in Christ—our true identity.

Today is a day like any other day. I stopped to pick up groceries on my way home from work. I took off my designer shoes, hung up my little black leather purse, and slipped off my jacket. Walking past the mirror in the hallway, I looked at my outfit, reassessing the cuteness, and decided it was definitely a repeat outfit. *I wonder if anyone noticed me today because my outfit was so cute*? While I love how it feels to be so put-together, some days it was just exhausting.

With groceries in hand, I began taking out food to prep dinner. I turned on a podcast to keep me company as I cooked. It was a lot of effort to cook dinner for just one person, but I am tired of settling for easy dinners. I love the taste of healthy food, even if it takes more preparation. While I sat there eating dinner at my dining room table alone, I began to feel overwhelmingly sad. Most days were good but some days are so hard. It is hard to be alone. It is hard to be 38 years old and have settled into this single life—my "single" identity—without hope that it will ever change.

I've been on a handful of dates since college but nothing ever went past a first date, and I haven't been asked out in over five years. I found myself trying harder to get the attention of men, but I was continually left feeling more disappointed. Tonight was one of those nights. What I hated most was the feeling that everything would be better if I acted out and masturbated, just this once. This was becoming a persistent evening feeling and I tried hard to resist it. Most of the time I could resist but only for a couple weeks; then I would give in, only to get the urge again a few days later. The cycle was never-ending and left me feeling horrible every time I acted out.

Tonight I was determined not to give in. I finished eating dinner, cleaned up, and then changed into my workout clothes. I needed to get my head in a better place. I needed to shift gears and get my mind thinking healthy thoughts. I tied my shoes and took off down the street for a brisk walk. As I walked, I took deep breaths and immediately started feeling better. Relaxed breathing always helped. When feeling triggered, I tried to go on walks and do meditative breathing. Walking and breathing was one replacement behavior that really helped me.

When I got back home. I opened the door, stepped in and took one last deep breath. I looked around my home and was grateful for having such a nice place to live. While still feeling discouraged from loneliness, I felt determined to work to broaden my perspective of healthy living, even as a single person. Although I felt exhausted from always trying to attract the attention of men and could not understand why they didn't like me, I was going to pray for patience for God's plan. As I prayed, tears streamed down my face. The sadness came and I allowed myself to feel the pain. I didn't try to numb it by acting out. I didn't try to run away from it. I felt it.

Susan

What things contributed to Susan's desire to masturbate?

____

____

____

____

In the end, Susan made a healthy choice to feel the pain. What do you think about that choice?

____

____

____

____

If you had a friend like Susan, how would you encourage her?

____

____

____

____

____

SOOTHING STRATEGIES

Stress seems to be constant in life. How we deal with stress is learned behavior. It is the ability to gently calm ourselves when we are triggered by what is happening around us. Depending on the type of environment in which we were raised, we may have learned how to soothe ourselves when feeling discomfort, pain, and anxiety. Our parents may have used distraction or a favorite toy to help us calm down when experiencing stress. Through this parent-child interaction we learn how to self-soothe, so that as adults, we are able to calm ourselves when feeling the pressure of our environment.

Since our soothing strategies are learned behavior, how did your parents self-soothe when they were stressed?

Have you found yourself using any of these same methods?

Unfortunately, not all children had this experience. Not all children learned how to self-soothe. Instead of developing healthy ways to soothe themselves, they turned to unhealthy behaviors in times of stress. Instead of learning how to calm themselves in a safe environment, they learned to survive by whatever means possible in a chaotic, unstable environment. Their self-soothing behaviors—disassociating, isolating, and medicating their pain—helped them survive an ongoing stressful lifestyle. Even as adults, this is their method of self-soothing.

- Numbing out on video games
- Binge watching Netflix, Hulu, videos, or TV
- Eating too much food or junk food
- Refusing to eat any food
- Finding new friends on Facebook
- Spending too much time on social media
- Obsessing over relationships
- Staying busy all the time
- Trying to control everyone and everything in our environment

Which of the above behaviors do you relate to most? Explain.

___

___

___

___

___

As we learned in chapter 2, when we experience stress—something in our environment that indicates a threat—it produces a cascade of physiological responses that initiate our fight-or-flight system. If a person was raised in an environment where they didn't learn healthy self-soothing strategies, their sensitivity to stress becomes acute to the point that even the smallest amount of stress will trigger a stress-response that is out of proportion to the situation.

At some point, whether we live with stress on a daily basis or encounter it occasionally, we will recognize the need for healthy strategies to combat stressful experiences. We have to develop a plan for self-soothing ahead of time so that when stress finds us, we can proactively work to calm ourselves.

Here are a few quick and easy methods for self-soothing:[153,154]

- Take a few deep breaths—this is one of the quickest ways to initiate a relaxation response in the brain.
- Prepare a hot beverage for yourself and drink it slowly, focusing on its smell, temperature, and taste.
- Wrap up in a warm blanket. Warm a blanket in the dryer and get cozy.
- Play calm and soothing music.
- Go out in the sun.
- Take a short walk.
- Talk to yourself in a positive and comforting way: "It's going to be okay."
- Laugh—YouTube your favorite funny video or find something to laugh about.
- Take a warm shower or bubble bath.
- Light a candle or diffuse essential oils. The scent of lavender is often used for soothing anxiety.

---

[153] Eddins, R. (2016). Grounding Techniques & Self Soothing for Emotional Regulation. Retrieved from https://eddinscounseling.com/grounding-techniques-self-soothing-emotional-regulation/.

[154] Tartakovsky, M. (2014). 10 Quick Strategies for Soothing Stress. *Psych Central*. Retrieved from https://psychcentral.com/blog/10-quick-strategies-for-soothing-stress/.

Following a stress-response, it is important that we complete a self-assessment, analyzing where we are physically, mentally, emotionally, and spiritually. Is our body feeling tense? Where are we emotionally—how are we feeling? What do we need spiritually? This self-assessment will help us determine the areas where we are still feeling stressed, allowing us to implement the proper self-soothing strategy. We need to take a holistic approach when developing our soothing techniques.

This week, begin creating a list of self-soothing strategies that will help calm yourself when feeling stressed. You may choose some of the activities listed above or create your own. Do your best to create strategies that are practical and easily implemented in your current season of life.

1. ______________________________

2. ______________________________

3. ______________________________

4. ______________________________

5. ______________________________

Now that you've created your list, share it with two trusted people who know you well enough to know when you're feeling stressed. Then, ask if they will remind you to use your list of self-soothing strategies when feeling stressed.

Who did you share your list with? ______________________________

Remember, we can't do this alone. Along the way, we need others to help us stay on the path toward lifelong health.

Looking Ahead

Complete the FASTER Scale, Group Check-in, Self-Care lesson, Thoughts/Feelings Awareness Log, and Change & Growth Analysis in your *Unraveled: Weekly Tools* before the next group meeting.

LESSON 2: BIBLICAL PROMISES

Our identity comes from Christ—who we are at our core and who we become is built from this foundation. When struggling with identity issues, we often ask ourselves, "What is it that God wants me to do?" or "Who is God creating me to be?" These are great questions, but they reveal a future-focused mindset.

Our core identity is not based on how we think God wants to use us in the future or what we hope to become someday. Our core identity comes from who we are right now, today, in Christ—who we have always been, from birth because God made us this way. We are exactly what God intended, but why can't we see it?

This is an interesting phenomenon: throughout our lifetime, our identity is constantly molded, smoothed, chipped, destroyed, and recreated, over and over and over again. Not our true identity, but the identity we want others to see. Our environment, the people who have influence, and the choices we make contribute to this process. But who were we before our life was tainted by the sins of this world? What unique qualities did God give us at birth—our personality, talents, and temperament—to shape our core identity?

EXAMPLES:

- **A sensitive heart**: others saw it as a weakness and called me names, but God made me sensitive to spiritual things.
- **Loving and compassionate:** sometimes twisted into a codependent behavior, but God designed me to practically and spiritually minister to others.
- **Belief in others:** trusted those who were not trustworthy, but God gave me a heart to trust Him and discern how to be loyal to those who can be trusted.
- **Forgiving:** taken advantage of by those who hurt me, but God gave me a forgiving heart and the ability to create healthy boundaries.

Name one unique quality God gave you at birth.

____

____

____

____

How has this quality been exploited, misused, or extinguished by the enemy?

____
____
____
____
____
____
____

This should make us angry! To think that God gave us a precious gift and the enemy of our soul twisted, manipulated, and used it against us and others is outrageous! To make matters worse, the enemy made us believe the lie—the lie that is now attached to our gift. The lie that causes us to doubt ourselves. The lie that keeps us in isolation. The lie that creates a divide in our relationship with God and others.

We need to be aware of how the enemy is using this lie against us. What lie is attached to your gifting?

____
____
____
____
____
____
____

Although the enemy has tried to use our gifting against us, used it to separate us from true relationship with God, he did not destroy it. He cannot destroy it. Do you know why? Because it is a core piece of our identity. Without question, we are made in the image of God. Therefore, the unique areas of gifting that shape our core identity are of God. In many ways, our DNA—the very core of our existence—is super-charged with the essence of God. While our environment, experiences, and behaviors influence our gifting, they cannot destroy our core identity that God intentionally put in us for His good and His glory. It can't happen.

So, why does it *feel* like the enemy of our soul destroyed our gifting? When we look for our true identity, why does it *feel* shameful, embarrassing, and hopeless? Why do we try so hard to create a fake identity, a facade that others will accept and love? Why do we work so hard to cover and hide our core identity?

Our greatest area of woundedness is our greatest area of giftedness.[155]

God gave us an amazing area of gifting, unique to us, and intended for God's glory. At some point, something happened, something deep in our core that caused us to believe that our gift was bad—not only is our gift bad, but we are bad. The shame of this experience created a catastrophic response that yielded years of self-destructive thoughts, feelings, and behaviors that continue to hold us hostage. The enemy has done everything in his power—steal, kill, and destroy[156]—to stomp the life out of our gifting, but we cannot continue to be the victim of his assault. We need to fight back. We need to discover who we are at our core. We need to become our identity.

MY CORE BELIEFS

Once we recognize that our core identity comes from Christ, we need to figure out what this means. This process takes time. We need to be intentional about spending time with God and in His Word so we can hear what He is saying to us. We need to give the Holy Spirit opportunity to speak truth into our life, to revitalize—bring back to life—our identity. Our core beliefs are attached to our identity and gifting, but they have been distorted by the enemy. It's time to let the truth set us free.

10

> *So Jesus said to the Jews who had believed him, "If you abide in my word, you are truly my disciples, [32]and you will know the truth, and the truth will set you free."*
>
> **JOHN 8:31-32 ESV**

As we spend time with God, through prayer and reading His Word, we not only gain a greater understanding of who He is, we also gain a greater understanding of our identity in Him. If we allow it, God will speak to us so clearly and so specifically that it cannot be denied.

I have a heart for children. This was especially evident when my husband and I started talking about adoption. We were both in our mid-50s, with two grown daughters and grandchildren. It seemed an unlikely path for a couple our age, but we felt confident in what God was calling us to do.

---

[155] Roberts, T. (2009). *Seven Pillars of Freedom Workbook*. Gresham, OR: Pure Desire Ministries International.

[156] John 10:10

I am the oldest of four children with one brother, a half-brother, and a half-sister. Although we had different dads, we were very close. I was very protective of my younger siblings, especially my younger sister.

Although it wasn't revealed until after I was married, I was sexually abused by my stepfather for many years. At one point, I told my mother about the abuse, thinking she would protect me, but that didn't happen. My mother confronted my stepfather and made some threats, but she was not about to stand up for me, especially if it meant experiencing another failed marriage. I felt responsible for the abuse and suffered in silence, but I also carried the burden of protecting my siblings from any form of abuse.

For many years, I struggled with identity issues. On one hand, I felt used, betrayed, exploited, unloved, and worthless. On the other hand, there was something in me that felt courageous, honorable, and brave. I wrestled with these conflicting feelings for years and couldn't make sense of what it meant.

I had a relationship with the Lord but didn't feel like God spoke to me in any specific way. A few months ago, I tried something new as part of my weekly Bible study. All the women in the group decided to start reading one psalm per day, meditating on that scripture passage throughout the day. I sought the Lord and grew in my love relationship with him. Although I didn't feel that God spoke to me in any profound way, I was diligent in reading through the psalms, enjoying my time with the Lord.

Then it happened. On day 82, while reading Psalm 82, God spoke to me. It was as though the words became energized as they jumped off the page:

> *Defend the weak and the fatherless; uphold the cause of the poor and the oppressed. [4]Rescue the weak and the needy; deliver them from the hand of the wicked.*
>
> **PSALM 82:3-4**

In the moment, my body felt warm as an indescribable peace covered me from head to toe. As tears fell from my eyes, I heard God's voice. I heard what He was saying.

"You are brave and strong. You protect and shield the innocent. You are resilient, defending the weak, giving grace to those in need. The fatherless will be safe in your arms."

This experience with God was invigorating. I knew it meant something, but not sure what to do next. Within a couple weeks, a missionary couple was visiting my church. They spoke about a specific need in the region they served where many children, mostly little girls, were abandoned. If not adopted by loving families, many would end up on the streets or sold into human trafficking.

As I listened to their plea, I knew exactly what God was asking me to do. These words echoed in my spirit, "The fatherless will be safe in your arms." Despite my past abuse, God was going to use me to rescue and protect these little girls. I was going to give them a home where they would be safe.

Brenda

Why did Brenda struggle with her identity?

____

____

____

____

What core beliefs were attached to Brenda's identity?

____

____

____

____

How did God affirm Brenda's identity in Him?

____

____

____

____

When our core beliefs do not align with our identity in Christ, it creates an internal struggle that we need to process. If our core beliefs keep us in isolation—unable to recognize God's voice in our life—we will miss out on experiencing God. We will miss out on what God is trying to do in us and through us.

What core beliefs are attached to your identity?

____

____

____

____

____

How do your core beliefs align with your identity in Christ? How do they differ?

Describe a time when you felt God speaking to you.

What scripture or biblical promise did God give you through this experience?

In many ways, our view of God shapes the way we live, the decisions we make, and even what we think about ourselves. The more we strive to create relationship with God, the easier it becomes to create relationship with others.

Looking Ahead

Complete the FASTER Scale, Group Check-in, Self-Care lesson, Thoughts/Feelings Awareness Log, and Change & Growth Analysis in your *Unraveled: Weekly Tools* before the next group meeting.

LESSON 3: SECURELY ATTACHED

Research suggests that our early attachment to caregivers can have a lasting impact on how we develop and behave in relationships.[157] In chapter 6, lesson 2, we learned about our attachment style—whether we had developed a secure or insecure attachment style.

Most of us who struggle with love, sex, and relationship addictions developed an insecure attachment style. We tend to exhibit some or all of the following behaviors in relationship. We:

- ☐ fear commitment and intimacy.
- ☐ pull away when things become difficult.
- ☐ are suspicious and untrusting of others.
- ☐ view others as unreliable.
- ☐ do not let others get emotionally close.

Or we:

- ☐ have mixed emotions about relationships, which creates conflict.
- ☐ feel misunderstood and unappreciated.
- ☐ constantly doubt the level of another's love and affection.
- ☐ feel that others lack commitment to the relationship.

Put a checkmark next to any of these behaviors that are or have been present in your relationships.

Of the behaviors you marked, which one do you struggle with most or is most prevalent in your current relationships?

____

____

____

____

[157] Coon, D. & Mitterer, J. (2013). *Introduction to Psychology: Gateways to Mind and Behavior.* Belmont, CA: Wadsworth Cengage Learning.

The cultural reality of our world today lends itself to an insecure attachment style. This is often observed in divorce and blended families. The attachment bond between parent and child is disrupted during divorce, creating for the child a lack of trust and attachment to new relationships.[158] This becomes especially challenging when remarriage and the blending or restructuring of the family takes place. For everyone involved—the biological parents, the stepparents, and the children—it requires the development of realistic expectations for relationship.

I was so excited to be married! I could not believe I found the perfect man, Jermaine, who was so willing to father my two children from a previous marriage. Although I was successful and independent during my years as a single mom, I found it difficult to bring up concerns in my marriage. I was afraid to talk with Jermaine about anything that was bothering me, thinking that it would make him feel stressed and question his decision to marry me.

This fear caused me to lose my voice, sacrificing my need to express my feelings and hypervigilant to keep the peace. When I felt hurt by Jermaine, I would remind myself how lucky I was to have a man willing to support me and my kids. I was even able to quit work and stay at home with the kids, which was a lifelong dream for me.

Jermaine also struggled and felt alone in his new role as a stepparent. When we got married, we had two more kids and he felt a stronger bond with his biological kids. Jermaine wrestled with guilt and shame because he didn't love all four kids the same. When my boys would come home from a weekend with their dad, they would talk about all the things he bought them and how much fun they had. Jermaine began to feel resentful toward the boys. He was working overtime to support all of us. Jermaine sacrificed things he wanted to do for himself, putting our needs first. When he heard the boys idolize their dad, who popped in and out of their life as he pleased, Jermaine felt very unappreciated.

I recognized that something needed to change. My family, all of us, need to learn how to be a blended family. Through an eight-week blended family class, we learned how to navigate many of the common problems found in blended families: bio parenting vs. stepparenting; loving the kids differently; loving the parents differently; blended siblings; minimizing guilt and shame; and there's no such thing as a perfect family.

This was liberating for the entire family. We learned how to navigate our blended family relationships. Jermaine, who often felt like an outsider, discovered how to effectively parent and stepparent his kids. I regained my voice, not just with

---

[158] Eagan, C. (2004). *Attachment and Divorce: Family Consequences.* Rochester Institute of Technology. Retrieved from http://www.personalityresearch.org/papers/eagan.html.

Jermaine, but with the kids, too, discovering the positive effects of healthy communication. The kids learned how to be in relationship with all their parents, creating a safe place where it was okay to love their bio parents and stepparents differently. Together, our family was learning how to cultivate a secure attachment, positively affecting our relationship and family dynamic.

Latisha

What factors created a disconnect in this blended family?

In what ways will these positive changes affect this family: the bio parents, the stepparents, and the kids?

As we pursue lifelong healing, we begin to recognize that change is possible. Our identity no longer reflects our trauma, pain, and shame. We don't have to remain in isolation. We can come out of the shadows. We can learn how to create healthy relationships with God and others. Once we grab hold of the fact that our identity is in Christ alone, anything is possible!

> *Therefore, if anyone is in Christ, the new creation has come:*
> *The old has gone, the new is here!*
>
> **2 CORINTHIANS 5:17**

Despite our past and the way we learned to attach to others, we can learn a healthy attachment style. We can learn to be securely attached.[159] What does that look like? People who are securely attached exhibit some or all of the following behaviors in relationship. They:

- have a stable and positive emotional bond with others.
- cultivate relationships through caring, support, and understanding.
- see themselves as friendly, easy-going, and likeable.
- think others are reliable, trustworthy, and well-intentioned.
- have a mutually healthy give and take relationship versus a one-way relationship.
- do not fear emotional closeness or abandonment.

Put a check mark next to any of these behaviors that are or have been present in your relationships.

Put an "X" next to any of these behaviors you would like to develop in relationships.

Of the behaviors you marked with an "X," which one do you want to start working on in your current relationships? Why? What is your plan to implement this new behavior?

---

[159] Ibid.

We want to feel securely attached. We want to learn a better way to maintain relationship without experiencing fear, shame, and isolation. If we didn't learn to be securely attached in childhood, or if it was dismantled by unhealthy relationships, it will take time and intention to gain ground in this area. We need to be patient and give ourselves grace as we learn to apply this in our lives.

As we continue to develop health in our relationship with God and others, it becomes insatiable. As we gain health in certain areas of our life, the more we want to experience health in all areas of our life.

REDEFINING SELF-ESTEEM

Self-esteem—having confidence in one's own worth or abilities—is a curious thing. To some extent, self-esteem is a term used to describe a person's sense of self-worth or value.[160] However, as we have learned, many of us who struggle with managing love, sex, and relationships are afflicted with low self-esteem. We lack confidence in ourselves and our abilities. We focus on our weaknesses, believing everyone else is better than us. We carry deep feelings of fear, shame, and worthlessness. To make matters worse, we don't believe others when they compliment or praise us in any way.

When someone compliments you, what is your normal response?

____

____

____

____

____

We become our own worst enemy. We create a vicious cycle of thoughts, feelings, and behaviors that perpetuate our worthlessness. We use relationships to determine our value. If our relationships last, we are worthwhile—we are loved. If our relationships fail, our core beliefs are confirmed—we are not worth having.

Somewhere in between, we create a cycle that reinforces this process. We are in a relationship. We put everything into the relationship, so we will feel loved and appreciated. When met with disapproval—real or perceived—we become fearful that someone has discovered our worthlessness. We try harder to please the other, often compromising or sacrificing our personal values. When this fails, we become desperate and needy, as if the core of who we are hangs on the acceptance or rejection from another person. When the relationship fails—and it usually does—we are left alone with ourselves.

[160] Cherry, K. (2017). *What Exactly Is Self-Esteem? Signs of healthy and low self-esteem*. Retrieved from www.verywellmind.com/what-is-self-esteem-2795868.

Here's the truth: our self-esteem cannot come from us. As we have learned, our identity is found in Christ. Our core beliefs must align with our identity. When these two aspects of our life are out of balance, or based on self-perception, we remain stuck in our unhealthy and addictive behaviors, looking for external definitions of our worth. We will continue to struggle with our self-esteem until we realize that what we need is God-esteem.[161] We were created with inherent worth, but a lack of nurture changed our self-perception. We need the Holy Spirit to speak truth into our lives and define us through God's grace. We need to replace our view of ourselves—our poor self-esteem—with God's view of us. God knows us at our core. He created each of us with unique gifts and abilities so that we could serve Him and others in relationship.

Raising awareness of our God-given gifts and abilities is a great place to start when building God-esteem.

Every good and perfect gift is from above, coming down from the Father of the heavenly lights, who does not change like shifting shadows.

JAMES 1:17

Use the following table to identify the different character qualities, abilities, and talents God has given you. If you can't think of any on your own, ask your spouse, friends, and family members. You can simply say, "What unique gifts or abilities do you think God has given me?"

For each God-given gift and ability you list, take a few minutes and visualize what you see God saying about you. Who does God say you are? How has your identity in Christ been shaped by your gifts and abilities?

Then, for each entry listed, find a scripture that reinforces this gifting from God. You may discover that some of your favorite scriptures align with your area of gifting. If nothing comes to mind, be patient. As you spend time with Him, meditating on His Word, pray and ask God to give you insight into what He wants you to hear. You may also want to look back at previous lessons for scriptures that provoked an emotional response or had special meaning.

---

[161] Wiles, J. (2018). *Self-Esteem or God-Esteem*. KingdomWorks Studios. Retrieved from https://conquerseries.com/self-esteem-or-god-esteem/.

GOD-GIVEN GIFTS AND ABILITIES	VISUALIZE: WHO DOES GOD SAY YOU ARE?	SCRIPTURE?
I am kind and accepting of others.	God says I am His daughter, created with a soft heart for others. I am able to reflect His love for them through my actions.	Therefore, as God's chosen people, holy and dearly loved, clothe yourselves with compassion, kindness, humility, gentleness and patience. **COLOSSIANS 3:12**
I like helping others.	God says He made me others-oriented, giving me a willing and helpful attitude toward others.	Let each of you look not only to his own interests, but also to the interests of others. **PHILIPPIANS 2:4**

Based on the previous exercise, in what ways have you discovered God-esteem?

God loves us and wants relationship with us. He wants us to see ourselves the way He sees us: as His beloved daughters. Our unique strengths and abilities are gifts from God—His continued blessing and a reminder of His grace in our lives. May we become ever mindful and aware of God's blessings in our life.

Looking Ahead

Complete the FASTER Scale, Group Check-in, Self-Care lesson, Thoughts/Feelings Awareness Log, and Change & Growth Analysis in your *Unraveled: Weekly Tools* before the next group meeting.

chapter eleven

THE REAL ME

LESSON 1: TAKING OFF THE MASKS

We have come a long way. We have identified new ways to challenge our unhealthy thoughts and replace them with new thoughts, using scripture and God's personal promises to us. Through the use of the FASTER Scale and other weekly tools, we are taking a proactive approach to recognizing when we are headed for relapse and practically intervening to get back to restoration. Every day we are learning what it means to live in health—we are creating our new identity.

At this point, some of us may finally feel like we are gaining sobriety in our lives: returning to a normal state of health, mind, and strength. Some of us may feel like we are in recovery, moving past sobriety and regaining control of something that was lost. We are beginning to recognize "the real me."

Early on in this process we identified the masks that were created by our past pain, trauma, and brokenness. Over the past several months, we have worked to set aside the masks that protected us and kept us safe, replacing them with healthy boundaries. As we have learned the value of healthy boundaries and behaviors, our need for authentic living has become more obvious. We want to fully embrace life without wearing masks, but fear it at the same time. Will we ever reach a point when we can live a mask-free life?

I have been in recovery for seven years. I continue to attend a weekly support group and have served as a leader or co-leader over the years. I enjoy helping women who struggle with love, sex, and relationship addictions discover what it looks like to live out their new-found health: to live life genuinely.

I constantly encourage the women in my group, saying, "This is a process. Lasting change takes time and intention. You can do this—be brave." It helps that I have my own story, my own struggle, to share with the other women. I know what it feels like to live life from behind a mask—masks worn to feel safe and loved, to cover guilt and shame, to manipulate others, and hide my true identity.

As I processed my past pain and trauma, I was able to put healthy boundaries in place to help me navigate healthy relationships. I have worked diligently to restore my internal boundaries, which shape my self-perception, self-talk, and self-esteem, knowing that my true identity comes from Christ. I no longer wear a mask—or multiple masks—portraying who I think others would like or accept more than the real me.

I have learned the importance of external boundaries and how they guard my proximity to others, how I physically interact with others, and how I communicate. I no longer hide behind a "they will think I'm weird" mask. For example, I only hug my close friends, not people I meet for the first time. I have learned that physical contact with some people—hugging people I really doesn't know—creates a flood of anxiety and fear, which causes me to seek isolation and return to unhealthy behaviors. I am now equipped to deal with these situations with confidence.

Just last week, I bumped into my friend Carol at Barnes & Noble. Carol was with her brother Jed, who was visiting from out of town. I know Carol is a "huggy" person and so is her family. Because I am friends with Carol, I hugged my friend. When Jed, basically a stranger, moved like he was also going to hug me, I put out my hand and said, "Let me shake your hand. It's a pleasure to finally meet you. I've heard so much about you!" It was appropriate, intentional, and reinforced my external boundaries.

After experiencing a divorce and several failed relationship, I took time off from dating during my first year of recovery. I recognized that I needed to pursue healing with a holistic approach: physically, mentally, emotionally, spiritually, and sexually.

Now, I have a whole new perspective on dating. With healthy boundaries in place, I am able to remain objective about my feelings and am not preoccupied or fantasizing about physical expectations. I am able to explore the personality, interests, and values of this new acquaintance in a healthy way. During the date, I am present and not worrying if there is going to be a second date. If there is only one date, I do not interpret it as rejection.

If tempted to put on a mask for protection or to hide my true identity, I use the tools I have learned in recovery to keep me in a healthy mindset. I am confident that God will bring along the right relationship in His time.

Leah

What part of Leah's story do you relate to most?

______

______

______

______

______

______

______

In what ways did Leah exchange unhealthy masks for healthy boundaries?

____
____
____
____
____
____

As you continue to move toward health, what unhealthy masks have you replaced with healthy boundaries?

____
____
____
____
____

What unhealthy mask do you still wear that needs to be replaced with healthy boundaries? What is the double bind you struggle with that keeps the mask in place?

____
____
____
____
____
____

DEVELOPING MY COMMUNICATION STYLE

Learning how to communicate well is an important step on the path toward healing. As we discovered in chapter 7, lesson 3, the art of communication—the process of sending and receiving of information—can be difficult, especially for those of us who struggle with managing relationships. However, it is never too late to learn how to effectively use our words in relationships. Many of our relational issues can be resolved by changing the way we communicate.

As we work to develop an assertive style of communication, we need to be intentional about putting new healthy behaviors in place. Too often, when we feel as though we don't have a voice—that our words fall on deaf ears—or we have learned to use our words to manipulate and control others, it can be challenging to practice a new method of communication. We need to make sure we are using our words to speak truth and life into our relationships.

Here are a few things to keep in mind when practicing a healthy and assertive communication style.

Pause before responding. It is no secret that many of us who struggle with managing relationships wear our emotions on our sleeve. When feeling overwhelmed, stressed, or exasperated, we let our emotions lead the way. Without giving it a second thought—literally, in the moment—everything we're feeling comes spewing out of our mouths and lands on the other person. This is not our intent, but it happens because we have not learned a healthy method of self-control in this area. We do not want to continue to be reckless with our words.

If we can learn to pause before responding, take a few seconds to collect our thoughts so that we are not so emotionally charged, we will be more effective at communicating what needs to be said in an effective manner. At times, it may be useful to count for three to five seconds (silently to yourself) before responding.

The words of the reckless pierce like swords, but the tongue of the wise brings healing.

PROVERBS 12:18

Take a deep breath. We have discussed the health benefits that come from taking time out of our day to practice relaxed breathing, but this is not the same thing. When we feel dismissed or overrun in conversations, it can bring out the worst in us. In a split second, we become the worst version of ourselves—we resort to yelling or using profanity toward those around us. This is not an effective form of communication.

In the heat of the moment, when we take a deep breath in preparation for what is going to be the next thing out of our mouth, what are we breathing in? Is it our pain? Our right to be heard? Our pride? Probably. But what if we thought of it this way: when we take a deep breath, we are filling our lungs with the Holy Spirit. As Christ followers, we have access to His Spirit anytime. As we develop healthy communication skills, why not use this to our advantage? Even when it comes to the way we communicate with others, we can choose, in the moment, to be the best version of ourselves. We need to continue to work toward developing a mindset for healing.

The heart of the godly thinks carefully before speaking; the mouth of the wicked overflows with evil words.

PROVERBS 15:28 NLT

The use of curse words. Some of us may have been raised in an environment where cussing or the use of profanity was acceptable behavior. Even if we did not grow up in this environment, we all have been faced with this choice. In the moment—when we stub our toe, get cutoff by another driver, or received an unexpected text—our emotions get the best of us and we respond by swearing.

What we don't often recognize it that using curse words is a defense mechanism. It is a way of avoiding our true feelings of pain, anger, or disappointment. We hide our feelings because we feel vulnerable and protect ourselves with cussing. It may empower us in the moment, but we are often still left with our true feelings. We need to develop a healthy way to acknowledge and express how we feel.

> *Out of the same mouth come praise and cursing.*
> *My brothers and sisters, this should not be.*
>
> **JAMES 3:10**

We can't take it back. Many of us have learned this the hard way. Once our words leave our mouth, we cannot take them back. We cannot undo the damage that is done by our hurtful words. Even if we were right and justified in saying what we said, could we have chosen a different method of communication to express how we were feeling? We may apologize and work to restore the relationship, but the thoughts and feelings that our words created for the other person cannot be undone.

This is a tricky area of communication. We need to be vigilant and acutely aware of how our words and methods of communication contribute to cultivating healthy relationships or disrupt and ruin relationships. We need to find the balance between saying what needs to be said—so we continue to move toward health—and saying it in a way to brings life to the relationship.

> *The tongue can bring death or life;*
> *those who love to talk will reap the consequences.*
>
> **PROVERBS 18:21 NLT**

Use I-statements.[162] The words we use in communication can determine the direction of the conversation. Our words can be divisive, causing others to feel under attack and defensive, or our words can express our needs and expectations in a healthy way. It is amazing how quickly a conversation can go sideways, not because our point of view is wrong, but simply because of the way we are communicating.

Using I-statements is an effective method for keeping the conversation about our feelings and expectations: "I feel unappreciated when I have worked so hard to keep our home clean and you leave your dirty socks on the living room floor." When having

---

[162] Riggenbach, J. (2013). *The CBT Toolbox: A Workbook for Clients and Clinicians*. Eau Claire, WI: PESI Publishing and Media.

difficult conversations, it is easy to resort to placing blame on others: "You obviously don't appreciate all the work I do around here!" This is not helpful when the goal is to bring about health and restoration in relationship.

> *Those who guard their mouths and their tongues*
> *keep themselves from calamity.*
>
> **PROVERBS 21:23 NIV**

Developing a healthy form of communication takes time and intention. This week, we are going to practice using I-statements in communication. To start, think of a current problem or issue in an important relationship. You can choose problems within one relationship or problems in various relationships. Use the following cards to work through the process of developing a healthy communication style.

EXAMPLE:

RELATIONSHIP WITH...	I FELT...
My husband, Derek	Unappreciated. Disrespected. Isolated. Resentful. Guilt. Angry. Alone.

CURRENT PROBLEM	WHAT I WANT TO SAY
He schedules evenings out with friends, without checking with me first, and when I've been home with the kids all week.	You totally take me for granted! I'm home raising YOUR kids and you don't even help! You don't appreciate the work I do with the kids all day! If anyone should be going out with friends, it should be me! I've earned it!

I-STATEMENTS
I feel unappreciated when you make evening plans and fail to include me in that decision. When I'm home with the kids all week, I begin to feel overwhelmed, isolated, and alone. I feel resentful and guilty at the same time. I could really use your help with the kids in the evenings. I know we both work really hard. I would love to work together to find a way that we can both experience an evening out with friends or plan weekly date nights.

EXAMPLE:

RELATIONSHIP WITH…	I FELT…
Roommate, Chelsea	Ignored. Fearful. Worried. Unimportant. Betrayed. Angry. Disappointed. Unsafe.

CURRENT PROBLEM	WHAT I WANT TO SAY
She invited a bunch of people to a party at our house, a house we rent from my parents. There were minors drinking. They broke a window and other household items. A fight broke out and the neighbors called the police. She was hungover and didn't help clean up the mess.	How could you do this? You didn't know half the people that were here, but you let them into our house! They destroyed the place! They broke a window, which YOU'RE paying for! You should be thankful the police didn't show up! They would have taken you to jail and rightfully so! I can't believe you would treat me this way! Get out!

I-STATEMENTS
I feel disappointed about what happened at the party. I felt worried and fearful by the amount of strangers that were in our home. I felt very unsafe. I feel that our relationship is not important to you. I feel a sense of betrayal in the way my parents' home was treated. I felt ignored when the police were called and I was trying to get everyone to leave peacefully. I would like to work together to make sure this type of thing doesn't happen again.

RELATIONSHIP WITH...	I FELT...

CURRENT PROBLEM	WHAT I WANT TO SAY

I-STATEMENTS

RELATIONSHIP WITH...	I FELT...

CURRENT PROBLEM	WHAT I WANT TO SAY

I-STATEMENTS

RELATIONSHIP WITH…	I FELT…

CURRENT PROBLEM	WHAT I WANT TO SAY

I-STATEMENTS

If developing a healthy communication style is a struggle for you, pray that God will help you guard your tongue.

Set a guard over my mouth, Lord; keep watch over the door of my lips.

PSALM 141:3 NIV

Looking Ahead

Complete the FASTER Scale, Group Check-in, Self-Care lesson, Thoughts/Feelings Awareness Log, and Change & Growth Analysis in your *Unraveled: Weekly Tools* before the next group meeting.

LESSON 2: HEALTHY SEXUALITY

When it comes to our sexuality, it can be challenging to identify what healthy sexuality looks like. Socially, we are bombarded by mixed messages from TV, films, and popular culture. We get the impression we should be able to have sex wherever, whenever, and with whomever we choose with no consequences. However, from our church, we may hear that we should never even think about sex, much less enjoy it. Neither of these approaches are biblical. We are sexual beings. God created us to have a sexual identity. Somewhere along the line, we humans really mess up this whole concept.

Our sexuality is shaped by many things but not just our biology. It is learned through relationship and experience. Growing up, we may have experienced an environment that encouraged healthy boundaries and we were given authority over our body, which made us feel safe, protected, and confident with our physical identity. However, when we experience abuse, neglect, and abandonment, this negatively affects our boundaries, disrupting our sexual and self-perception. Boundary violations include:

- Emotional: "Stop crying! You're such a baby!"
- Intellectual: "You are so stupid!"
- Physical: slapping or pinching
- Sexual: inappropriate touch or words

Our sexual perception is unique to us. If we have a healthy sense of our value and worth—a balanced and accurate self-esteem—our internal boundaries protect our sexual perception. When our self-perception is broken—when our sense of value and worth is unhealthy—it impacts and shapes our sexual perception. We believe the lies:

- "I'm pretty, but not as pretty as..."
- "I will only get a boyfriend if I..."
- "If I'm skinny, I will be loved."
- "I have to be porn-ready for relationships."
- "My husband will leave me for someone else if I'm not..."
- "I have to dress a certain way to feel sexy."
- "I fantasize that I am someone else to orgasm during sex with my husband."

- "I have to get free from this addiction before anyone will love me."
- "I have to act like someone else just to get a guy to notice me."

What negative messages have contributed to your view of sexuality?

Our sexuality is complex. As women, our view of healthy sexuality becomes complicated by body image issues, comparing ourselves to other women, and the shame we hold on to as a result of our sexual experiences. It's no wonder we have difficulty understanding and experiencing healthy sexuality.

When you think of healthy sexuality, what thoughts, feelings, and behaviors come to mind?

I am very involved in church and mentor other women. I am a worship leader, volunteer at women's ministry events, have the perfect marriage, well-behaved kids, and am extremely kind to everyone. However, I have a secret. Every day, I live under a cloud of shame from something that happened when I was a little girl.

When I was eight years old, I started to explore what it would be like to kiss someone. It started out as simple curiosity, but quickly grew into something I couldn't stop. I began by making out with my teddy bear, pretending it was a boy I liked from school. One day when my neighbor friend Kate was over, I told Kate we should kiss. We kissed a few times, and then wanted to kiss again with the lights off and longer. This continued for several months. Eventually we tried experimenting in other sexual ways and included other neighbor girls as well. I knew it was wrong, but the excitement and the shame drove me to want it more. A couple years went by and Kate moved away. Eventually I stopped seeing the other girls in the neighborhood. Kate held all our friends together and with her gone, it wasn't the same.

After Kate moved, I felt very guilty about everything I had done and what I made the other girls do too. I felt flawed. I never wanted anyone to find out what I did with my friends. The thought of anyone knowing became my worst fear. I buried this secret deep inside and carried the guilt with me every day. My anxiety grew over the years, but on the outside, I worked hard to make sure it looked like I had it all together.

I may have made my life look great, but the shame from my early sexual experiences with other girls was driving my perfectionist behavior. It had been more than 30 years, but I still worried about someone finding out or running into one of those neighbor girls from my past. To make matters worse, I never told my husband about it. My own sexuality was so tainted by shame, I constantly struggled to sexually connect with my husband. It didn't matter how much I tried to forget it. Unless I took the time to process and deal with the guilt and shame, I would not be able to experience healthy sexuality.

Beth

What part of Beth's story do you resonate with most?

____

____

____

____

If Beth were your friend and confided in you about her secret, what step toward healing would you recommend for Beth?

____

____

____

____

Due to the very nature of our sexual development and curiosity, many of us have similar sexual experiences from our childhood. How do we know if the experience was an innocent childhood encounter or something that we still need to process?

____

____

____

____

For those of us who are parents, what thoughts and feelings does this stir up when thinking about our children?

____

____

____

____

____

____

In practical terms, what does it mean for us to develop a mindset for healthy sexuality? What does this look like on a daily basis? What does this look like behaviorally?

As women, the development of our sexuality is important. Whether we are married or single, we have to learn what it means to live out our sexuality in a healthy way. For many single women with previous sexual experiences through masturbation or encounters with others, we need to discover what it means to live as sexual beings as God intended and not filled with shame and regret, but fueled with the knowledge that our sexuality was created by God for good. For married women, many of us carry our shame and regret into the marriage, unable to recognize how our self-perception and sexual identity inhibit true connection with our spouse.

I love having sex with my husband and regularly reach orgasm during sex. Before having sex I heard about so many women who couldn't orgasm and I knew that wouldn't be a problem for me. Truthfully, I was proud to marry as a virgin who didn't have a problem in the orgasm department. For several years, I figured out the secret to successful orgasm by masturbating a couple times a week but that wasn't a big deal, right?

In my dating history, I was close but never gave into sex before marriage. Instead, I would get intimately physical with my boyfriends without crossing "the line" and then masturbate when I was alone. I never looked at porn: instead, I allowed my mind to wander into the world of fantasy where I took on the role of a sexy woman dressed in skimpy clothes, dominating the man I was with. The men in my fantasies would change from time to time, but what really turned me on was thinking about how sexy I looked. Although my fantasy may not have been influenced by porn, my perception of what a woman should look like during sex was heavily skewed by images I saw in movies, store catalogs, and social media.

Fast forward ten years after our wedding night. We had "good sex" for ten years and I never had a problem with masturbation after we got married. Most of the guilt and shame I had about my masturbation issues were in the past. Since I didn't masturbate after getting married, it seemed like a non-issue. However, while having sex with my husband, my mind would wander deep into the same exact thoughts I had when I used to masturbate. Every...single...time. In fact, if I didn't let my mind wander into my fantasy world, I knew I wouldn't reach orgasm. If my fantasy got interrupted, it wouldn't happen either.

In those ten years of having sex a couple times a week, I never once orgasmed without escaping into my fantasy world where I was a sex idol. My brain was responding to my fantasy rather than the amazing reality that was right in front of me. I was incapable of experiencing real, healthy sexual intimacy with my husband and had absolutely no idea what I was missing.

Kora

Why do you think Kora was unaware of what was happening in her mind?

____

____

____

____

____

What do you think Kora's husband thought about her behavior during sex? Do you think he knew what was going on in her head?

____

____

____

____

____

How can you relate to the struggle with fantasy that Kora experienced?

____

____

____

____

____

____

When it comes to living out our sexuality in a healthy way, we have to be intentional. We have to understand and identify how our thoughts, feelings, and behaviors contribute to our sexual health. Are we consciously choosing to move toward healthy sexuality or are we constantly pulled back into unhealthy sexual behaviors? Once we have developed this awareness, we can begin to replace our unhealthy sexual behaviors with new behaviors that promote a holistic approach toward healing physically, mentally, emotionally, and spiritually. Remember, it's not enough that we simply stop an unwanted behavior—we have to replace the behavior with something that will keep us on the path toward lifelong healing.

The following table describes many of the differences between unhealthy sexuality and healthy sexuality.[163]

UNHEALTHY SEXUALITY	HEALTHY SEXUALITY
• Degrades & shames	• Respectful
• Demanding & obligatory	• Fun & exciting
• Victimizes & exploits	• Victimless
• Lacks emotional attachment	• Intimate
• Needs dominated by one	• Mutuality in needs expressed
• Built on dishonesty	• Trust is foundational
• Unsafe, creating fear	• Safe
• Serves to medicate pain	• Serves to connect emotionally
• Meets self-focused needs	• Creates warmth & oneness
• Compromises values & beliefs	• Deepens values & beliefs
• Reflects a double life	• Authentic

In each column above, which behaviors do you resonate with most? Why?

____

____

____

____

____

____

[163] Roberts, D. (2010). *Pure Desire for Women: Eight Pillars to Freedom from love addiction & sexual issues*. Gresham, OR: Pure Desire Ministries International.

Briefly describe a time when your behaviors or the behaviors of another reflected unhealthy sexuality in the relationship. What was the outcome of that experience?

Briefly describe a time when your behaviors or the behaviors of another reflected healthy sexuality in the relationship. What was the outcome of that experience?

We have to be intentional about our pursuit of healthy sexuality. From the previous chart, in what area do you want to improve your approach to healthy sexuality? What is that going to look like for you?

ACKNOWLEDGING MY NEEDS

All of us have needs: physically, mentally, emotionally, and spiritually. However, when we have experienced deprivation in these areas, it often leads us to create distorted beliefs that make us feel we are undeserving.[164] Those of us who struggle with relationships often miss the fact that healthy relationships are founded on reciprocal interaction—both individuals giving and receiving. In fact, because we desperately seek love and acceptance, we become quite skilled at giving in relationships, but not as comfortable receiving in relationship.

Receiving in relationship requires asking for help. Many of us who struggle with love, sex, and relationship issues were raised in an environment where asking for help was a sign of weakness. It was risky. It left us open to painful experiences. We learned that having needs was unacceptable. In many ways, this left us unable to recognize our own needs, let alone how to get our needs met.

As we continue to learn how to be in relationship with others, it's important to develop a realistic expectation of our needs. Here are a few examples of common needs.

Physical: Water, food, clothing, shelter, exercise, sleep

Mental: Quality time with others, learning new things, quiet time alone

Emotional: Feeling safe, cared for, and loved; finding meaning in life

Spiritual: Quality time with God, reading the Bible, going to church, finding purpose

Identifying and acknowledging our needs can become challenging, especially if we cannot separate the difference between our wants and needs. Most of us would agree that getting coffee at our favorite local coffee shop would most often fall into our wants category. However, suppose we are having a difficult week, and when texting a friend about it, she suggests we meet for coffee to talk. Realistically, we can admit that quality time with a friend meets our mental need, but meeting at our favorite coffee shop is also going to meet the emotional need of feeling cared for in a difficult time.

As we work to understand what health looks like for us, we first must raise an awareness to our basic needs, as well as recognize the needs that may be uniquely ours.

---

[164] Riggenbach, J. (2013). *The CBT Toolbox: A Workbook for Clients and Clinicians*. Eau Claire, WI: PESI Publishing and Media.

This week, use the following table to identify some of your needs. Be specific. Also determine whether the need is physical, mental, emotional, and/or spiritual. You may see some overlap in the type of need being met.

MY NEEDS	TYPE OF NEED

Raising an awareness to our needs is a positive step on our path toward lifelong health. As we develop a realistic perspective surrounding our needs, it's important to recognize that we can always look to our heavenly Father and He will meet our needs.

> *"So don't worry about these things, saying, 'What will we eat? What will we drink? What will we wear?' [32]These things dominate the thoughts of unbelievers, but your heavenly Father already knows all your needs. [33]Seek the Kingdom of God above all else, and live righteously, and he will give you everything you need."*
>
> **MATTHEW 6:31-33 NLT**

Looking Ahead

Complete the FASTER Scale, Group Check-in, Self-Care lesson, Thoughts/Feelings Awareness Log, and Change & Growth Analysis in your *Unraveled: Weekly Tools* before the next group meeting.

LESSON 3: INTIMACY

What is intimacy? In today's culture, this word has become synonymous with sex. We often hear people say, "We were intimate," meaning that they had sexual intercourse. Many people have sexual intercourse and don't have intimacy. Many people have intimate relationships with others, but not sexual relationships with them. So why is this concept of intimacy so challenging?

In many ways, intimacy describes a closeness to another person with whom we feel warmth and affection. We have a unique attachment to them, unlike most of our relationships. We are confident in the relationship. We can be ourselves—the good, the bad, and the ugly—without the fear of judgment or rejection. We are loved and accepted. We are safe.

Intimacy is a result of first feeling secure in our own self-worth. From this position of security we share our self, our emotions, our intellect, our mind and, at times, our bodies. We can, in our own security, reveal ourselves in safety—and we receive this reality from another without judgment, allowing them to feel their own emotions without intervention. The result of this type of appropriate giving and receiving is intimacy.

My husband turned his back so I quickly changed out of my clothes and into pajamas without him seeing me. We have been married five years, but I still feel uncomfortable every time I am changing around him. When we are having sex, I really try to be a little more relaxed, but it is challenging for me to be naked. In the midst of having sex, I often feel self-conscious, tensing up all over, and my mind begins racing to other places. I start making the grocery list and thinking about my presentation at work the next day. Needless to say, sex is not something I enjoy; I try to have a good attitude about it and have sex with my husband at least once a week. I often wonder, "What is wrong with me? Why can't I enjoy sex with my husband like I am supposed to?"

I grew up in a very strict Christian home. My father was a pastor and talking about sex in my home was a huge taboo topic. If we were watching a movie as a family and any scenes came up with kissing or other forms of appropriate affection, my father would immediately fast forward the scene, saying, "We don't need to see that." If it was anything more than kissing, my father just skipped over the scene without saying a word. When I turned 14, my parents handed me a little a booklet that talked about sex and said, "You should probably read this at some point." I read the booklet and felt so much shame reading it. My parents probably had good intentions, but the way they chose to approach the topic of sex created an extremely shame-filled environment.

I steered clear of boys until I met my husband in college. We kissed a little while dating, but tried to maintain good physical boundaries before marriage. Once we got engaged and with our wedding night approaching, I began to think more about sex. I wanted to be excited about sex, but my whole childhood did not set me up for healthy sexual intimacy with my husband. My body would become so turned off physically, mentally, and emotionally every time we had sex. Even the thought of sex made me tense. It left me questioning over and over, "What is wrong with me?"

Even more confusing is that outside of the bedroom, we are especially close and everything else in our marriage is great! I can't help but wonder if we could experience more connection with a better sexual relationship.

Heidi

In what ways did Heidi's family of origin contribute to her negative and confusing perspective about sex?

____

____

____

____

____

Why did Heidi struggle with being naked in front of her husband?

____

____

____

____

____

If you were Heidi's friend, what suggestions and encouragement would you offer her regarding her intimacy issues?

____

____

____

____

____

PERSONALIZING INTIMACY

Intimacy can be a challenging concept to grasp. In our modern culture, intimacy often refers to sex, but it is really so much more. In so many ways, intimacy is a social construct. It is not based on a specific, sustainable definition, but one that is more fluid, continuously changing based on subjective human interaction.

Historically, the word intimacy has carried several interesting meanings.[165]

- Collaboration with at least one other person
- Existing in the thought and affection of another
- A level of sexual involvement: greater sexual involvement=greater intimacy
- Correlated with the health and happiness of the relationship
- The act of revealing personal information to others
- A very special instance of self-disclosure
- The emotional bonding individuals feel toward one another

Even still, the meaning of intimacy and its role in relationship continues to change. There is much debate on whether intimacy is something confined to a sexual relationship or if intimacy can possibly exist in a variety of relationships. One thing is clear: intimacy refers to a mutual satisfaction of needs and a closeness to another human being on a variety of levels.

For the purpose of this exercise, we're going to focus on the relationship of couples. Intimacy in relationship is often observed on several levels.[166]

Emotional intimacy: experiencing a closeness of feelings

Social intimacy: the experience of having common friends and similarities in social networks

Intellectual intimacy: the experience of sharing ideas

Sexual intimacy: the experience of sharing general affection and/or sexual activity

Recreational intimacy: shared experiences of interests in hobbies, mutual participation in sporting events

Think of intimacy as a process: something that occurs over time and never reaches completion. Too often, couples think they have arrived at intimacy. With this mindset, they fail to maintain or improve the level of intimacy in their relationship. In other cases, since intimacy carries an individual level of subjectivity, many couples differ on their expectation of intimacy in the relationship. There is no single way to measure the

---

[165] Schaefer, M.T. & Olson, D.H. (1981). Assessing intimacy: The PAIR Inventory. *Journal of Marital and Family Therapy*, 1, 47-60.

[166] Ibid.

acceptable or ideal degree of intimacy in any relationship; however, there is a way to assess the realized and expected level of intimacy in a relationship.

The PAIR Inventory—Personal Assessment of Intimacy in Relationships—is used to gather information on five types of intimacy in a relationship. Individuals, either dating or married, evaluate the relationship based on their current perception (realized), and also based on what they would like the relationship to be (expected).

Although the score may have meaning worth exploring, the PAIR Inventory is not intended to simply reveal a score within each category of intimacy. It is most effective in identifying differences in the *realized* and *expected* levels of intimacy a couple may have for the relationship. Ideally, each partner would fill out the inventory twice: first indicating how the relationship "is now" and then as they would "like it to be." From the information gathered, a scored profile is plotted on a graph, providing a visual representation of the couple's realized and expected levels of intimacy.

To get the best results from this assessment, it is ideal to involve our partners in this exercise. This can be especially challenging when our relationships are stressed. As hard as it is, be brave. Including our partners in this exercise will enhance what we can learn from it. We have done the hard work for months and have experienced change in ourselves and those around us. Using this exercise will teach us and our partners how we can become more intimate in our relationship.

When using this inventory, here are a couple things to keep in mind: this is a self-assessment based on individual *feelings*. There are no right or wrong answers. **It is important to rate each statement honestly based on your perception.** At its core, this inventory is giving insight to the current levels of intimacy in the relationship, as well as providing areas of intimacy for the couple to improve.

The five-point scale ranges from "strongly disagree" to "strongly agree." When reading each statement, decide how well the statement describes your relationship. It may be helpful to think of each statement in the context of "does not describe me/my relationship" (strongly disagree) or "describes me/my relationship" (strongly agree).

Within the context of this workbook, the PAIR Inventory provides a realistic view of each partner's needs and the degree to which they are being met. In many ways, it takes the "magical concept of intimacy out of the clouds of romance"[167] and puts it in a context that is useful in helping couples identify areas of strength and weakness in their relationship. It gives couples the opportunity to experience new levels of intimacy as they grow together in relationship.

Note: Many of us who struggle with relationships may not currently be in a relationship. If so, we can still use the PAIR Inventory as an insightful tool to raise awareness of the

[167] Schaefer, M.T. & Olson, D.H. (1981). Assessing intimacy: The PAIR Inventory. *Journal of Marital and Family Therapy*, 1, 47-60.

discrepancies between our perceived and expected levels of intimacy in relationship. As we continue to learn how our behaviors influence our interactions with others, this tool can shed light on the specific areas of intimacy where we may need to change and grow.

If this is the case, fill out the PAIR Inventory based on your feelings of a recent or previous relationship. Use the Intimacy Profile graph as a visual of your scores. When completed, answer the questions found on page 315.

PERSONAL ASSESSMENT OF INTIMACY IN RELATIONSHIPS (PAIR)[168]

PHASE 1:

*Rate each statement based on how **it is now** in your relationship. Write the number that corresponds with the best answer.*

1	2	3	4	5
Strongly Disagree	Disagree	Don't Know	Agree	Strongly Agree

In my relationship now...

____ **1.** My partner listens to me when I need someone to talk to.
____ **2.** We enjoy spending time with other couples.
____ **3.** I am satisfied with our sex life.
____ **4.** My partner helps me clarify my thoughts.
____ **5.** We enjoy the same recreational activities.
____ **6.** My partner has all the qualities I've ever wanted in a mate.
____ **7.** I can state my feelings without him/her getting defensive.
____ **8.** We usually "keep to ourselves."
____ **9.** I feel our sexual activity is just routine.
____ **10.** When it comes to having a serious discussion, it seems we have little in common.
____ **11.** I share in very few of my partner's interests.
____ **12.** There are times when I do not feel a great deal of love and affection for my partner.
____ **13.** I often feel distant from my partner.
____ **14.** We have very few friends in common.
____ **15.** I am able to tell my partner when I want sexual intercourse.
____ **16.** I feel "put-down" in a serious conversation with my partner.
____ **17.** We like playing together.
____ **18.** Every new thing that I have learned about my partner has pleased me.
____ **19.** My partner can really understand my hurts and joys.
____ **20.** Having time together with friends is an important part of our shared activities.
____ **21.** I "hold back" my sexual interest because my partner makes me feel uncomfortable.

[168] Ibid.

_____ **22.** I feel it is useless to discuss some things with my partner.
_____ **23.** We enjoy the out-of-doors together.
_____ **24.** My partner and I understand each other completely.
_____ **25.** I feel neglected at times by my partner.
_____ **26.** Many of my partner's closest friends are also my closest friends.
_____ **27.** Sexual expression is an essential part of our relationship.
_____ **28.** My partner frequently tries to change my ideas.
_____ **29.** We seldom find time to do fun things together.
_____ **30.** I don't think anyone could possibly be happier than my partner and I are when we're with one another.
_____ **31.** I sometimes feel lonely when we're together.
_____ **32.** My partner disapproves of some of my friends.
_____ **33.** My partner seems disinterested in sex.
_____ **34.** We have an endless number of things to talk about.
35. I think we share some of the same interests.
_____ **36.** I have some needs that are not being met by my relationship.

*Complete the following calculation to obtain your **realized** level of intimacy in each category. Add the score for each numbered statement as listed below. After calculating each category score, obtain the correlating percentage from the table below.*

EMOTIONAL INTIMACY | Add scores for 1, 7, 13, 19, 25, and 31: __________ Percentage: _______

SOCIAL INTIMACY | Add scores for 2, 8, 14, 20, 26, and 32: __________ Percentage: _______

SEXUAL INTIMACY | Add scores for 3, 9, 15, 21, 27, and 33: __________ Percentage: _______

INTELLECTUAL INTIMACY | Add scores for 4, 10, 16, 22, 28, and 34: __________ Percentage: _______

RECREATIONAL INTIMACY | Add scores for 5, 11, 17, 23, 29, and 35: __________ Percentage: _______

CONVENTIONALITY SCALE* | Add scores for 6, 12, 18, 24, 30, and 36: __________ Percentage: _______

PERCENTAGE CONVERSION TABLE

Percentage conversion: the following list indicates the corresponding percentage based on the potential inventory score. The percentages are round to the nearest whole number.

30 = 100%	25 = 83%	20 = 67%	15 = 50%	10 = 33%	5 = 17%
29 = 97%	24 = 80%	19 = 63%	14 = 47%	9 = 30%	4 = 13 %
28 = 93%	23 = 77%	18 = 60%	13 = 43%	8 = 27%	3 = 10%
27 = 90%	22 = 73%	17 = 57%	12 = 40%	7 = 23%	2 = 7%
26 = 87%	21 = 70%	16 = 53%	11 = 37%	6 = 20%	1 = 3%

**The Conventionality Scale is included and scored separately in order to assess how much the individual is attempting to create a good impression.*

PHASE 2:

Rate each statement based on how ***you would like it to be*** *in the relationship. Circle the number that corresponds with the best answer.*

1	2	3	4	5
Strongly Disagree	Disagree	Don't Know	Agree	Strongly Agree

In my relationship, I would like it if...

____ **1.** My partner listens to me when I need someone to talk to.

____ **2.** We enjoy spending time with other couples.

____ **3.** I am satisfied with our sex life.

____ **4.** My partner helps me clarify my thoughts.

____ **5.** We enjoy the same recreational activities.

____ **6.** My partner has all the qualities I've ever wanted in a mate.

____ **7.** I can state my feelings without him/her getting defensive.

____ **8.** We usually "keep to ourselves."

____ **9.** I feel our sexual activity is just routine.

____ **10.** When it comes to having a serious discussion, it seems we have little in common.

____ **11.** I share in very few of my partner's interests.

____ **12.** There are times when I do not feel a great deal of love and affection for my partner.

____ **13.** I often feel distant from my partner.

____ **14.** We have very few friends in common.

____ **15.** I am able to tell my partner when I want sexual intercourse.

____ **16.** I feel "put-down" in a serious conversation with my partner.

____ **17.** We like playing together.

____ **18.** Every new thing that I have learned about my partner has pleased me.

____ **19.** My partner can really understand my hurts and joys.

____ **20.** Having time together with friends is an important part of our shared activities.

____ **21.** I "hold back" my sexual interest because my partner makes me feel uncomfortable.

____ **22.** I feel it is useless to discuss some things with my partner.

____ **23.** We enjoy the out-of-doors together.

____ **24.** My partner and I understand each other completely.

_____ **25.** I feel neglected at times by my partner.

_____ **26.** Many of my partner's closest friends are also my closest friends.

_____ **27.** Sexual expression is an essential part of our relationship.

_____ **28.** My partner frequently tries to change my ideas.

_____ **29.** We seldom find time to do fun things together.

_____ **30.** I don't think anyone could possibly be happier than my partner and I are when we're with one another.

_____ **31.** I sometimes feel lonely when we're together.

_____ **32.** My partner disapproves of some of my friends.

_____ **33.** My partner seems disinterested in sex.

_____ **34.** We have an endless number of things to talk about.

_____ **35.** I think we share some of the same interests.

_____ **36.** I have some needs that are not being met by my relationship.

*Complete the following calculation to obtain your **expected** level of intimacy in each category. Add the score for each numbered statement as listed below. After calculating each category score, obtain the correlating percentage from the table below.*

EMOTIONAL INTIMACY | Add scores for 1, 7, 13, 19, 25, and 31: __________ Percentage: _______

SOCIAL INTIMACY | Add scores for 2, 8, 14, 20, 26, and 32: __________ Percentage: _______

SEXUAL INTIMACY | Add scores for 3, 9, 15, 21, 27, and 33: __________ Percentage: _______

INTELLECTUAL INTIMACY | Add scores for 4, 10, 16, 22, 28, and 34: __________ Percentage: _______

RECREATIONAL INTIMACY | Add scores for 5, 11, 17, 23, 29, and 35: __________ Percentage: _______

CONVENTIONALITY SCALE* | Add scores for 6, 12, 18, 24, 30, and 36: __________ Percentage: _______

PERCENTAGE CONVERSION TABLE

Percentage conversion: the following list indicates the corresponding percentage based on the potential inventory score. The percentages are round to the nearest whole number.

30 = 100%	25 = 83%	20 = 67%	15 = 50%	10 = 33%	5 = 17%
29 = 97%	24 = 80%	19 = 63%	14 = 47%	9 = 30%	4 = 13 %
28 = 93%	23 = 77%	18 = 60%	13 = 43%	8 = 27%	3 = 10%
27 = 90%	22 = 73%	17 = 57%	12 = 40%	7 = 23%	2 = 7%
26 = 87%	21 = 70%	16 = 53%	11 = 37%	6 = 20%	1 = 3%

**The Conventionality Scale is included and scored separately in order to assess how much the individual is attempting to create a good impression.*

CREATE A PROFILE

Use the percentages from each inventory to create a profile on the graph below. Make sure to use a different line designation for the results of each inventory (e.g., solid, dashed, or dotted lines; various colored pens or pencils).

Based on the numbered scale on the edge of the graph, place a dot at the appropriate percentage point for each vertical line indicating a category of intimacy. After all five dots are positioned on the graph, connect the five dots with a line. Complete this process for your inventories and for your partner's (additional PAIR Inventories are located in the appendix). See page 341 of the appendix to see what a completed graph should look like.

Mark on the graph the Conventionality Scale score for each partner, but do not include this plot point in the drawn lines. The Conventionality Scale score shows that the information can be trusted when partners score within 18 points of one another.[169] This score assesses the truthfulness of each partner's answers, indicating whether they are trying to make a good impression or "faking" their answers.

INTIMACY PROFILE OF PAIR SCORES

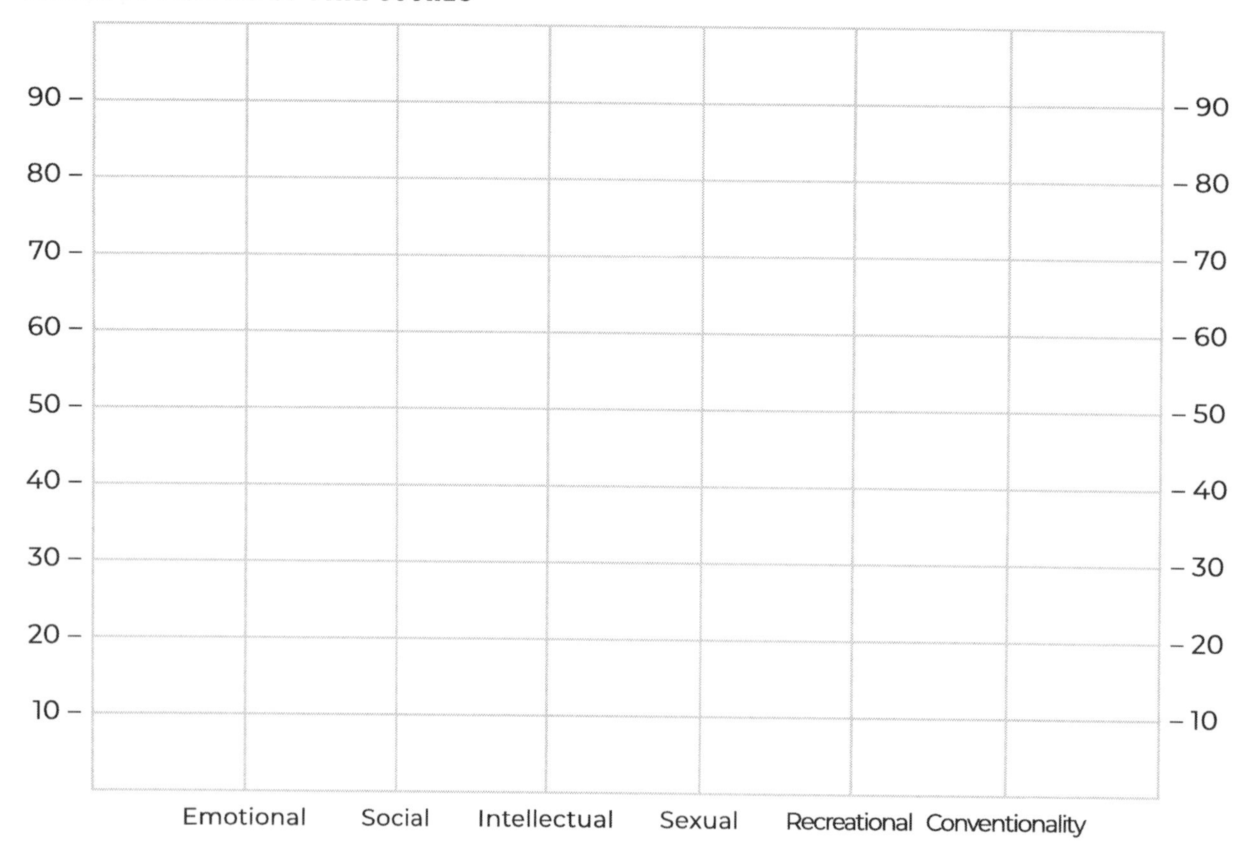

[169] Schaefer, M.T. & Olson, D.H. (1981). Assessing intimacy: The PAIR Inventory. *Journal of Marital and Family Therapy*, 1, 47-60.

When the profile is complete, use the following questions to talk through the results.

In what areas of intimacy do you recognize a moderate to severe discrepancy between your perceived and expected scores?

In what areas of intimacy do you recognize a moderate to severe discrepancy between your partner's perceived and expected scores?

In what area(s) are you and your partner closest in your perceived level of intimacy?

In what area(s) are you and your partner closest in your expected level of intimacy?

What fears surface when looking at your perceived and expected scores?

Based on your Intimacy Profile, what area of intimacy do you and your partner want to start improving? What's your next step in this process?

If you are currently single, answer the following questions based on your results from the Intimacy Profile.

- *In what areas of intimacy do you recognize a moderate to severe discrepancy between your perceived and expected scores?*

- *In what area(s) are your perceived and expected scores closest?*

- *What does this tell you about yourself and your perceptions of intimacy?*

As with many other areas of our lives, we can learn new ways to create intimacy in relationship. Raising awareness is a great step in the right direction.

Looking Ahead

Complete the FASTER Scale, Group Check-in, Self-Care lesson, Thoughts/Feelings Awareness Log, and Change & Growth Analysis in your *Unraveled: Weekly Tools* before the next group meeting.

chapter twelve

INTENTIONAL LIVING

LESSON 1: WHAT DOES RECOVERY LOOK LIKE?

Throughout this process we have used the tools in this workbook and the support of this group to help us gain a new perspective on managing love, sex, and relationships. We have done the work to keep us on the path toward lifelong healing. However, as we continue to move forward, we must consider all aspects of our health and the application of everything we have learned. What does it look like to live in recovery every day?

I have struggled with a love addiction for many years. For several months, I have worked diligently to gain health in this area through a support group. Although I experienced relapse a couple times early in the process, I have been making great strides in my recovery, recognizing the family of origin issues that influence my addictive behaviors. I have processed the shame of my unhealthy relationships and behaviors: having sexual relationships with married men, men in general, and with a couple women during college—thinking sex was an action that reflected love and acceptance.

As my group is coming to an end, I am worried that without the daily work and continued support, I will fall back into my old behaviors. I am determined to keep moving forward in my healing, committed to establishing sobriety one day at a time.

Every day, I will spend time meditating on God's Word to keep my mind focused on healing. I will focus on eating healthy foods and getting the appropriate amount of sleep at night—I know that feeling hungry and tired can contribute to relapse. I will walk with a friend three times a week because I know I won't do it on my own. I will monitor my thought-life, paying close attention to negative thoughts or feelings that might pull me toward unhealthy behaviors.

I also plan to maintain weekly contact with my accountability partners—and more frequently if I am triggered or find myself sliding into dangerous behaviors. Due to our strained relationship, every time I plan to spend time with my mother, I will call an accountability partner before and after the visit.

Recognizing the benefit of community, I have decided to join a weekly Bible study to meet other women in my church. When I feel ready and after seeking wise counsel from my accountability partners, I will return to the young adults group at church and begin to establish healthy relationships with single men.

I am on the road to recovery.

Lucy

What is Lucy doing well to maintain sobriety?

What other proactive steps would you recommend for Lucy?

Living in sobriety requires a "one day at a time" approach. We have worked hard to make sense of our past—how our pain, trauma, and life experiences contributed to our addictive behaviors—so we can freely move forward, unencumbered by the weight of our past. We need to implement healthy behaviors on a daily basis to keep us on the path toward lifelong health. We need to live intentionally.

> *Not that I have already obtained all this, or have already arrived at my goal, but I press on to take hold of that for which Christ Jesus took hold of me. [13]Brothers and sisters, I do not consider myself yet to have taken hold of it. But one thing I do: Forgetting what is behind and straining toward what is ahead, [14]I press on toward the goal to win the prize for which God has called me heavenward in Christ Jesus.*
>
> **PHILIPPIANS 3:12-14**

We have learned how to maintain health, but what does that look like on a daily basis? We need to create a sobriety plan—the positive behaviors that we are committed to doing on a daily or weekly basis to support our continued health. It is important that we devise a holistic sobriety plan that is realistic and crafted specifically to our needs: physically, mentally, emotionally, and spiritually.

Use the following space to begin creating a sobriety plan.[170] Don't worry about filling in all the blanks. Be specific about what positive behaviors you need to put in place on a daily or weekly basis to maintain sobriety. Circle whether the need is daily or weekly.

In order to **physically** maintain sobriety, I need:

- ______________________________ daily/weekly
- ______________________________ daily/weekly
- ______________________________ daily/weekly
- ______________________________ daily/weekly
- ______________________________ daily/weekly
- ______________________________ daily/weekly

In order to **mentally** maintain sobriety, I need:

- ______________________________ daily/weekly
- ______________________________ daily/weekly
- ______________________________ daily/weekly
- ______________________________ daily/weekly
- ______________________________ daily/weekly
- ______________________________ daily/weekly

In order to **emotionally** maintain sobriety, I need:

- ______________________________ daily/weekly
- ______________________________ daily/weekly
- ______________________________ daily/weekly
- ______________________________ daily/weekly
- ______________________________ daily/weekly
- ______________________________ daily/weekly

[170] Triangle SAA (2017). Spring Step Retreat. Track 1, Step 1. 51.

In order to **spiritually** maintain sobriety, I need:

- ______________________________ daily/weekly
- ______________________________ daily/weekly
- ______________________________ daily/weekly
- ______________________________ daily/weekly
- ______________________________ daily/weekly
- ______________________________ daily/weekly

When we create a sobriety plan—positive behaviors we can implement in our daily lives—it help us learn how to walk out our healing in a practical way.

RECOVERY ACTION PLAN—REVIEW

Recovery is a process. As we continue to change and grow in our understanding and development of lifelong health, our needs change as well. Over the past several months we have observed significant changes. Six months ago, what we needed to maintain sobriety might look different than what we need today. In chapter 1, lesson 3, we developed a Recovery Action Plan based on our needs and expectations at the time.

Now that we have gained sobriety over many of our compulsive and addictive behaviors, it is a great time to review and make changes to our Recovery Action Plan.

PERSONAL REVIEW

Take the time to review your Recovery Action Plan during the next group. Look at the items you had listed as natural and logical consequences. Do you need to make adjustments? Have you discovered or identified more natural consequences? Look at the logical consequences next and decide if any of those need to be revised. Now that you have gained more understanding about yourself and your needs, is there a consequence that needs to be increased or decreased so it appropriately aids in accomplishing your health and relationship goals?

By this time, you may have established and maintained sobriety for a few months and need to look at what might have led to a current relapse. For example, if you were viewing pornography and masturbating before and have gained sobriety in that area, you may want to look at other things that lead you toward relapse. Perhaps fantasizing or flirting with married men is still an issue. Take time to add those things to your Recovery Action Plan while still keeping your previous relapse listed.

If you are still struggling with your original relapse, we suggest continuing to use these tools, repeat the group, and seek counseling for further investigation and guidance.

What new discoveries did you make about your recovery?

What changes did you make to your Recovery Action Plan?

Our road to recovery may change based on what's happening in our life. When things are going well, we may take great strides toward health, but when life is challenging, we may end up on a slight detour. Use the tools we've learned to maintain forward motion toward lifelong healing.

Looking Ahead

Complete the FASTER Scale, Group Check-in, Self-Care lesson, Thoughts/Feelings Awareness Log, and Change & Growth Analysis in your *Unraveled: Weekly Tools* before the next group meeting.

LESSON 2: LIVING IN SOBRIETY

When it comes to living in sobriety—living every day with a mindset for lifelong health and healing—we have to consider where we have struggled in managing love, sex, and relationships, and what it will look like for us to walk out our healing.

For some of us, this may require that we take one year off from dating so we can focus on our personal recovery. For others, we might need to put healthy boundaries in place with people in our lives who are not healthy: family, friends, and coworkers. We might have to set hard boundaries around our social media use and overall online behaviors. We may need to invest in marriage counseling so we can pursue a healthy marriage with our spouse. We might want personal counseling. Perhaps we need to change jobs, join a book club, take a vacation, enroll in a cooking class, buy a treadmill—whatever it is that will help us establish sobriety and keep us moving toward lifelong health is worth it.

Living out our sobriety is unique to us: there is no "one size fits all" plan. Over the past months, we have learned how our past trauma held us captive in our addictive behaviors—how fear, isolation, and shame created our cage, locked with a key of deception. Now, as we have processed our trauma in a healthy way and developed new tools and strategies to change our thoughts, feelings, and behaviors, we are ready to face life head-on, empowered by our new-found freedom!

Easier said than done. In fact, many of us may be feeling anxious and fearful about living in sobriety. In the past, we had our coping behaviors to get us through life; albeit unhealthy, they met our need in the moment. Now, we may feel as though we are facing life with a bag full of tools, but not enough experience in how to best use all our new tools.

Don't be afraid. If we have learned only one thing in this process, it is that God is with us. He knew that we would be right here, right now, feeling exactly what we're feeling. This is no surprise to God. He has brought us this far and He will continue to lead the way.

O Lord, you have examined my heart and know everything about me. [2]You know when I sit down or stand up. You know my thoughts even when I'm far away. [3]You see me when I travel and when I rest at home. You know everything I do. [4]You know what I am going to say even before I say it, LORD. [5]You go before me and follow me. You place your hand of blessing on my head. [6]Such knowledge is too wonderful for me, too great for me to understand!

PSALM 139:1-6

As you consider what living out your sobriety might look like for you, what are some of your fears?

____

____

____

____

____

____

____

What excites you about living out your sobriety?

____

____

____

____

____

____

____

When you think about what God is going to do in you and through you as a result of your healing, how is Psalm 139:1-6 an encouragement to you?

____

____

____

____

____

____

I am doing great! With the help of my support group, I have been sober from my love addiction for six months. My previous pattern of feeling lonely, going out with friends for drinks, and hooking up with random strangers is behind me. Although I had experienced several STD and pregnancy scares over the past 13 years, I am feeling empowered by my new-found freedom. I have put safeguards in place to help me stay sober: attend group each week; complete daily recovery work; create accountability partners; invest in healthy self-care; do not go to bars; only drink alcohol at home; avoid toxic relationships from the past; and practice assertive communication.

On my way home from work, I stopped by a local restaurant to pick up food for dinner. I was surprised to see Bonnie there, an old friend from college who had recently moved back to the area. We talked easily as if no time had passed. Before long, we made plans to go out to dinner on Friday night. I wanted to meet Bonnie at the restaurant on Friday, but Bonnie insisted that we drive together.

Bonnie picked me up as planned. She also invited a few other girlfriends from college to meet us at the restaurant. In an attempt to pick a central location, we were now going to a different restaurant. As Bonnie continued to tell me the new agenda for the evening, I sat quietly. I could feel myself becoming anxious and wasn't sure what to do. I was feeling out of control.

Before we got to the restaurant, I began implementing my exit strategy. I texted a friend from group and told her what was happening. The friend was encouraging and ready to help: she could come and pick me up within 20 minutes if needed. Bonnie suggested we all sit in the bar, so we could be seated more quickly. I spoke up and said I would prefer to wait for a table in the restaurant area. The others agreed, but ordered drinks while they waited. When I ordered a non-alcoholic ice tea, I received a few questioning looks from my girlfriends. I simply responded, "I don't drink alcohol when I'm out. It has contributed to many poor decisions in the past and I'm trying to be more intentional with the choices I make."

Not only was that an acceptable explanation, but two other women told me how their alcohol use had contributed to unhealthy behaviors and they commended me on my courage to make a healthy choice. Periodically throughout the evening, I texted my friend from group to let her know how I was doing. Although the evening went well, I made some additions to my exit strategy: drive my own car when meeting friends and ask ahead of time if any plans have changed.

Jill

How was Jill proactive in maintaining her sobriety and health?

For Jill, this was a fire drill—a way to practice her exit strategy in a real-life situation. What other options did Jill have to stay safe and maintain sobriety?

BUILDING MY SUPPORT TEAM

Developing healthy relationships is vital to our recovery process. Many of us who struggle with managing love, sex, and relationships have been hurt in relationship. We continue to believe the lie that isolation will keep us safe. We need to continually remind ourselves that lifelong healing happens in relationship—it happens in community.

This is an area where we need to have balance and where we need to be intentional. We need to assess the relationships we have in our lives: determine the role of each relationship, as well as recognize where we might be missing a key relationship.

When we think about the relationships we have in our lives, what comes to mind? We should have a few close relationships—people who are safe and know everything about us. We also have relationships with people (whether we like it or not) who are not safe, who we would not trust with personal information.[171] Then, we have relationships that fall somewhere in between—people we would trust with some personal information but not everything.

[171] Riggenbach, J. (2013). *The CBT Toolbox: A Workbook for Clients and Clinicians.* Eau Claire, WI: PESI Publishing and Media.

We all have individual stories with unique experiences, but we need to find healing together. When building our support team, we need to consider this truth: who is better equipped to walk through the healing process of love, sex, and relationship addictions than someone who has experienced healing from love, sex, and relationship addictions? Who is better equipped to help a woman walk through the divorce process than a woman who has navigated divorce successfully? Who is better equipped to mentor a woman with a blended family than a woman with a blended family? We are better together.

Use the following diagram to visually build your support team.

Do you see any areas that might need to be filled through a new healthy relationship?

Examples: mentor, spiritual mother, older woman with grown kids who can help me parent better.

____

____

____

____

____

Could any of your current relationships meet this specific need?

____

____

____

____

____

____

What are the benefits of having people in your life who facilitate support and healing?

What feels scary or causes hesitation in allowing others to help you continue to move toward health?

We can't do this alone. We need to walk out our health with others. We need support. We need community.

Looking Ahead

Complete the FASTER Scale, Group Check-in, Self-Care lesson, Thoughts/Feelings Awareness Log, and Change & Growth Analysis in your *Unraveled: Weekly Tools* before the next group meeting.

LESSON 3: COMFORTING OTHERS

Why did we join this group? Were we looking to escape the destruction of our sexually compulsive and addictive behaviors? Were we drowning in the shame of our past? Were we searching for lifelong healing? Many of us would respond with, "Yes, yes, and yes."

Now that we have experienced the amazing gift of health and freedom and are confidently headed down the path of recovery, what's next? God's grace in continuing to bring us to a place of healing is remarkable! God has done a miraculous work in us to get us to this point. Now, He wants to continue to work through us to bring healing to others.

God is intentional. He brought healing and restoration to our life so we could pass it along to others—so we could show others the way.

> *All praise to God, the Father of our Lord Jesus Christ. God is our merciful Father and the source of all comfort. 4He comforts us in all our troubles so that we can comfort others. When they are troubled, we will be able to give them the same comfort God has given us.*
>
> **2 CORINTHIANS 1:3-4 NLT**

This scripture is very clear: God did not bring us comfort from our troubles so we could be comfortable.[172] He comforts us so we can comfort others: "*When they are troubled, we will be able to give them* ***the same comfort*** *God has given us.*"

Perhaps we already recognized that our healing was not just for us. Our change and growth throughout this process has significantly impacted all our relationships: marriage, kids, family, friends, coworkers, and more. The health we're experiencing is spilling out into the relationships around us. The transformation is incredible! But, is God asking you for more—is He asking you to do something bigger than you could have ever imagined?

What do you think God is asking you to do with your healing?

____

____

____

[172] Stumbo, N. (2016). *Healing Woundedness*. Pure Desire Conference.

How does this align with what you had planned to do with your healing?

When we consider all the work we've done to get to this place of healing, God's presence and provision is obvious. It has been emotionally painful. At times, the honesty and vulnerability was grueling. There have been tears.

Yet, in His most gracious and caring way, God had to move us from where we were to where He is, so that He could do something wonderful in us and through us.[173] This experience—our healing process—was God's way of moving us into position so that He could use us to fulfill His plan and purpose. Only God could use our addiction to love, sex, and relationships to bring about His glory in our life and in the lives of others.

In what way has God uniquely equipped you to comfort others?

I was reeling from the pain of my husband's betrayal. I tried reading my entire Bible, listening to sermons, seeking advice from mentors, and cutting off all social media and TV. Months had gone by and nothing relieved my pain. Anger and hurt bubbled under the surface. I often lashed out at my husband and children. I was plagued with guilt and shame for the way I was acting, but I was stuck. I felt angry with the people at church, who just kept telling me to read my Bible and pray more. I prayed for God to bring me some help. When I realized that there was no one at my church who could lead a healing group for me, I decided to do it myself.

On *Small Group Sign-Up Sunday*, as I stood behind a table in the lobby of my church, I could feel the blood rushing to my face. Women asked what my group was about and I could barely explain it without breaking down in tears. Regardless of how it felt, I knew I needed deep healing and no one else was going to get this going. The more I verbalized my pain—even to the strangers in the lobby—the less it stung.

[173] Blackaby, H. & King, C. (1990). *Experiencing God: Knowing and Doing the Will of God*. Nashville, TN: LifeWay Press.

I ended up taking a group of women through the small group. My group knew that I was a mess and needed it just as much as they did. Week after week, I continued to lead, mess and all. I went to my group and felt the weight of my pain lifting off me as I shared my answers and then listened as women just like me shared their answers.

The more I dug into my pain, the more I realized that I had decades of my own pain and trauma that I had never dealt with. As I saw women finding hope, it inspired me to be brave, using my story to encourage more women. I wanted every woman living with secret shame to know that there was real hope and freedom. I needed them to know they were not alone: who is better to offer that assurance of hope than someone who has experienced their same pain?

I learned that stuffing my feelings inside will not take them away. It may help stop the behavior, but that destructive root will continue to have its grip in me until I take the time to dig in and pluck it out. I learned that the Holy Spirit and a group of women using practical tools were exactly what I needed to locate the toxic root of my pain. I learned what it looked like to trust God with my life and my story.

I spent the next year working on myself and the past behaviors that had led to my struggle with sex, love, and relationships. I also discovered that my unhealthy behavior and mindset contributed to marrying an addict. I now feel unashamed: free in my own skin, and able to share openly and honestly with anyone who needs to hear about what God has done in my life. This includes my own kids. I share with small groups, at conferences, women's brunches, and anywhere else that God opens the door. I am now addicted to seeing lives radically changed through the healing power of God's grace.

They triumphed over him by the blood of the Lamb
and by the word of their testimony.

REVELATION 12:11

Valentina

What motivated Valentina to lead a healing group for women?

____

____

____

____

____

What did Valentina learn about herself and her own healing process?

When you think about sharing your story with others, how does it make you feel?

What part of your healing story might inspire others to pursue hope and healing?

USING MY RESOURCES

It has been suggested that 90 percent of the things we worry about never happen.[174] Through this group, we have worked to retrain our brain—implementing new healthy behaviors—so we can realistically assess what is happening in our environment. Even though we have new skills in place, we can still become blindsided by unexpected life stressors. When this happens, we need to feel prepared.

All of us have resources at our disposal when life goes sideways—when we experience an anxiety-provoking event. In that moment, we may not be able to think rationally or mentally compile a list of resources to help us navigate the stress in a healthy way. As we continue to explore what it means to live out our recovery—to live intentionally—we need to plan ahead for any potential disruption to our healing. We need to identify our resources and understand how they help us when we're faced with an overwhelming or stressful situation. We need to plan ahead.

Use the following table to identify your resources and how they help you when feeling overwhelmed or stressed. Indicate how each resource will help keep you holistically healthy: physically, mentally, emotionally, and spiritually. Be specific. Try to list 10 resources—based on the situation—you want to ensure that you will have options.

EXAMPLES:

MY RESOURCES	HOW DOES THIS HELP ME?
I am a good problem-solver.	This helps me feel emotionally and mentally confident that I will find a solution to the problem.
I am resilient.	This helps me mentally, remembering that whatever happens I will be okay.
Faith in God	This helps me spiritually and mentally keep my eyes on God and not on my situation.
My Pure Desire group	This helps me mentally and emotionally know that I am not alone.
Breathing and meditation	This helps me to physically calm down, so I can think clearly.
My parents' house	This helps me physically and mentally, knowing that I always have a safe place to go.

[174] Riggenbach, J. (2013). *The CBT Toolbox: A Workbook for Clients and Clinicians*. Eau Claire, WI: PESI Publishing and Media.

MY RESOURCES	HOW DOES THIS HELP ME?

If you cannot think of 10 resources, ask your group members for help.

For quick reference, here is a list of resources and tools found in *Unraveled*:

UNRAVELED RESOURCES CHEAT-SHEET

THE NEXT STEP?

We did it! We have survived the mental strain of unpacking our past pain and trauma, the emotional ups and downs, and the spiritual revival of our soul—all of which have strengthened our foundation for lifelong healing. Through this unraveling process, we have learned how to manage love, sex, and relationships. But our journey doesn't end here.

This is a new beginning. A new way of walking out our health with the tools and mindset for lasting change. Living every day with our focus on the pursuit of healthy relationship with God and others. We cannot do this alone. We need to continue our healing in community.

How is God calling us to use our healing for others? For some of us, it may include going through this study again as a leader or co-leader. Perhaps God is calling us to invest in our marriage through personal counseling or a study for couples. Maybe God is calling us to take this curriculum beyond our church, to women in our community who desperately need God's healing grace.

God brought us to a place of healing not just for us, but for others so the glory and grace of God would be evident in our lives. As we continue to walk the path of lifelong healing—taking one step at a time, one day at a time—may God open our eyes to where we need to pass along the hope and grace of His healing in our lives.

I pray that God, the source of hope, will fill you completely with joy and peace because you trust in him. Then you will overflow with confident hope through the power of the Holy Spirit.

ROMANS 15:13 NLT

APPENDIX

THE DISCLOSURE PROCESS

Disclosing the extent of our sexual history is challenging. We may struggle with wanting to free ourselves from the burden of our sexually compulsive and addictive behaviors; and at the same time, wanting to bury the truth of our behaviors deep within our soul, so that no one ever discovers our secret.

However, one truth remains: **to carry secrets is to carry shame.**[175] The more we hold on to our secrets and shame, the more our addiction will control us. Disclosure is an essential part of the process by which we find lasting freedom. It is key to regaining healthy control in our lives.

FORCED DISCLOSURE

There are different forms of disclosure. A **forced disclosure** happens when our addictive behaviors are discovered by our spouse. This is the worst case scenario: no one—ourselves, our spouse, or our children—has the necessary support and tools they need to handle the situation.

A forced disclosure may become necessary in some cases: if we have been caught in the act; when illegal activity has occurred; when our sexual activity involves other people and we have put our spouse at risk of STDs; when our spouse is unable to move forward in the relationship, despite our involvement in a recovery group.

STAGGERED DISCLOSURE

At times, especially early in recovery, we may feel an urgency to tell our spouse some of our sexual history. We may choose to leave out pieces or specific events because they are too terrible or we may not be healthy enough to remember the full extent of our sexual history. This is very common. We have learned that honesty is a part of the recovery process, but have only become dangerous. We fail to understand the extent of how this form of disclosure, a **staggered disclosure**, continues to retraumatize our spouse every time we reveal bits and pieces of our sexual history.

---

[175] Carnes, P. (2015). *Facing the Shadow: Starting Sexual and Relationship Recovery* (3rd ed.). Carefree, AZ: Gentle Path Press.

FULL DISCLOSURE

The best form of disclosure is defined as a full, fact-based reporting of our sexual history and is usually recommended after we have established six months of sobriety. When possible, disclosure should be done with a Certified Sex Addiction Therapist (CSAT) or Pastoral Sex Addiction Professional (PSAP). Many couples, however, will walk through disclosure as part of their group experience.

Although the full disclosure process happens after sobriety has been established, it is critical to recovery that we learn to be transparent while working toward sobriety. Relapse that occurs during the recovery process should be disclosed to our group members and our spouse. Immediately after relapse occurs, our Recovery Action Plan should be implemented. Breaking free from our sexually compulsive and addictive behaviors requires us to live an honest lifestyle, break isolation, experience consequences, and give those we have hurt the respect and dignity to make informed choices. If our spouse is involved in this healing process, they will have their own Recovery Action Plan. If we are working on our recovery but still keeping secrets, then shame will keep us stuck.

In many ways, disclosure is beneficial to our healing.[176]

- It destroys the secret life we're living.
- It makes our commitment to accountability real.
- It enables us to let go of our shame and guilt.
- It empowers our spouse to make healthy choices.
- It allows our spouse to face the trauma our addiction triggered.

The disclosure process is difficult, not just for us, but for those we've hurt through our addictive behaviors. It is important that we take responsibility for our behaviors, which is possible after we gain an understanding of our addiction, break denial, and establish several months of sobriety. We need to be in a place of accountability and honesty.

While much of this information pertains to disclosure among married couples, these steps should be followed for dating or engaged couples who choose to go through the disclosure process.

As you prepare for disclosure, use the following steps to walk through this process.

Write out your full sexual history and discuss it with your group leader thoroughly before you engage in the disclosure process with your spouse or family.

- Include the time frame when referring to each incident where you acted out and how many incidents happened during that time frame.

---

[176] Roberts, T. (2014). *Seven Pillars of Freedom Workbook* (3rd ed.). Gresham, OR: Pure Desire Ministries International. 200.

- Include sex acts that don't involve a physical act, such as flirting or planning to act out.
- Include financial information.
- Include health issues or health risks such as exposure to STDs.
- Acknowledge if there is someone else who the spouse may know or run into.
- Refer to the spouse in the second person (I betrayed YOU when...).
- Stick with information sharing—do not justify any of your addictive behaviors.

Work with your spouse to find a time for disclosure that is conducive to an honest conversation. Allow time following the disclosure to process it emotionally. If it is not possible to meet with a CSAT or PSAP as recommended, both parties should have their group leader or support person there during the disclosure process. Including outside people in the disclosure process should always be at the choosing and comfort level of the betrayed spouse.

STEPS FOR YOUR BETRAYED SPOUSE

Write out questions that are needed to establish truth, understanding, and forward motion in recovery. Keep in mind that restoration and healing, not curiosity, should be the driving force behind the questions. Examples of commonly asked questions:

- In what ways have you lied about or hidden behaviors from me?
- What are the addictive behaviors you are/were involved with?
- What are the time frames of these behaviors?
  - What was the frequency and duration?
- Has your behavior involved another person/people?
  - How many other partners were there?
  - Where did these encounters take place?
  - Do I know any of the people you were sexually involved with?
  - Have you cut off all contact with your other sexual partners?
- Has any of your sexual acting out included same-sex relationships or behaviors?

Share your questions with your spouse before the disclosure, so they have time to formulate honest, thorough answers. These may be shared through the group leader or trusted advisor.

If you're not already in a *Hope for Men* group, join one for support and empathy.

Share questions with your group leader or another trusted advisor familiar with the disclosure process. This advisor might suggest omitting certain questions to help you avoid questions that are overly detailed or hold more potential for pain than healing.

DISCLOSING TO YOUR CHILDREN

PD Podcast: Episode 021 - Disclosing to Your Kids

At some point, this process may include disclosing to your children. Your children may not know exactly what's happening, but they can feel the tension between their parents. They don't need to know all the details, but they need some information to feel safe in their environment. Use the following guide to help disclose to your children in a way that is age-appropriate.

FOR PRESCHOOL CHILDREN:

- They need to know you are not going to leave them.
- They are not in trouble and they did not cause the problem.
- They need to know you love them.

FOR ELEMENTARY CHILDREN:

- This is not their fault.
- Will something bad happen—separation or divorce?
- Are you going to leave?

FOR MIDDLE SCHOOL CHILDREN:

- What will happen to me if you divorce?
- What is so bad about sex? (Help them understand healthy sexuality.)
- How are you going to get better?

FOR TEENS AND YOUNG ADULTS:

- How could you do this to our family?
- How does this relate to me? (You ruined my life.)

The best time to disclose to children is when you and your spouse have experienced some healing, and can engage in this disclosure process together. This helps defuse their fear of divorce. Here are a few more things to keep in mind when disclosing to children:

- Let your child's level of interest be your guide. They may need fewer details than you think.
- Let them know what the recovery process looks like, so they don't think they have to become the caretaker.
- If needed, provide emotional support for your child through the church or a counselor.
- Create a culture of healthy sexuality in your home from what you have learned in the recovery process.
- If your child is struggling in life, wait for disclosure until you and your spouse agree that the time is right.

We can't let our shame and fear keep us stuck in our compulsive and addictive behaviors. As we have learned, facing our fear is a huge part of recovery. If we want to continue on the path toward lifelong health, it will include the disclosure process. This will keep us moving forward as we continue to learn how to manage love, sex, and relationships.

PAIR INTIMACY PROFILE—EXAMPLE GRAPH

Cheyenne requested marriage counseling for herself and her husband, Derek. They have been married 12 years. Cheyenne complained that she does not receive any support from Derek. She feels she is "not important" to him and that she "doesn't count" in the relationship. Although Derek admitted that he is not as involved in the relationship as Cheyenne wants, he doesn't know how to change the situation.

The graph below reflects the degree of *perceived* and *expected* intimacy in each category for Cheyenne and Derek.

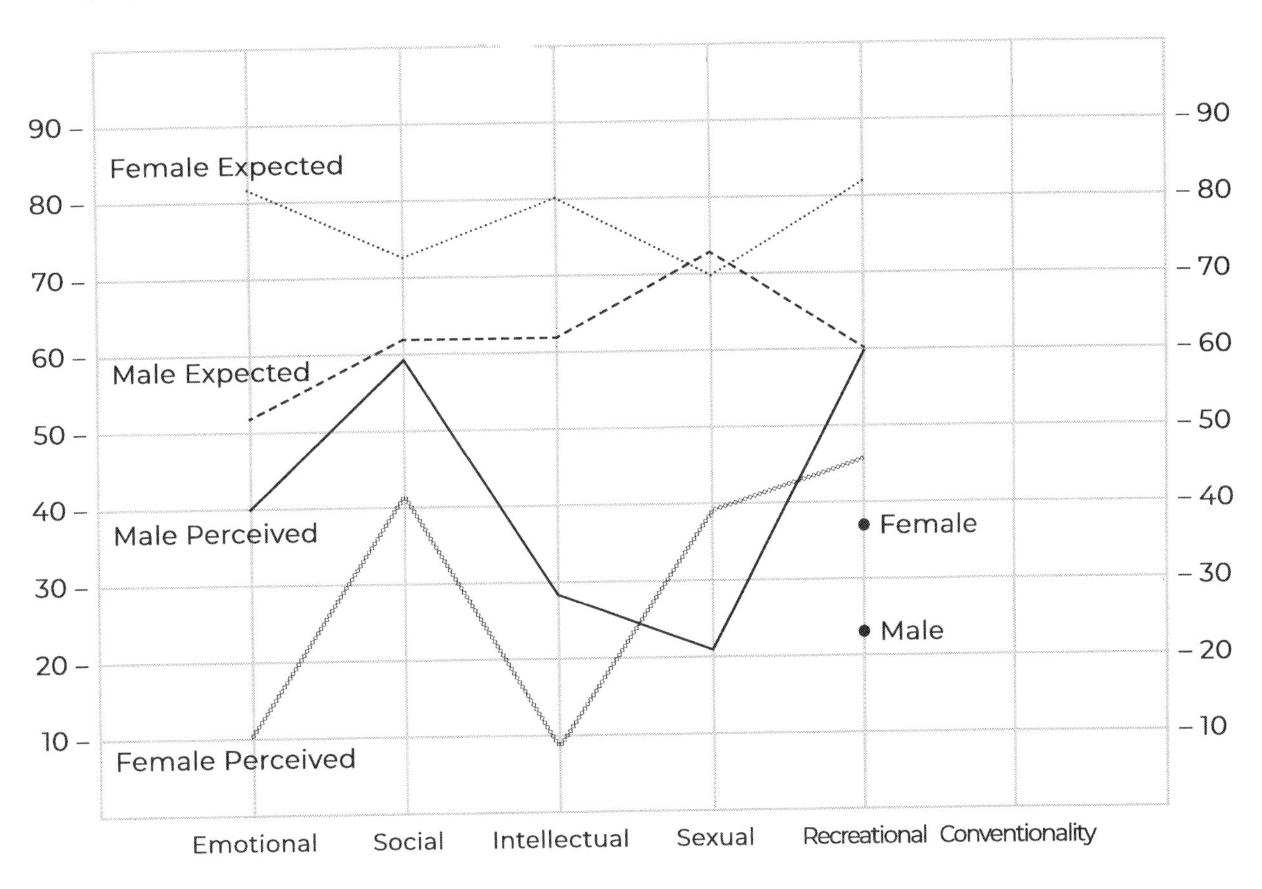

Based on the results, Cheyenne demonstrates a severe difference between her perceived and expected scores on her Emotional, Intellectual, and Sexual intimacy scales. A clear difference also exists for Social and Recreational intimacy.

Derek's scores indicate a severe difference between his perceived and expected scores on his Intellectual and Sexual intimacy scales. His perceived and expected scores are more closely aligned in the other areas.

When there is a severe difference in the perceived and expected scores, this indicates that an individual is not receiving what they would like to receive in this area of intimacy. These areas of unmet needs are a great place to begin building intimacy.

Their Conventionality Score indicates that the information can be trusted: Cheyenne, 37; Derek, 24. The Conventionality Scale score needs to be within 18 points of one another for a trustworthy score. This score assesses the truthfulness of each partner's answers, indicating whether they are trying to make a good impression or "faking" their answers.

PERSONAL ASSESSMENT OF INTIMACY IN RELATIONSHIPS (PAIR)[177]

PHASE 1:

Rate each statement based on how ***it is now*** *in your relationship. Write the number that corresponds with the best answer.*

1	2	3	4	5
Strongly Disagree	Disagree	Don't Know	Agree	Strongly Agree

In my relationship now...

____ **1.** My partner listens to me when I need someone to talk to.
____ **2.** We enjoy spending time with other couples.
____ **3.** I am satisfied with our sex life.
____ **4.** My partner helps me clarify my thoughts.
____ **5.** We enjoy the same recreational activities.
____ **6.** My partner has all the qualities I've ever wanted in a mate.
____ **7.** I can state my feelings without him/her getting defensive.
____ **8.** We usually "keep to ourselves."
____ **9.** I feel our sexual activity is just routine.
____ **10.** When it comes to having a serious discussion, it seems we have little in common.
____ **11.** I share in very few of my partner's interests.
____ **12.** There are times when I do not feel a great deal of love and affection for my partner.
____ **13.** I often feel distant from my partner.
____ **14.** We have very few friends in common.
____ **15.** I am able to tell my partner when I want sexual intercourse.
____ **16.** I feel "put-down" in a serious conversation with my partner.
____ **17.** We like playing together.

[177] Schaefer, M.T. & Olson, D.H. (1981). Assessing intimacy: The PAIR Inventory. *Journal of Marital and Family Therapy*, 1, 47-60.

_____ **18.** Every new thing that I have learned about my partner has pleased me.
_____ **19.** My partner can really understand my hurts and joys.
_____ **20.** Having time together with friends is an important part of our shared activities.
_____ **21.** I "hold back" my sexual interest because my partner makes me feel uncomfortable.
_____ **22.** I feel it is useless to discuss some things with my partner.
_____ **23.** We enjoy the out-of-doors together.
_____ **24.** My partner and I understand each other completely.
_____ **25.** I feel neglected at times by my partner.
_____ **26.** Many of my partner's closest friends are also my closest friends.
_____ **27.** Sexual expression is an essential part of our relationship.
_____ **28.** My partner frequently tries to change my ideas.
_____ **29.** We seldom find time to do fun things together.
_____ **30.** I don't think anyone could possibly be happier than my partner and I are when we're with one another.
_____ **31.** I sometimes feel lonely when we're together.
_____ **32.** My partner disapproves of some of my friends.
_____ **33.** My partner seems disinterested in sex.
_____ **34.** We have an endless number of things to talk about.
_____ **35.** I think we share some of the same interests.
_____ **36.** I have some needs that are not being met by my relationship.

*Complete the following calculation to obtain your **realized** level of intimacy in each category. Add the score for each numbered statement as listed below. After calculating each category score, obtain the correlating percentage from the table below.*

EMOTIONAL INTIMACY | Add scores for 1, 7, 13, 19, 25, and 31: _____________ Percentage: _______
SOCIAL INTIMACY | Add scores for 2, 8, 14, 20, 26, and 32: _____________ Percentage: _______
SEXUAL INTIMACY | Add scores for 3, 9, 15, 21, 27, and 33: _____________ Percentage: _______
INTELLECTUAL INTIMACY | Add scores for 4, 10, 16, 22, 28, and 34: _________ Percentage: _______
RECREATIONAL INTIMACY | Add scores for 5, 11, 17, 23, 29, and 35: _________ Percentage: _______
CONVENTIONALITY SCALE* | Add scores for 6, 12, 18, 24, 30, and 36: _______ Percentage: _______

PERCENTAGE CONVERSION TABLE

Percentage conversion: the following list indicates the corresponding percentage based on the potential inventory score. The percentages are round to the nearest whole number.

30 = 100%	25 = 83%	20 = 67%	15 = 50%	10 = 33%	5 = 17%
29 = 97%	24 = 80%	19 = 63%	14 = 47%	9 = 30%	4 = 13 %
28 = 93%	23 = 77%	18 = 60%	13 = 43%	8 = 27%	3 = 10%
27 = 90%	22 = 73%	17 = 57%	12 = 40%	7 = 23%	2 = 7%
26 = 87%	21 = 70%	16 = 53%	11 = 37%	6 = 20%	1 = 3%

**The Conventionality Scale is included and scored separately in order to assess how much the individual is attempting to create a good impression.*

PHASE 2:

*Rate each statement based on how **you would like it to be** in the relationship. Circle the number that corresponds with the best answer.*

1	2	3	4	5
Strongly Disagree	Disagree	Don't Know	Agree	Strongly Agree

In my relationship, I would like it if...

____ **1.** My partner listens to me when I need someone to talk to.

____ **2.** We enjoy spending time with other couples.

____ **3.** I am satisfied with our sex life.

____ **4.** My partner helps me clarify my thoughts.

____ **5.** We enjoy the same recreational activities.

____ **6.** My partner has all the qualities I've ever wanted in a mate.

____ **7.** I can state my feelings without him/her getting defensive.

____ **8.** We usually "keep to ourselves."

____ **9.** I feel our sexual activity is just routine.

____ **10.** When it comes to having a serious discussion, it seems we have little in common.

____ **11.** I share in very few of my partner's interests.

____ **12.** There are times when I do not feel a great deal of love and affection for my partner.

____ **13.** I often feel distant from my partner.

____ **14.** We have very few friends in common.

____ **15.** I am able to tell my partner when I want sexual intercourse.

____ **16.** I feel "put-down" in a serious conversation with my partner.

____ **17.** We like playing together.

____ **18.** Every new thing that I have learned about my partner has pleased me.

____ **19.** My partner can really understand my hurts and joys.

____ **20.** Having time together with friends is an important part of our shared activities.

____ **21.** I "hold back" my sexual interest because my partner makes me feel uncomfortable.

____ **22.** I feel it is useless to discuss some things with my partner.

____ **23.** We enjoy the out-of-doors together.

____ **24.** My partner and I understand each other completely.

____ **25.** I feel neglected at times by my partner.

____ **26.** Many of my partner's closest friends are also my closest friends.

____ **27.** Sexual expression is an essential part of our relationship.

____ **28.** My partner frequently tries to change my ideas.

____ **29.** We seldom find time to do fun things together.

____ **30.** I don't think anyone could possibly be happier than my partner and I are when we're with one another.

____ **31.** I sometimes feel lonely when we're together.

____ **32.** My partner disapproves of some of my friends.

____ **33.** My partner seems disinterested in sex.

____ **34.** We have an endless number of things to talk about.

____ **35.** I think we share some of the same interests.

____ **36.** I have some needs that are not being met by my relationship.

*Complete the following calculation to obtain your **expected** level of intimacy in each category. Add the score for each numbered statement as listed below. After calculating each category score, obtain the correlating percentage from the table below.*

EMOTIONAL INTIMACY | Add scores for 1, 7, 13, 19, 25, and 31: ________ Percentage: ______

SOCIAL INTIMACY | Add scores for 2, 8, 14, 20, 26, and 32: ________ Percentage: ______

SEXUAL INTIMACY | Add scores for 3, 9, 15, 21, 27, and 33: ________ Percentage: ______

INTELLECTUAL INTIMACY | Add scores for 4, 10, 16, 22, 28, and 34: ________ Percentage: ______

RECREATIONAL INTIMACY | Add scores for 5, 11, 17, 23, 29, and 35: ________ Percentage: ______

CONVENTIONALITY SCALE* | Add scores for 6, 12, 18, 24, 30, and 36: ________ Percentage: ______

PERCENTAGE CONVERSION TABLE

Percentage conversion: the following list indicates the corresponding percentage based on the potential inventory score. The percentages are round to the nearest whole number.

30 = 100%	25 = 83%	20 = 67%	15 = 50%	10 = 33%	5 = 17%
29 = 97%	24 = 80%	19 = 63%	14 = 47%	9 = 30%	4 = 13 %
28 = 93%	23 = 77%	18 = 60%	13 = 43%	8 = 27%	3 = 10%
27 = 90%	22 = 73%	17 = 57%	12 = 40%	7 = 23%	2 = 7%
26 = 87%	21 = 70%	16 = 53%	11 = 37%	6 = 20%	1 = 3%

**The Conventionality Scale is included and scored separately in order to assess how much the individual is attempting to create a good impression.*

CREATE A PROFILE

☐ *Use the percentages from each inventory to create a profile on the graph below. Make sure to use a different line designation for the results of each inventory (e.g., solid, dashed, or dotted lines; various colored pens or pencils).*

Based on the numbered scale on the edge of the graph, place a dot at the appropriate percentage point for each vertical line indicating a category of intimacy. After all five dots are positioned on the graph, connect the five dots with a line. Complete this process for your inventories and for your partner's (additional PAIR Inventories are located in the appendix). See page 341 of the appendix to see what a completed graph should look like.

Mark on the graph the Conventionality Scale score for each partner, but do not include this plot point in the drawn lines. The Conventionality Scale score shows that the information can be trusted when partners score within 18 points of one another.[178] This score assesses the truthfulness of each partner's answers, indicating whether they are trying to make a good impression or "faking" their answers.

INTIMACY PROFILE OF PAIR SCORES

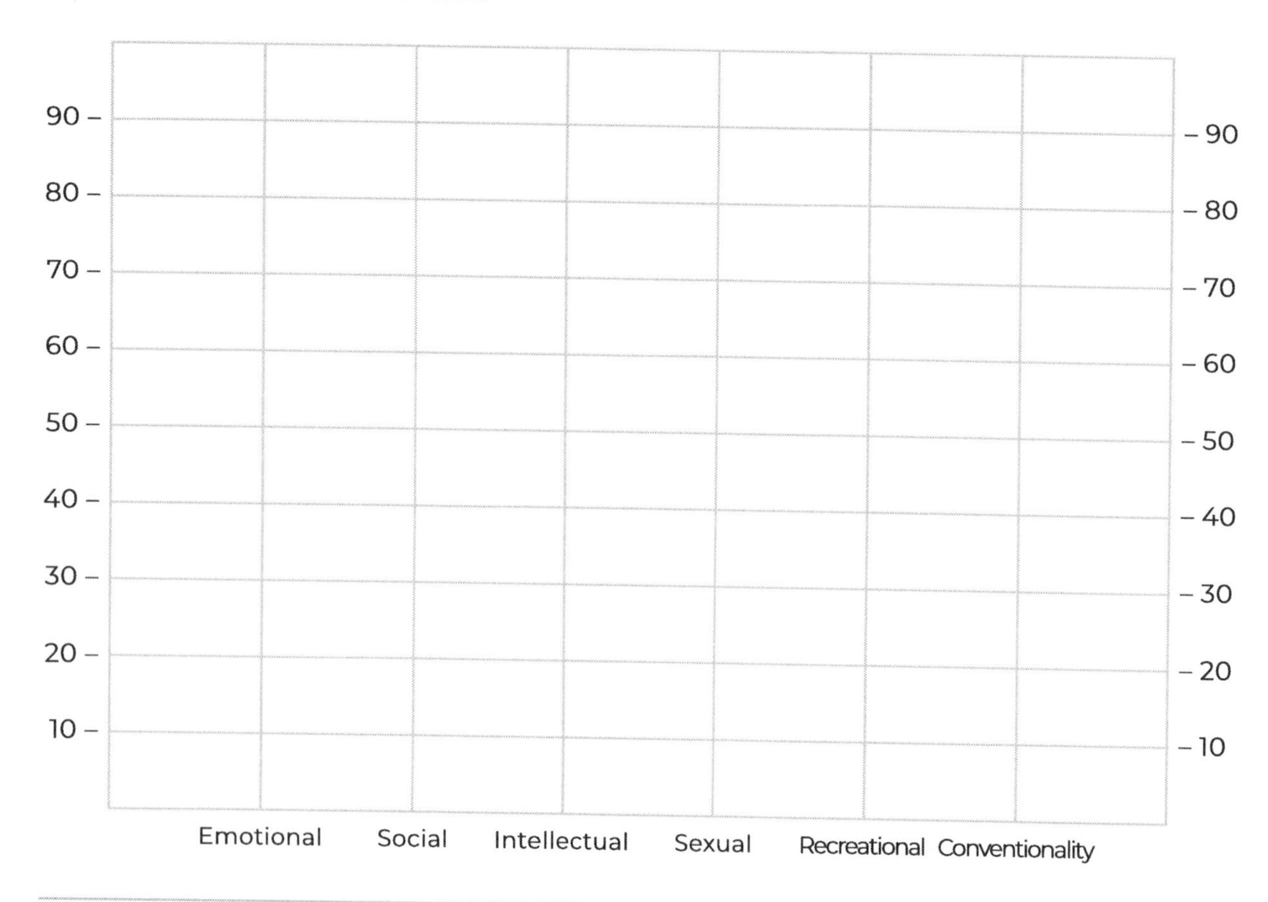

[178] Schaefer, M.T. & Olson, D.H. (1981). Assessing intimacy: The PAIR Inventory. *Journal of Marital and Family Therapy*, 1, 47-60.